# HOME
# FARM

# HOME FARM

complete food self-sufficiency

# MICHAEL ALLABY

with COLIN TUDGE

READERS UNION
Group of Book Clubs
Newton Abbot

This edition was published in 1977 by Readers Union
by arrangement with Macmillan London Limited

Copyright © Michael Allaby and Colin Tudge 1977

Full particulars of RU are obtainable from
Readers Union Limited, PO Box 6, Newton Abbot, Devon.

Printed in Great Britain by
Lowe & Brydone Printers, Limited
for Readers Union

# CONTENTS

# Introduction

Britain is an industrial nation. We all know it, and any textbook on history or economics will confirm it. We earn our living by making things and then selling them. These activities bring us an income and part of that income we spend on buying the food we need. We buy food wherever we can find it most cheaply. For many years we were supplied mainly by our farmlands overseas, in North America and Australasia where food can be produced economically in large amounts, by farmers who looked on Britain as their motherland. More recently we have come to rely on our new partners in Europe, who also produce large amounts of food that are surplus to their own needs.

It was not always so. At one time we grew all our own food, and if some of us did not eat too well that was more the fault of our social system than of our farming methods. It may not be so in the future, for the cheap food on which we have come to rely is cheap no longer. Our food import bill is now in the order of £5,000 million a year, and we are less wealthy than we were. It is plain common sense and good housekeeping to try to become a little more self-reliant.

The conventional view of Britain as an exclusively industrial nation is only partly accurate. We are also a major agricultural nation, even today. More than 80 per cent of the total land area of the United Kingdom is devoted to agriculture or forestry, and if our bill for imported food is large, it would be twice as large were it not for our own farmers producing half of what we eat. Since the eighteenth century, and possibly for longer, British farmers and agricultural scientists have been in the forefront of developments and innovations that have improved farming techniques. Yields are high, and the British farmer or farm worker feeds more people than his counterpart in most countries – perhaps in any.

When people talk of the efficiency of British agriculture, usually they mean either the output per man-hour or, more subtly, the delicate balance that has been achieved between input costs and output: the value we get for our money. British yields of many crops are lower, for example, than those of Holland, but if we were to increase them the cost of doing so would make all our food much more expensive than it is.

We live in a time of rapid change, however, and complacency is a luxury we cannot afford. The sharp rise in energy costs has demonstrated that the efficiency with which labour is used on our farms has been achieved not by the use of magic plants that grow by themselves, but by the substitution of machines and chemicals for human beings. This has increased the productivity of the land, but at the expense of a loss of that personal attention to small details that characterizes true mastery of any craft. As the farm labour force has dwindled farming has become more profitable for those who remain, but some operations that cannot be mechanized have been abandoned.

At the same time, most of us have lost touch with the land and with rural life. Our preoccupation with manufacturing industry has made us urban-minded, so that even agricultural policies have been devised on the basis of similarities between agriculture and industry that are much more hypothetical than real.

If we are to grow more of the food we eat it is probable that more of us will need to become involved directly in the production of food, and it is certain that agriculture, horticulture and, to a lesser extent, aquaculture will play a much more important part in our lives than they have done in the recent past.

We know this, of course. In the past few years seed merchants have found it difficult to keep up with the demand for vegetable seeds from amateur gardeners, and the once-declining allotment scheme has been revived so that demand for allotments now exceeds the available supply in many towns. This is a very substantial change. It is less than a decade since an official report recommended that the few remaining, mainly neglected, allotments be converted into 'leisure gardens'. The demand for work places on farms, and the search for smallholdings by people from towns who want to become farmers, is now intense, as anyone who writes about farming can testify. In one way or another, people are much more rural-minded than they were; they are becoming involved in food production.

In this book we have tried to explore a few of the possibilities by describing some of the many ways in which food is produced – and is likely to be produced in the future. This is not a textbook, for you cannot learn how to farm or garden from a book, but in explaining how food is produced we hope also to provide at least rudimentary instruction for those who wish to start producing it. We have aimed for completeness, and we explain what actually happens on farms today, so that some of the techniques we describe are not practicable on a smallholding; but where this is so, we often describe a smaller-scale version of the same enterprise. In the case of dairying, for example, we explain the principles of commercial farming, but we also explain how to buy and manage a house cow – and goat. We describe intensive poultry and pig farming, but we also describe the 'backyard' versions of both.

There are two main areas of controversy in modern farming. The first concerns the use of grains to feed livestock. Our view is that the large intensive livestock units (the 'factory farms') that depend on imported feedgrains are inappropriate in the world of the late 1970s and 1980s. We find them aesthetically displeasing and think they are probably cruel – though it is difficult to be precise about this – but we warn that traditional systems, badly managed, were often no less displeasing, and undoubtedly cruel.

The second controversy concerns the use of agricultural chemicals. We describe what actually happens, and we also explain the principles that underlie organic methods of husbandry, but we do not advocate one or other system. The differences between them are more of emphasis than of rigid principle. Fertilizers and even modern pesticides are not evil and their use is not a sin. Their misuse, on the other hand, is.

The subject divides itself conveniently into sections. We begin with a general outline of farming in Britain, to show how the enterprises on any particular farm are determined by soil types, climate, topography, and personal preference, all mediated by economics. We deal too with more practical matters, such as drainage, and we describe the most common farm implements and machines.

This takes us into the production of plant crops, on both a farm and a garden scale, the one merging naturally into the other, for some – such as potatoes – can be grown on either scale. We deal with vegetable gardening and the growing of tree and soft fruits. We give an outline of major developments imminent in arable farming, such as new crop varieties (especially of potatoes) and new ways of supplying nitrogen. The last plant crop, or group of crops, we describe is grass, which is the basis of livestock farming.

Most of us are familiar with the main breeds of cattle, less familiar with those of pigs, and possibly bewildered by the large number of sheep breeds. We describe the main ones in each case. We explain how it is that there are so many sheep and comparatively few cattle and pigs, and the ways in which the situation may change with the elimination of some old breeds and the introduction of new ones. We deal with poultry, and we suggest that more could be made of species that are not farmed at present, or that are farmed but only on a small, or experimental scale.

By widening the scope of livestock farming we can make better use of marginal environments and of very small areas. Food production in towns, even in window boxes and inside houses and flats, is more practicable than many people realize. Some of us keep a few hens in the back garden already, but do we remember how to raise rabbits for food? Or even guinea pigs? If this demands space at present used for other purposes, perhaps we can economize. There is no reason for not bringing the herb garden indoors, for example.

This sounds like fun (and it is), but there is a serious purpose as well. If it were necessary, very substantial amounts of food could be produced within towns. We show how a sewage works might be adapted for this purpose, and we take a fairly typical small area in an industrial city and describe how it might be used to produce an impressive quantity of food. It is possible to go further, by producing single-cell proteins from micro-organisms grown on a wide range of nutrients that require no use of land at all, apart from the space occupied by the industrial plant itself.

Finally we consider fish. Fishing is a traditional industry, of course, and interesting in that it is the last remnant of the hunting culture which at one time provided all our animal food. We explain the main fishing methods, and list the principal fish species landed at each of the major ports. Fish farming – aquaculture – is emerging as a viable way of producing freshwater fish in Britain, and research into farming marine fish is very advanced and may be applied commercially within the next few years. We describe the work that has been done and some of the exciting possibilities in, for example, fish breeding.

The possibilities are almost endless, and this is a book of possibilities. If we exploit even a few of them we will move much nearer to feeding ourselves, and that will make the future more secure – and a great deal more enjoyable.

# LAND

# What grows where?

The main factor determining the kind of farming system that will thrive in a particular locality is economic. It is far less a question of what can be grown than of what can be grown for sale at a competitive price.

If you were prepared to import soil, place a whole area under cover, and supply artificial lighting, heating and water control, then in theory you could grow bananas at the North Pole, or wheat on the sea bed. The cost of doing so, however, would be very high, and you would find it impossible to sell your produce in competition with bananas from Central America or wheat from Norfolk. If you chose to live at the North Pole, or on the sea bed, it might be possible for you to produce food for your own consumption, but even then you might find it cheaper to buy food from farmers working in more favoured localities.

The idea of growing crops under the sea or in the Arctic sounds absurd – and it is absurd, although schemes rather like it have been suggested as a desperate technological strategy for feeding people in developing countries, whose main problem is that they are too poor to buy as much as they need even of food grown a kilometre down the road. At a lower level, however, it is less absurd. Poor soil can be improved and induced to grow crops it could never have supported without improvement; irrigation and drainage (see p.18) can place water where it is needed, when it is needed; hedges and shelter belts of trees can reduce wind speeds and raise the temperature of soils; crops can be bred to tolerate climates other than those in which they evolved naturally. On a limited scale, even the length of the day can be modified – as it is with artificial lighting in intensive livestock units (see p.152).

Since almost anything is possible, what happens in practice is determined by the amount of change to the local environment that is necessary, the cost of that change, and the economic benefit to be derived from it.

## Soils

The first factor to examine is the soil itself: not the fertility of the soil, which is a temporary phenomenon that can be altered quite easily, but the inherent character of the soil, its type.

Most of Britain was covered at one time by mixed deciduous forest, and the most common soils are those associated with forests: brown forest, acid brown, grey-brown podzolics and podzols. Their organic content was derived originally from leaf litter and other plant remains. Where the primeval forests were deciduous – in warmer and drier areas – the soils are inherently less acid than in the areas once covered by coniferous forest, which supplied less organic matter and much of that in the form of pine needles that decompose only slowly. Podzols are generally poor, acid soils, from which most nutrients have been removed by leaching. They are often rather grey in colour, and like ash in consistency when dry. You will find them on heaths and upland moors, often supporting heather, ling, bracken and gorse. Elsewhere they are waterlogged, and a layer of acid peat has accumulated over a hardpan, usually rich in iron oxides.

Forest soils make good farm land, although they may require regular liming to prevent them

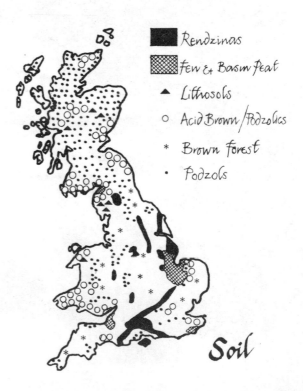

Rendzinas
Fen & Basin Peat
Lithosols
Acid Brown / Podzolics
Brown Forest
Podzols

Soil

from becoming too acid. It seems that once the forest is cleared, podzolization begins and a podzol is the natural end-product, unless the process is arrested by good farming. Podzols can be reclaimed in many cases, by deep ploughing to break up the pan, the use of fertilizer to supply almost all the major nutrients (see p.30), the installation of drainage (see p.18) and the growing of one or two pioneer crops that are ploughed in to supply organic matter. It is a rather slow business, but if you have a farm with some poor soil of this kind on one part of it, you could turn it into useful pasture within a couple of years, and eventually it might become quite productive crop land. Unless you are rich, however, it is not a good idea to buy a farm that consists of nothing but podzol.

Under the downs, the Wolds of Lincolnshire and Yorkshire, the Cotswolds, the Chilterns and in one or two other areas, you will find rendzinas. These are fertile soils, light sandy loam to loam in texture, that overlie chalk. Their limitation is their thinness. Most of them cannot be ploughed to a depth of more than 15cm or so, which is a pity as they are not acid and support large populations of soil organisms, so that if they were deeper they would be very good farm soils indeed. As it is they are used mainly as grassland for the grazing of sheep. In some places farmers have used slightly deeper rendzinas to grow barley every so often, exploiting the fertility contributed by the sheep. It is the sheep and rabbit which have given us the typical landscape of the downs, and as sheep farming has declined, and as the rabbit population has been reduced by myxomatosis, the grass has tended to be replaced by scrub as the land begins to revert to its former covering of shrubs and low trees with necessarily shallow roots.

The peat soils that occur in the Fens of East Anglia and on either side of the northern end of the Bristol Channel are almost pure compost. Most peats, however, are waterlogged and acid – often very acid. They are formed by the accumulation of organic matter under conditions too wet to allow normal decomposition. Drained and well ploughed they can be the most fertile of all soils, although when exposed to the air their decomposition accelerates, so they become a gradually dwindling asset. In Ireland and in parts of Scotland peats are still cut for fuel, in pieces rather larger than a house brick, built into 'walls' to dry out during the summer for use in the winter.

In the uplands many soils are very thin: erosion keeps pace with soil formation and their name, 'lithosol', suggests a soil that is mostly rock. They provide some rough grazing.

## Climate

No matter how fertile a soil is in terms of nutrients, crops will grow there only if they are supplied with the water they need, and if temperatures and the amount and intensity of daylight are adequate.

Climate is determined partly by latitude, but in a country as small as Great Britain the topography is much more influential. Height above sea level affects average temperatures and these affect rainfall.

Weather systems generally move from west to east, so that in Britain the western side of the country is wetter than the east. Wheat, which requires warm, dry weather before harvest, can be ripened successfully only on the eastern side of the country. Oats, which prefer cooler, moister conditions, are grown more widely in the west and north: this is why oats were the traditional staple food of the Highland Scots. The west grows excellent grass, in Devon and Cornwall for dairying and some beef, in Herefordshire for beef, in Cheshire, Lancashire and north into Cumbria for dairying, in south-west Scotland for dairying and some beef and, further north still, for beef.

In the very far north of Scotland the long, dark winter reduces the length of the growing season and this limits the range of crops that can be grown.

The climate is changing. There has been much discussion about this over the past few years, and despite large areas of uncertainty that still exist, some facts are becoming evident. For whatever reason, our climate is growing cooler, and our weather less predictable. The drought of 1975–6 and the widespread flooding early in 1977 are characteristic of a general weakening of the weather systems all over the northern hemisphere. The summer anticyclones tend to be more reluctant to move, so that long periods of dry weather are broken violently. Over the past twenty years or so the growing season has become shorter by about ten days.

We should not make too much of this. Probably there will be another ice age sometime in the next ten thousand years, but it is rather unlikely that Britain will be under the ice sheet by the end of this century! On the other hand, we cannot afford to ignore the short-term implications. Conditions in North America may become more difficult than they have been for the past thirty years, so that it may be unwise to plan on the assumption that American production will increase. Canadian and Soviet production of cereals may decrease, since their crops are grown rather close to the existing geographical limit. In Europe, research should be (and is being) directed to the development of crop varieties that are less sensitive to day-length and temperature.

## Topography

Apart from its effect on climate, topography exerts an influence of its own, and this, too, is one that changes according to the economic climate.

Some land, though fertile, is too steep for a tractor to work. The tractor is a robust machine, but it is prone to topple over if it is taken on to steep land, and most of the accidents to farm workers in Britain are caused by tractors rolling. New tractors are required by law to be fitted with safety cabs to protect the driver, but the

difficulty remains. So you will still see many fields on hillsides that are used only as permanent grassland.

A couple of generations ago, when all cultivation was horse-powered, many of these fields grew crops, for a horse can work land that is too steep for a tractor.

Where steep land is cultivated, cultivations should always follow the contours fairly closely. Ploughing across the contours (up and down a hillside rather than along it at a more or less constant height) is a major cause of soil erosion, as the rain flows down the furrows, carrying the soil with it. In countries that have much labour and little good lowland, hillsides are terraced. This provides a series of small areas of level ground and minimizes erosion. The technique is little used in Britain, mainly because the high cost of making the terraces could not be recovered from the sale of food in a reasonable time.

Fields on the north-facing slope of a narrow valley may be uncultivated because they are shaded for virtually all of the time, either by the hill of which they are part, or by the hills on the opposite side of the valley.

### Idiosyncracy of farmers

Despite the physical opportunities or limitations in an area, you will still see differences. In a dairying region some farmers will prefer one breed to another, and this will affect the arable crops they grow, since the dietary requirements of the various cattle breeds vary slightly.

Differences may also reflect the amount of capital the farmer has to invest, and the kind of lifestyle he prefers. Cattle, and especially dairy cattle, require constant attention. This means the farmer must find someone to stand in for him if he goes away even for a weekend. The purely arable farmer can leave his crops much more easily, and so is much freer. However, the fertilizer, machinery and fuel that are necessary in arable farming mean that it is expensive to begin. A herd of cattle can be worked up from a small initial stock by breeding, and by buying in animals a few a year. The farmer who entered farming recently is likely to be repaying loans, with high rates of interest; this may compel him to farm more intensively than he would wish. The farmer who inherited his land, or who has farmed it for a long time, may have low fixed costs, so that he can afford to adopt a more relaxed approach.

If it is the relationship between soils, climate,

Climate

Cold dry winter / Cool dry summer

Cold dry winter / Warm dry summer

Mild dry winter / Warm dry summer

Cold wet winter / Cool wet summer

Mild wet winter / Cool wet summer

Mild wet winter / Hot wet summer

topography and economics that have formed the broad patterns of farming in the different parts of Britain, it is the personal choices and the differing private circumstances of individual farmers that have supplied much of the richness of our landscapes. Just as a human community is composed of individuals whose differing tastes and idiosyncracies provide cohesiveness and variety, so, when transferred to the landscape, they have provided the diversity that we find aesthetically pleasing and that allows for ecological stability.

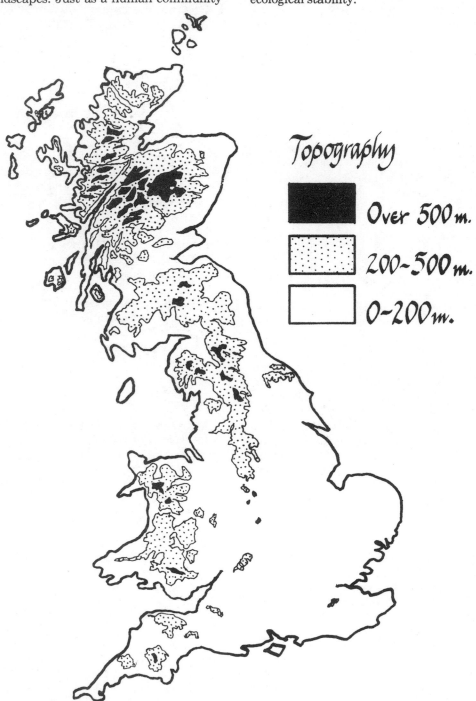

Topography

Over 500 m.

200-500 m.

0-200 m.

# Rural landscapes

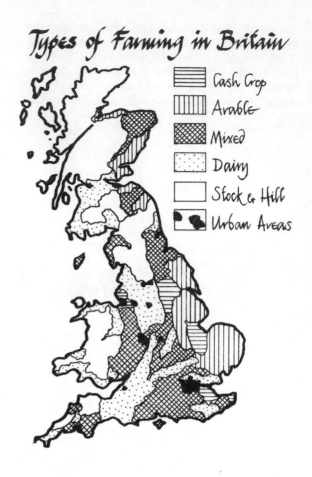

Types of Farming in Britain

- Cash Crop
- Arable
- Mixed
- Dairy
- Stock & Hill
- Urban Areas

It is often said that there is no truly natural landscape in Britain. Everything is man made. This is a slight exaggeration, but only a slight one. If it is the climate and topography that have determined farming systems, it is practical aims of the farmers themselves that have created the detail of what we see. Trees have been planted for a reason; hedges were made to enclose land (and many of them are no more than a century or two old) and they were removed when the need for them disappeared.

Because each type of land use is associated with a particular kind of landscape it is possible to correlate the two – so that if someone mentions, say, an arable farm, or a dairy farm, you will be able to picture it, and a glance at the landscape will tell you at once the kind of farming that is practised on it.

Intensive market gardening and fruit growing is unmistakable. Orchards, of course, are semipermanent features, although you may not be able to identify the fruit being grown if you visit them in winter. Much vegetable growing is done on rather small holdings, so you will find more dwelling houses than on most farms. There will be little or no grass, but the fields will be smaller than on many arable farms. The area will be not far from a large urban centre: proximity to the market is important when you are growing highly perishable produce. The main market-gardening areas in Britain are found in Kent, Worcester and Herefordshire, Gloucestershire, Cambridgeshire – Bedfordshire – Hertfordshire, East Yorkshire, Lancashire between Liverpool and Manchester, and the biggest area of all, south Lincolnshire, north Cambridgeshire (Isle of Ely) and north Norfolk. This is the very flat region, which includes Holland, of mainly fen peat soils, so fertile that it is farmed on a large scale, very intensively, to produce vegetables and flowers for widespread distribution.

At the other extreme, the highlands are largely uncultivable and of little agricultural value, though they may provide some rough grazing, for sheep or possibly for such new farm animals as red deer (see p.148).

At a slightly lower altitude, the hill sheep and stock farm is usually steep and wet. It will look green all year round (except when it is covered with snow). The fields will be of medium size, although there may be no field boundaries as such on the higher ground. Where there are boundaries, they are likely to be dry-stone walls, or stock-proof hedges with few trees. Hill sheep wander where they will, which is what makes hill sheep country so good for walking. The hills, the fells of the north, the downs (because of the character of their soils, see p.11, rather than their altitude) and the upland moors, all are used for sheep farming. Cattle, on the other hand, are enclosed in fields, and generally at lower levels and in more sheltered places. They require longer, lusher grass than the short, springy species that grow higher.

On the lower hills, and generally on the western side of the country, you will find

14

pastoral farming. This can be based on dairying, beef or sheep, or any mixture of the three, but the most usual enterprise is dairying. The fields will be fairly small and enclosed in strong, tight hedges, often with trees to provide additional shelter for the animals and, from time to time, a cash crop of timber. In general, the richer pastures are used for dairy cattle and the poorer ones for beef.

It is no coincidence that the best fields are closest to the farm centre – not, at least, if the general layout of the farm has remained essentially unchanged for a long time. These are the fields that are dunged most heavily, as they are crossed by stock to and from the central area of the farm, and where animals are wintered under cover the manure that is mucked out from the yards tends to be applied more to nearby fields than to remote ones: it may be bad farming, but it is very human! In a few years this may make little difference and on more modern, better managed farms the practice may have been stopped. However, many of our farms have stood for centuries, and over that kind of timescale the difference in the quality of fields becomes very pronounced.

Where arable crops can be grown as well as grass, it is almost certain that they will be, to cut the cost of bought-in feeds that are necessary to augment the grass supply for high dairy production. They may also provide a very useful income in their own right. A mixture of arable and stock farming is called mixed farming, and you will find it practised widely in central southern England, the Midlands, the North-East and the North-West and in Aberdeenshire, and to a lesser extent in most other regions. Mixed farming is the basis of traditional high farming: the system of husbandry introduced from northern Europe in the eighteenth century that gave a new lease of life to the existing system and, incidentally, led to the enclosure of much open land. It tends to be very stable and is sustainable for long periods of time, the arable crops feeding the stock and supplying bedding, the grass and manure feeding the soil, and the farm income derived from the sale of animal produce and arable surpluses.

Until quite recent times mixed farming was practised much more widely. A combination of economic pressures and the availability at a low price of agricultural chemicals made it possible to dispense with livestock in the areas best suited for cereal growing, and so much of East Anglia, Lincolnshire, south-east Yorkshire and parts of eastern Scotland as far north as Kincardineshire are devoted exclusively to arable farming. The departure of livestock removed the need for many of the hedges; the introduction of larger machines, and especially the combine harvester (see p.27), made larger fields desirable; and the reduction in the size of the labour force made hedge maintenance difficult. The combination of these factors has led to the appearance of what is sometimes called the 'prairie landscape': great fields of 50 hectares or more, stretching as far as the horizon unbroken by hedge or tree. Despite the seasonal appearance of combines working three or more in formation, the landscape is not truly that of the prairies and the farming is very different. The soils, derived from those characteristic of deciduous forest (see p.10) are not those of the prairie grasslands, and the climate is much milder and wetter. Thus British 'prairie' farming is much more intensive than would be possible in North America, and British yields per unit area are roughly double North American yields. One cause of the Oklahoma dust bowl was the assumption by immigrant Europeans that they could farm the prairies the way they were farmed back home.

Wherever a river provides a sufficient flow of water that is unpolluted and that is reasonably certain to remain unpolluted – which means well upstream of any town – you may find a fish farm. Fish farms occupy little space compared with any other kind of farm, but they can produce prodigious quantities of fish by raising them more intensively than is possible with mammals. In southern England small quantities of trout are produced on farms, and the number of farms doing this is likely to increase in years to come. In one or two parts of England and Scotland salmon are farmed. Salmon farms are less common, since they require very special conditions (see p.206).

Marine fish may also be farmed in the future, taking over to some extent from the sea fishing that is traditional all round the coast. The number of sites suitable for cultivating sea fish is limited in England and Wales, but in the Scottish sea lochs there are many sites. A marine fish farm is likely to consist of a few buildings on shore, with good access roads, open-air tanks for hatching eggs and rearing juveniles, and, in the water, nets or cages suspended from moored rafts or floats.

# Water means life

Even in our damp climate water shortages can occur, as we saw in 1976, and one of the first industries to be affected is agriculture. In drier climates this problem is more acute and more permanent. Many civilizations have been based on the skill with which they managed limited water resources.

Most of the civilizations failed – in the Fertile Crescent of Mesopotamia and the Indus Valley, for example – partly because their irrigation systems failed. The exception is Aztec Mexico. It fell because it was overthrown by the invading Spanish. Its water management was, perhaps, the most sophisticated the world has ever seen. It was developed in the fourteenth century AD and it is hard, even now, to think of ways in which it could have been improved. Yet the most advanced agricultural tool involved was the digging stick.

Now a German teacher of biology, working in Peru, has devised independently a system for producing crops in the tropics that is almost a modern version of the old Mexican system – of which he knew nothing.

In Britain, medieval monks drained the swamps and marshes that occupied large areas – in Somerset for example – to provide some of the best pasture in the country. Water management is vital.

### The chinampas
Aztec Mexico was ruled from a city that rose as an island in the cente of a huge lake. In the winter dry season the lake evaporated to become five smaller lakes. The lakes lay in the Valley of Mexico, 2.5km above sea level.

Large areas were drained by digging canals that intersected at right angles to form a grid pattern. The mud scooped out to make the canals was piled on the ground between, so that a pattern of rectangular raised beds was formed. These were secured by posts and vines and eventually by trees, mostly willows. Each bed, or 'chinampa', was about 90 metres long and 4.5–9 metres wide. As the canals were kept clear, the mud continued to be piled on top of the chinampas and the water weeds, which grew in profusion, were collected and used as a green manure. It was probably the great rafts of water weed being towed to the farm plots that gave rise to the Spanish interpretation of the chinampas as 'floating gardens'.

At one end of each plot was a seed bed. Mud was placed in a layer over a layer of water weed, and when the mud dried it was cut into squares. One seed was sown in each square and covered with manure, in Aztec days human excrement, but today animal manure. The seed was watered and when it sprouted it was moved, complete with its cube of mud, to the chinampa proper. The only crop not grown in this way was maize. Fish were raised in the canals.

The system worked only because there was a continual supply of fresh water to prevent the accumulation of salts left behind as the water evaporated in the hot sun. The fresh water came from springs, channelled into the canal system; and when, in the time of Montezuma I (1440–68), this proved inadequate, causeways were built to bring in water from further afield.

New plots were created by digging more canals, and when the beds became too high – which meant the upper soil dried out too quickly – soil was removed and redistributed among other plots.

No one knows what crop yields were achieved, but each household had six to eight members, and much of what they produced was paid in taxes, the income to the capital amounting to thousands of tonnes of produce each year.

### 'Uta culture'
Uta culture is the name given to the somewhat similar system devised by Rudolf Sessler for Peru, but which may also be adapted to a temperate climate.

The system begins with a series of shallow canals, about 80cm deep and of a similar width, lying parallel to one another. Water flows in at one end of the first canal and down it, up the second, down the third, and so on until it flows back to the river from which it came.

The canals are lined with an impermeable material, such as heavy-duty polythene sheeting, and raised beds are built between the canals, retained by low walls or partitions. The beds are used to grow a wide range of crops, and fish can be raised in the canals themselves. Sediment and weed that accumulates in the canals can be used as fertilizing material on the beds, so that nutrients are constantly recycled. Excess rainfall drains into the canals, but during dry weather the beds are kept moist by water ris-

ing through the soil by capillary attraction, and since the canals are lined the water cannot be lost. It is a constantly recycling system and apart from vegetables it can be made to produce feed for livestock, whose manure can also be returned. A filter at the exit will trap material that might otherwise leave the plot entirely, if this should prove necessary, and some barrier is needed to fence in the fish.

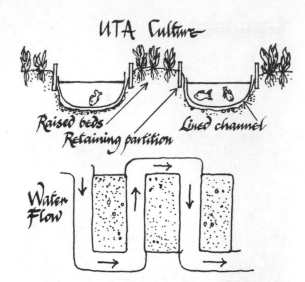

## Water hyacinth

The water hyacinth is a remarkable plant. It can produce more than 17 tonnes of plant material (wet) per hectare per day, and between 17 and 22 per cent of this is protein. The US National Aeronautics and Space Administration has found that not only can this plant material be processed to produce feed for livestock, methane gas, and fertilizer, but as an added bonus the plant is remarkably efficient at removing pollutants, especially heavy metals, from water. At NASA's National Space Technology Laboratories at Bay St Louis, Mississippi, they have designed a complex that ignores the manatees (perhaps they would cause difficulties on space ships) but takes the weeds in at one

end, pumps out purified water at the other, and produces methane and fertilizer as well as running a cattle and poultry farm along the way.

Water hyacinths grow only in warm, tropical waters, but at least the experience of NASA, not to mention that of the Mexicans centuries earlier, shows that water weeds can be used in food production.

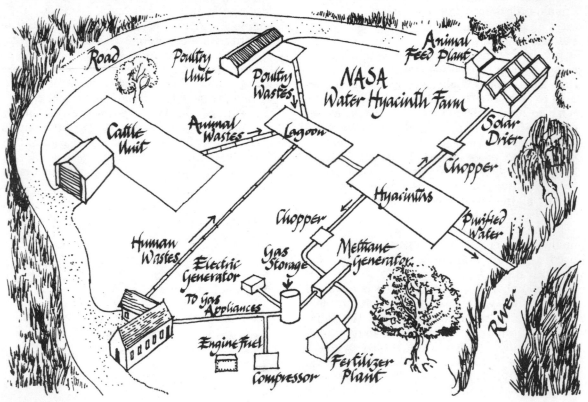

# Drainage

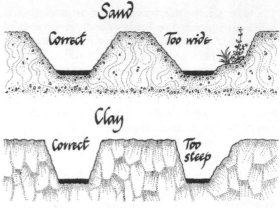

When water enters a soil some of it moves horizontally, some vertically. Water reaches a soil from rain, from melting snow, or by flowing downhill from land higher up a slope. Some of this water flows close to the surface, but much of it flows at a deeper level.

If the water table rises too close to the surface, problems arise that must be solved if the land is to be farmed efficiently. Apart from visible waterlogging, crop yields will be reduced, shallow-rooting, creeping kinds of weeds will flourish, such crops as are produced may be more difficult to handle, and animals will suffer from poor grazing and an increased risk of infection from parasites such as flies and flukes, and from foot rot.

The first step in draining land is usually to dig a ditch or to clear out an old, choked ditch. This may be all that is needed, but if not then mole drains or tile drains may be necessary.

## Ditches
Apart from hedges, ditches are probably the most common small-scale feature of the British rural landscape. Usually, but not always, they exist to carry away surplus water. They may also serve to mark a boundary, or to act as a 'wet fence' to retain farm animals. In some cases modern farmers dispense with ditches and use underground pipes instead. Pipes can be used effectively where the volume of water is not great, and especially if the need is to carry away the outfall from field drains rather than a larger, more dispersed flow.

Piping is expensive, but so is the proper maintenance of ditches, and where pipes can be used they do liberate a little more land for cultivation.

The purpose of a drainage ditch is to collect water at the lower end of a field, so preventing it from entering the next field down the slope. Roadside ditches prevent water from undercutting or flowing across the surface of roads. The ditches themselves are linked so that eventually they discharge, usually into a stream or river. Thus, to help dry out a field that is too

wet, the ditch is dug at the upper boundary, not the lower one.

Digging a ditch is more complicated than it may sound. Its depth must be determined by measuring the level at which the water is flowing, its width depends on the volume of water to be carried (if it is too narrow it will overflow and if it is too wide it will choke with weeds), and the angle of its banks depend on the type of soil – steeper sides in clay than in sand.

## Moling
Drainage may be needed either because the quantity of water entering the field is too great – in which case a ditch may cure the problem – or because the water table is too high. It may be too high because of the natural structure of the soil, with impermeable material lying rather close to the surface, or because the use of heavy machinery, or trampling of wet ground by cattle ('poaching'), has compacted the soil into a 'hardpan' within about 30cm of the surface. A ditch will not cure this situation: the pan must be broken.

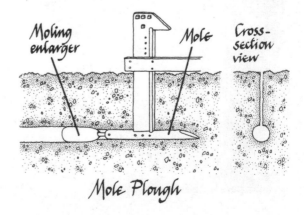

This is what moling aims to achieve. A mole is a metal cylinder, usually about 8cm in diameter, with one end sharpened. Often it has an 'enlarger' behind it: a second, slightly larger cylinder that can rotate to widen the hole.

The mole is mounted on a blade whose length is adjustable, and fixed to a bar on the rear of a tractor. A hole is dug to the required depth to insert the mole, and then the mole is dragged down the field. It cuts a hole through the soil which stays open because it is formed by the compaction of the soil around it, but the slit cut by the blade above it closes over. A mole drainage system will last for five to ten years, depending on the type of soil.

Moles are usually dug at a depth of 50–70cm, and they will drain the land above them at an angle of about 45°, so they are commonly spaced 2.5–3 metres apart.

Mole drains require a considerable power to dig. It is a job for a tractor, and if the soil is heavy it may need a large tractor. Often the work is undertaken by a contractor, and for registered farmers grants are available to help with the cost.

## Tiles

Tile drains last much longer, but involve much more work and much more expense. Most farmers do not have the equipment to install them. However, grants are available, and as the system should last for several lifetimes the initial cost may be worth while.

Narrow channels are cut in the soil to the required depth. Generally this is much the same as the depth for moles, but a tile is said to drain the land to either side to a distance equal to about eight times its depth.

The channels are covered with a layer of gravel, or simply made smooth and level. Short (about 25cm) lengths of unglazed pipe with an inside diameter of about 10cm are laid end to end and well butted together. Where they feed into a ditch, the outfall must be at least 15cm above the bottom of the ditch and the final 1.5 metres of piping must be rigid and frost-proof. The drain is then covered with straw or more gravel and finally the earth is replaced.

Tile drains may be laid in a simple, parallel fashion at intervals down the field, or in a more complex herringbone pattern, using ready-made junction pipes. The side drains are smaller (say about 7.5cm) than the main drains and their purpose is to improve the drainage of very heavy land.

### General notes

The Ministry of Agriculture, Fisheries and Food publishes a set of excellent simple pamphlets on drainage called *Field Drainage,* available from regional offices of the Ministry. The Ministry also has drainage advisers, and farmers who believe they have a drainage problem are encouraged to consult the Ministry. The drainage adviser will also provide information on the size of the grant available – it will cover about half the cost – and how to obtain it.

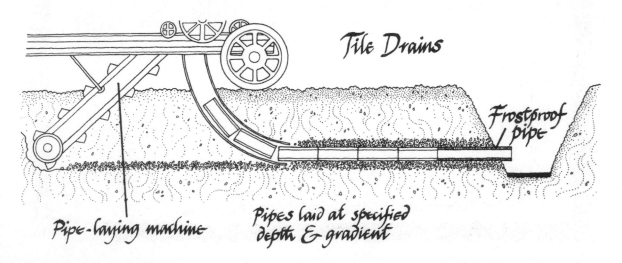

Tile Drains

Frostproof pipe

Pipe-laying machine

Pipes laid at specified depth & gradient

19

# Crop implements

### The plough

The purpose of ploughing is to invert the topsoil, burying and so killing many annual weeds, opening up the soil to the action of frost – which breaks up large lumps of earth as the expanding ice splits them apart – burying surface residues and debris, and assisting drainage (but see p.18).

The plough in most common use in Britain is the mouldboard plough, designed to plough one or more furrows at a time, depending on the type of soil and the power available to draw it.

The first part of the plough to make contact with the soil is the coulter. This may be shaped like a knife, or it may be a hard steel disc about 40cm in diameter. The knife type has the advantage of preventing the plough from choking, especially if the plough is of the reversible type (see below). In front of the coulter there may be a skimmer or jointer, a blade that skims off (hence its name) a narrow strip of surface soil ahead of the coulter.

The coulter makes a vertical cut in the soil ahead of the blade of the plough itself, and its height can be adjusted.

The main cut is made by the ploughshare, made from steel or, less commonly, from cast iron. The share is detachable and consists of a point at the upper end and a swept-back wing.

The share cuts through the soil; the mouldboard turns the furrow over and as its name suggests it is shaped so that the soil will move past it, up and over. The upper edge of the mouldboard is called the shin, and in some models this is detachable. The mouldboard must be designed and constructed so that soil does not stick to it: it must slide past as smoothly as possible.

The share and mouldboard are attached to a vertical beam which in turn is attached to a horizontal beam (called simply the beam), to which is also attached the 'coulter stalk', the arm bearing the coulter and skimmer – the height and relative positions of coulter and share being adjusted by a pivoted lever, so that raising the coulter moves the share forward and vice versa.

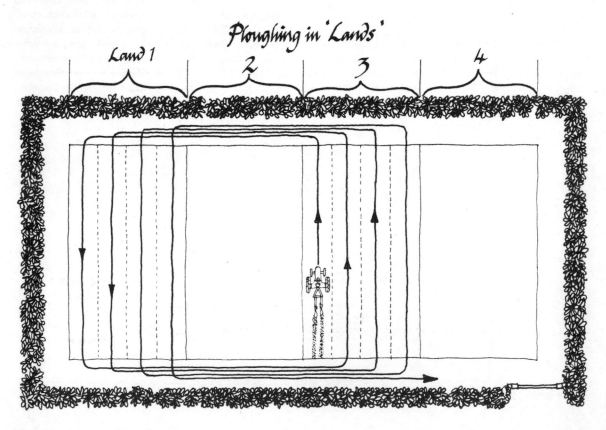

Ploughing in 'Lands'

Land 1    2    3    4

There are several versions of the basic mould-board plough, but the most important variant is the reversible plough. The design of the mould-board is such that a furrow will be turned to one side only: to left or right. By mounting a left-hand and a right-hand plough to either side of an arm in such a way that rotating the arm lowers one and raises the other, the same implement can be made to turn furrows to either side. The reversible plough makes possible one-way ploughing. Imagine a plough that turns a furrow across a field. It then turns about and cuts a second furrow, moving in the opposite direction. If the mouldboard is fixed – say a right-hand one – the first furrow will be turned to the right and the second furrow will be turned in such a way as to fill in the first furrow. This problem can be overcome by devising a ploughing pattern that has the plough crossing the land in one direction only – ploughing 'in lands' – or by using the reversible plough.

The mole attachment (see p. 18) is also a type of plough, and the third type is the chisel plough. This consists of three to five rigid or spring steel tines fixed to a tool bar and drawn through the soil, which it shatters to a depth of 35cm or more, but without turning over the top-soil. Disc ploughs, which scoop shallow, semi-circular grooves, are not much used in Britain.

**Ploughing in lands:** This is the traditional ploughing pattern. The plough is taken around the boundary of the field to mark out a single shallow furrow. This outer edge of a field is the 'headland', and it must be wide enough to permit the tractor and plough to turn in it, so that it begins each furrow in correct alignment.

The field is divided into lands, or plots, of a convenient width – usually about 12 metres – their alignment depending on the shape and slope of the field but generally aiming to allow the longest possible furrows and so the minimum amount of turning.

Each plot is ploughed in the same direction, but so that the direction of ploughing alternates from one land to the next. Markers are set up at either side of the field to ensure the opening furrow is straight. Ploughing begins in land three. The plough moves along the headland and enters land one, heading in the opposite direction, returning to the second furrow in land three. When one and three are ploughed, the plough turns into lands two and four, working in a similar fashion. However, if the ridges in land

one lie to the left, those in land two will lie to the right, and so forth, so that the finished field is marked with double ridges and double furrows at alternate land boundaries. Finally the headland itself is ploughed in either a clockwise direction ('gathering') or anti-clockwise ('casting').

**No-ploughing:** In some senses, ploughing is controversial. There is a school of thought which holds that it is positively harmful: oddly enough, for many of the reasons that most farmers believe it to be beneficial. Burying weeds means that organic matter is placed at too low a depth to be of use as a source of nutrients to growing crops; opening up the soil tends to dry it out; exposing the soil increases the danger of damage from wind (erosion) and rain (capping, whereby heavy rain can batter the top few millimetres into a smooth, impermeable layer from which further water runs off without draining to the plant root region beneath).

The theory has found little support among British farmers and its arguments are not very convincing scientifically, at least not for most parts of Britain. No doubt there are soils that are better left undisturbed, but in general the clearing of weeds and the aeration of the soil do more good than harm.

That said, there is a danger of creating a 'plough pan', a hard impermeable soil layer just below normal ploughing depth caused mainly by the repeated movement of machinery over the land. A plough pan will cause poor drainage. In most cases the cure is simply to plough to a greater depth once in a while (subsoiling), using either a much larger and heavier mouldboard plough, or a chisel plough.

It is possible today to avoid all mechanical cultivation of the soil, using chemical treatments to achieve weed control, and although this is not widely practised at present, mainly because of its high cost, it may become more popular in the future (see p.40).

**Ploughing virgin land:** If you travel in land that has never been cultivated, or that has not been cultivated for a very long time, you may see evidence of particularly deep ploughing. The aim here is to open up virgin soils, which may be poorly drained and are probably acid, prior to planting a 'pioneer crop' – the first crop to be sown on new land, more for the benefit of the soil than for the crop itself.

# Cultivating machinery

## Rollers

The roller is used to flatten and consolidate land after ploughing, especially on newly ploughed grassland. The old smooth roller – like a garden roller only larger – has been largely superseded by the Cambridge roller, which is made from a series of ribbed rings. Its advantage is that it smashes large clods of earth and is not so prone to form an impermeable cap on the soil surface as is the smooth roller. Towed by tractors, rollers are generally worked as **a** triple gang, a long roller in the centre preceding two shorter ones towed behind and to the sides.

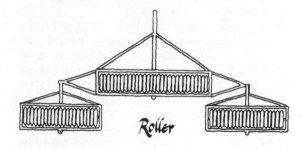

*Roller*

## Cultivators

Cultivators cut through, and so break up the ground. They are to the plough what the garden fork is to the spade. There are two main types, rigid tine and spring tine. Rigid tines can also be spring mounted, so that if they meet an obstruction, such as a large stone, the tine moves back and up on a pivot, to clear the obstacle, then springs back into its original position. The curved, pointed tip of the tine is called the 'share'.

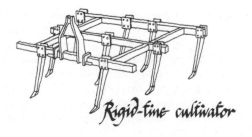

*Rigid-tine cultivator*

The spring tine achieves the same advantage by being itself a spring, made from steel.

Rigid- or spring-tine cultivators are particularly useful for cultivating between rows of vegetable crops (e.g. potatoes, brassicas, etc.) that are grown commercially in straight rows.

The rotary cultivator is similar to the garden rotavator, but larger in scale and operated from a tractor. It consists of a series of six or more sets of blades mounted on arms or wheels at right angles to the axis around which they rotate. Towed across the land they chop up the soil into fine particles and throw it slightly upwards, so that it falls back well aerated.

*Spring-tine cultivator*

## Harrows

The harrow is the farm equivalent of the garden rake. It works a ploughed (and perhaps rolled) soil to a fine tilth. It also compacts the soil to some extent, which may or may not be desirable.

The simplest harrow of all is a large clump of gorse (called furze, or whin, in some parts of the country) which at one time was sown deliberately, mainly as a fuel crop but also to some extent for harrowing and even, in hard times, as food for livestock. Cattle and horses will eat gorse when there is nothing else.

You will be lucky to see gorse being used in this way today. The harrows you will see are of several types, all doing the same job, but very different in appearance.

**Disc harrow:** The disc harrow consists of a series of cutting discs mounted on an axis, and often used in tandem, so that a second row of discs is pulled behind the first, and at a different angle. A two-gang tandem can be pulled on either side of a tractor, making a four-gang tandem.

*Tandem disc harrow*

**Spring-tine harrow:** The spring-tine harrow is an arrangement of springy, curved blades or knives.

*Spring-tine harrow*

**Zig-zag harrow:** This consists of a frame, or more usually three frames, arranged in a Z-shaped pattern, with a rigid straight or curved tine at each intersection.

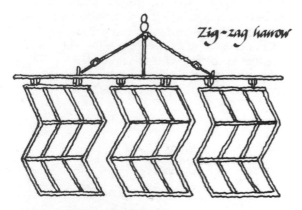

*Zig-zag harrow*

**Chain harrow:** This is a section of chain-link matting, completely flexible so that it follows the undulations of the land, with or without spikes projecting down from the links, depending on the purpose for which it is used.

On grassland, for example, a plain chain harrow will spread manure evenly after grazing and improves the grass for later mowing. On ploughed land it will help remove some troublesome weeds such as couch grass (sometimes called 'twitch'). The spikes aerate the soil a little. If fertilizer is to be used, they will help it to penetrate.

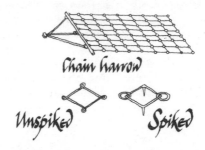

*Chain harrow*

*Unspiked*            *Spiked*

### Weeders and hoes

Weeders may be versions of harrows or, more usually, rotary cultivators, designed simply to uproot, chop, bury and generally abuse weeds. Land can be levelled and clods crushed by an arrangement that looks rather like a five-bar gate, dragged flat over the land.

Hoes are meant for working between rows, so the arrangement on the tool bar behind the tractor must be precise. A farm hoe blade does the same job as a garden hoe – it cuts off weeds just below the ground surface – but the angle at which the blade enters the soil is adjustable. The hoe blade, or series of blades, may be mounted in the same framework as two discs. The discs run on either side of the crop plants, cutting a narrow channel to either side of them, while the hoe cuts between the channels, disturbing the top layer of soil.

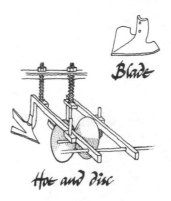

*Blade*

*Hoe and disc*

## Thinners

For thinning out row crops a device is used that consists of a set of rotating arms, often five of them, each arm having at its end a small, rectangular blade. As the arms rotate, each blade in turn is brought across the crop row at right angles, so removing any plant it encounters. Each set of blades works one row, so that five sets of blades work five rows simultaneously. Each set of blades rotates in the opposite direction to that of the next set, to prevent the apparatus from being swung to the side. The blades are adjustable and the distance that is left between the remaining plants can be controlled. This is only one pattern of thinner: there are others.

## Manure spreaders

There are two types of manure spreader, the trailer and the rotary spreader. The trailer consists of an endless belt floor that moves the manure toward the rear, where it meets two sets of flails. These are mounted one slightly above and in front of the other, and each has a number of arms. As they rotate they pick up the manure and throw it with some force into a rotating helical-shaped spreader that throws it upward and to the rear. It aerates the amnure as it spreads it, and the trailer spreader is an ideal implement for making compost on a farm scale (see p. 117).

Manure spreader

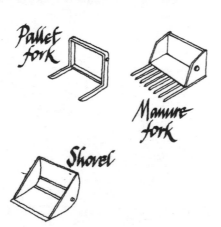

Thinner

## Loaders

Tractors can be mounted with hydraulically powered arms at the front or rear, and these may be used with a range of tools, most commonly the shovel, manure fork and pallet fork, for lifting different kinds of load.

The rotary spreader can handle semi-liquid or liquid manure (which a trailer spreader cannot), it pulverizes the materials more completely, and it achieves a more even spread. It consists of a cylindrical container with a central spinning axis to which are attached flails made from chain.

Chains can be substituted for the helical spreader at the rear of trailer spreaders.

Liquid manures (slurry, see p. 116) are more often spread by pumps or tankers.

Pallet fork

Manure fork

Shovel

Rotary Spreader

## Fertilizer distributors

The most common types are based on a spinning disc. A funnel-shaped feeder allows the fertilizer to drop on to a disc that is spinning rapidly in a horizontal plane, so throwing it outwards in all directions. Sometimes the disc itself is contained in a housing from which pipes protrude at intervals, in which case the fertilizer is ejected from the pipes.

The distributor is used in conjunction with a trailer fitted with either an endless belt floor, or a centrally mounted helical auger, so that the material in the trailer is constantly pushed to the rear and into the feeder funnel.

## Sowing

The final process, after the land has been ploughed, rolled, harrowed, cultivated and worked to a fine tilth, is sowing. Obviously, row crops, which include anything except wheat, oats, barley or rye, must be sown in rows. Cereals (what the British call 'corn' – American corn is maize, which is a row crop) used to be sown broadcast, and still can be. Provided labour is available it is the cheapest way to do the job.

To ensure the seed is distributed evenly over the field, it is best to divide the field into plots, share the seed equally among the plots, and place the bags so that each plot receives its own share and none of the seed belonging elsewhere.

Each plot is then walked by a person holding a bag or basket containing the seed, which is scooped out by hand and thrown in a single sweeping gesture. To ensure even coverage it is best to divide even this process into two parts, halving the seed, and walking each plot twice, the second time at right angles to the direction of the first sowing. With a little practice it is possible to sow seed quite evenly in this way.

Similarly, row crops can be sown by hand, although this is a more laborious not to say back-breaking business.

**Seed drills:** The alternative is the seed drill. Invented many, many years ago, this is perhaps the simplest of farm implements. It consists first of a hopper or tank in which the seed is placed. The bottom of the hopper has holes which can be covered by a sliding plate whose position is adjusted by a lever, so that the size of aperture is regulated. This controls the rate at which the seed falls through a funnel-shaped dispenser and

down a tube (the 'coulter tube') and into the coulter, which is a hollow spike open on one side, that makes a narrow groove in the soil (a drill) into which the seeds are placed.

There are many refinements, particularly in the way the seed is fed into the coulter assembly.

Seed drills are specialized to some extent to accommodate different kinds of seed, and the coulter may be in the form of a single disc, double disc (arranged so that the discs meet at their lower edge and cut a V shaped groove), or a hoe blade. Fertilizers are also applied by seed drills on many farms. Grass seed, which should not be planted in rows, requires a slightly different mechanism in which rotating brushes throw the seed through apertures in the rear of the dispenser.

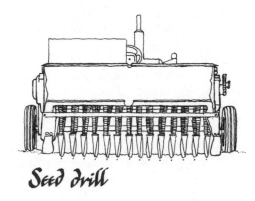

## Seed drill

Potato planting presents special problems. A large, strong coulter, more like a plough, cuts a drill. A large wheel with projecting blades forms cups, into each of which a seed potato is fed. The potatoes are carried downwards and fall from the bottom of the wheel into the drill. The potatoes can be fed manually, working one row at a time, or sowing three rows at a time.

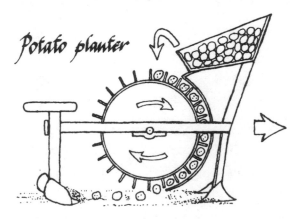

## Potato planter

# Harvesting Machinery

## Foraging

Traditionally, foraging is the provision of any kind of food for livestock. In practice, it means the harvesting of a forage crop: a crop grown specifically as food for livestock and intended to be harvested while it is still green. So that it may be stored the crop must first be dried or ensiled (see Grass conservation, p.106).

The green crop is cut, using a mower very like a lawn-mower but larger, with a rotating set of blades that cut against a fixed plate. The flail harvester and flail mower are refinements of the basic design. After the crop is cut, it is thrown upwards along a chute and discharged high enough from the ground for it to feed directly into a trailer. A rotary scythe, with a horizontal spinning disc like a rotary garden lawn-mower, is used rarely on farms. The main alternative to the mower is cutting based on reciprocating knives, like a garden hedge-trimmer, but mounted horizontally. If the crop is to be moved from the field for drying or ensiling, the flail harvester or mower has the obvious advantage of

saving an entire operation by delivering the crop into a trailer as it is cut.

If the crop is left lying in the field, small quantities can be lifted and moved for ensiling using a buckrake mounted on a tractor.

## Haymaking

Making hay is a poor way of storing grass, since much of the nutritional value is lost, but it is traditional and will not disappear from our farms overnight.

The herbage is cut and left to dry in the field. It must be spread out and turned over as often as is necessary.

If the weather is fine – and for haymaking fine weather is vital – the tedder follows close behind the mower. 'Tedding' is derived from the same root as the Welsh word 'teddu', which means 'to spread out'. The tedder lifts the swathe left by the mower, throws it up and over, and leaves it open so that air can penetrate.

The grass must then be spread, or scattered, using mechanical rakes. Spreading is sometimes used instead of tedding – it does less damage to the crop – particularly after the crop has been soaked by heavy rain.

Before the dried hay can be moved from the field it must be gathered, which most usually means making two swathes into one, with the

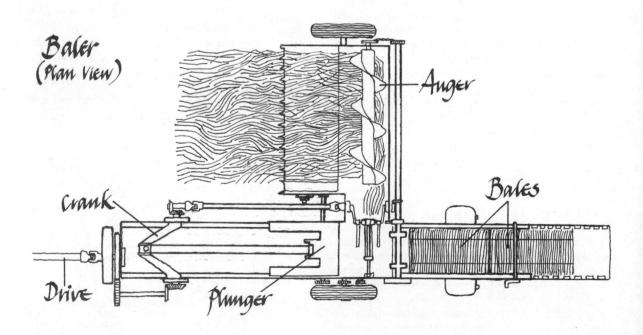

Baler (Plan View)

Auger

Crank

Bales

Drive

Plunger

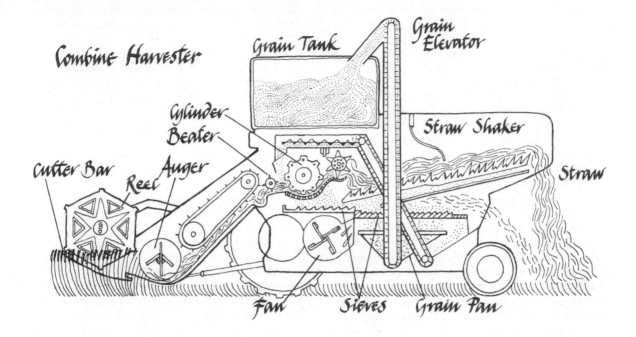

Combine Harvester

machinery moving between the two swathes; side-raking usually takes two swathes at a time and discharges both to the same side of the rake, so having a gathering effect.

To accelerate drying, hay is sometimes crimped by being passed between fluted rollers, or crushed between smooth rollers.

The baler consists of revolving tines which lift the hay on to a feed table, where it comes into contact with an auger or other type of conveyor, which feeds it into a chamber under increasing pressure, where it is packed tightly into a bale, tied automatically, and discharged. There are now machines that can move round the field collecting the bales of hay (or straw after combining) and stacking them.

## Cereal crops

Cereals can be cut by scythe, or with a reaper and binder, but today the combine harvester has superseded all other machines. It is the size of combines – although the size does vary, all of them are large – that has necessitated fields larger than those that existed previously in many areas, and so has led to the removal of many hedgerows in a process that often has gone much further than is required for good modern farming.

Designed originally only to harvest grains, the combine used to spend all but about three weeks of the year lying idle. Modern combines are rather more versatile and can harvest other crops, such as peas and beans, as well.

A modern combine harvester performs four operations, and sometimes five. It cuts the crop; it separates the grain from the ear; it separates the grain from the straw, pumping the grain into a tank and baling and discharging the straw; it separates weeds and rubbish from the grain; on some machines it also screens the grain, which assists in its grading.

Individual components vary in their design, but all combines consist of the same basic parts. At the front is the cutter bar, which can be raised and lowered. This is similar to a mowing machine, but the blades are often serrated, which makes for cleaner cutting of straw and less need for sharpening.

Above the cutter bar there is a reel, which rotates the crop and gathers it into the machine. This reel is driven by a belt or chain, and its position can be adjusted according to the length of the straw.

The crop is then gathered by an auger, which drives it to the feed conveyor, which carries it up and back to the feeder beater and threshing cylinder, which separate the grain from the ear and the grain from the straw. All those parts of the machine from the cutter to the feeder beater are known as the 'header'.

The threshing cylinder, or drum, is edged with beater bars and rotates in a curved grid, called the concave. The turning of the cylinder draws the crop across the bars of the concave and rubs the grain out of the ears.

Most of the grain falls through the concave on to a shaker beneath and thence, through two sieves, into the grain pan, from which it is taken to the grain tank.

The straw, meanwhile, is carried back to the stripper beater, which transfers it to the straw shaker, where it is agitated to remove the kernels of grain that it still contains. The grain recovered in this way falls through to the shaker, sieves and grain pan, while the straw is ejected, loose or baled according to the type of machine.

The two sieves through which the grain must pass are blown by a current of air from a fan, so that the grain is first cleaned of dust and chaff and then sifted and winnowed. A separate system exists to catch grain that falls from the machine and to return it.

Most combine harvesters today are self-propelled, but there are still some in use that are trailed.

Despite the fact that it looks like an ungainly toy built with a child's construction kit, the combine harvester has revolutionized cereal farming, and the way of life associated traditionally with it. Because of the speed at which it works, the harvest has a much better chance of being gathered at exactly the right time, and so losses have been much reduced. On the other hand, it has been blamed for the acute weed problem on many arable farms. Whereas at one time the crop would be taken to one place on the farm to be threshed, so that weed seeds caught in it were all deposited in one small area, the combine threshes as it goes and distributes the weed seeds all over the field.

The efficiency of the combine has reduced the requirement for labour on farms, perhaps more than any other machine apart from the tractor, which replaced the labour-intensive horse. School holidays are still long in the summer to allow children to take part in the grain harvest.

Today, one man drives the combine, a second ferries the grain from the combine's tank to the bins. Two men and one machine are all that is needed.

**Root crops**
Until quite recently, potato harvesting was also labour intensive – and backbreaking. Today a large labour force is needed only when the weather has been so bad that machinery cannot get on to the land. Potatoes are harvested by machine.

There are several types of potato harvester, but the most common are the spinner and the elevator.

The spinner type is trailed by a tractor and powered from the tractor. It consists of a share, triangular in shape, which lifts a slice of earth, and a rotor with tines – the spinner – which throws the potatoes to one side and through a screen, which prevents them from being thrown too far and also knocks some of the earth from them. In some models the tines feather as they are carried up and over, and are extended only in the lower positions. The spinner type of harvester leaves the potatoes on the surface for subsequent collection by hand.

The elevator type, which may be trailed, semi-mounted or mounted, has a share which lifts the earth, which is then fed on to an endless belt elevator made from rods linked to one another. The potatoes are carried upward, and then descend past agitators. The movement, first of being carried by the rods and then of being agitated, shakes off most of the earth. Usually the potatoes are left on the ground, but elevators can be linked to feed the harvested crop into trailers.

Sugar beet is usually harvested nowadays by a complete harvester. The machine begins by removing the tops, which are sliced off and thrown to one side. An alternative design lifts the beet complete with top and removes the top later, allowing the root to fall on to a conveyor and throwing the top out to the rear. The root is lifted by shares, which may be triangular or slightly concave splayed wheels. The advantage in topping the beet after it is lifted is mainly the protection afforded to the cutting edges which do not then encounter stones.

As the root is passed by a linked rod elevator to the point at which it is discharged into a container, or trailer, it is agitated to remove much of the earth that clings to it.

# Flail-Harvesting

# Sugar Beet Harvesting

In-Line     Offset (Rear Attached)   Offset (Side Attached)

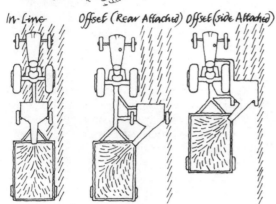

# Potato Harvesting

Spinner-Type Harvester

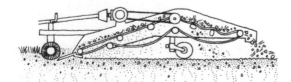

Elevator-Type Harvester

# Side-Raking

Tedding     Timing     Side-Raking

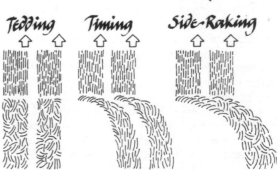

29

# Fertilizers and fertility

'Fertility' implies three things: a supply of appropriate nutrients, matching the crop's changing requirements throughout the season; a correct level of acidity (pH), to ensure that those nutrients remain available to the plant; and a good soil structure to ensure, above all, that the roots have enough air and water to be able to utilize the food you give them. The boring debate about whether 'organic' or 'artificial' fertilizers are better is out-moded. The bulky organics and the more precisely formulated and concentrated artificials can and should complement each other: the organics, in general, providing a groundswell of broad-spectrum, long-term fertility and helping to maintain and improve soil structure, and the artificials meeting precisely the immediate requirements of each hungry crop.

For the best results you must know precisely which nutrients each crop requires, and in what proportions (grass, for example, can take far more nitrogen than cereals), and you must also know what your own soil lacks, so that you know what to add. For example, expensive phosphates are often applied wastefully to soils that already have enough. To be in the top league of growers you should seek the help of professional soil chemists.

First, though, here are some guiding principles. A plant consists mostly of carbon, which it gets from the air as carbon dioxide, and water, which it gets from the soil. It needs in addition a variety of other elements, nutrients, which it also gets mainly from the soil ('mainly' because deficient trace and sometimes other minerals can be introduced conveneintly through the leaves). The chief nutrients, which must be attended to afresh with each crop, are nitrogen (N) introduced as nitrate or ammonium salts, phosphorus (P) introduced as some form of phosphate, and potassium (K) or potash introduced as various salts. In the second league of

nutrients, requiring more occasional and specific topping up, are calcium, magnesium, sulphur and, for some plants such as sugar beet, sodium. The trace metals, which are vital but only in minute amounts, include iron, manganese, boron, copper, zinc, molybdenum and cobalt. Most soils naturally contain adequate amounts of these metals.

Nitrogen poses the greatest problems. In general, yield is directly related to the amount of N applied; ICI suggests that the average amount applied to grass in the UK, 52kg per hectare, provides less than 65 per cent of the return that could be achieved. But you can put on too much: an excess on cereals, for example, makes them grow too tall and 'lodge' (see pp.34 and 49); an excess on grass may produce more herbage than you can cope with. Application is subject to the law of diminishing returns, so that the eight-fold increase in N application since the turn of the century has increased overall yield by only one-and-a-half times.

The time and place of application are critical. The early application of N to grass in the spring can give a spurt to growth that will support livestock three weeks earlier than would be possible otherwise, so saving winter feed. If you apply before the soil is warm enough to support growth, however, and especially if rainfall is high, then most of the fertilizer will simply leach away. Again, fertilizer scattered vaguely between the rows of row-crops will not reach the roots: modern machines sometimes introduce fertilizer precisely into the seed drills (see p.25). Farmers know these problems, but nevertheless 50 per cent of the nitrogen applied artificially is believed simply to wash away.

The ideal soil structure must reconcile the opposing requirements for water and air. A waterlogged soil, such as badly drained clay, suffocates the plants; a too open, airy structure, such as sand, dries them out. You need sponginess – a network of pores with water adhering to the sides, and air coursing between. It is this open but water-loving structure that bulky organic material is best able to provide. With such a structure, added artificial nutrients are least likely to be washed away.

Finally, because of the organic activity within it, most soil tends to become progressively more acid. Lime in various forms is added to restore neutrality, but again you must be precise. Test the acidity with a pH meter (several types are available) before applying exactly the amount of lime the suppliers calculate is necessary. Too much is wasteful, and possibly harmful.

## Nitrogen fixation

Industry makes nitrogen fertilizer by 'fixing' atmospheric nitrogen – combining it with hydrogen to form ammonia ($N_2 + 3H_2 \rightarrow 2NH_3$), which is then applied to the fields either as an ammonium ($NH_4$) salt, or is oxidized first to nitrate, the form in which plants absorb it. Some bacteria and blue-green algae also carry out this process, not by employing the metal catalysts and white heat that industry requires, but by gentle enzyme action in the cold soil. Worldwide, this natural fixation contributes at least three times more N to the soil than comes from artificials, and perhaps ten times as much, and for most of the world's crops it is the sole source of added nitrogen. Rice in the Far East, for example, is fertilized mainly by blue-green algae. The fertilizer industry is expanding rapidly to meet a world demand for nitrogen that will increase sevenfold by AD 2000, but it requires ever greater quantities of ever more precious energy. Small wonder that many scientists are now striving to abet the natural fixing process.

Nitrogen-fixing bacteria in the soil are of three main kinds: those that live free; those that prefer the rhizosphere (plant root region) and form loose associations with plant roots; and those that live within the root itself, forming intimate symbiotic relationships, with the bacteria providing nitrogen for the plant, and the plant giving carbohydrate (produced by photosynthesis) to the bacteria.

The best known of these symbiotic relationships is between the leguminous plants (such as peas, beans and lupins), and the *Rhizobium* bacteria that live in nodules on their roots. This relationship was first described in the nineteenth century, although the legumes' ability to bolster the growth of subsequent crops, or that of plants grown alongside, was recognized long before that. Today, clover is deliberately encouraged in some grass swards; clover, vetches lucerne and sainfoin are grown as partly self-fertilizing green forage crops (see p.98); and lupins, peas and beans contribute to many a rotation. Much of the nitrogen fixed by a legume may be leached out in winter if the crop is ploughed in during autumn, but the 100kg of N per hectare contributed by a close clover sward, for example, is not to be despised.

Many attempts are being made now to increase the legumes' power to fix nitrogen. The amount fixed is related directly to the rate of photosynthesis, which probably could often be increased. Most temperate plants, for example, have in-built mechanisms to restrain photosynthesis, which could be bred out or inhibited chemically. Again, *Rhizobium*'s nitrogen fixation is inhibited by the ammonia that it itself produces, so that soya, for example, will not respond to overlarge applications of artificial fertilizer, because the excess simply suppresses the *Rhizobia* in the roots. Less sensitive *Rhizobium* strains could be developed: the antibiotics industry has shown how flexible bacteria can be.

Yet the most exciting recent discovery is that many non-leguminous plants also form symbiotic relationships with nitrogen-fixing bacteria. alder and myrtle are two common examples. If this ability is not peculiar to legumes, why should it not be conferred on a whole range of food plants – and in particular the grasses, which include the cereals?

Here, too, nature has beaten us to it. Johanna Döbereiner in Brazil has shown that the bacterium *Spirillum lipoferum* fixes nitrogen within the roots of several tropical grasses, and even in some strains of maize, the best of which, apparently, fix nitrogen as efficiently as soya. *Spirillum* and its maize hosts are resolutely tropical, but many other tropical crops have been adapted to temperate regions.

British scientists are trying to arrange a marriage between wheat and the nitrogen-fixing bacteria already adapted to northern climates. The main problem is to produce a wheat that will play host to the bacteria. One approach is to use cell-fusion techniques to try to 'borrow' the necessary genes from leguminous plants, virtually forming a hybrid between totally unrelated species that could never be crossed naturally. *Rhizobium* is the most obvious bacterial candidate, but the free-living nitrogen-fixing *Azotobacter* might also be induced to live in plant roots.

Plant breeders have usually simply modified wild species. Only occasionally, as with the swede or cauliflower or the modern maizes, have they produced plants so different from their ancestors as to be virtually man-made. A nitrogen-fixing wheat would be the supreme artifice. It would also be the greatest agricultural development since the domestication of the potato.

# The pesticides

Fashions change in pesticides, as they do in every branch of agriculture. The two outstanding natural insecticides, extracted from plants, are nicotine, taken from tobacco, and pyrethrum, from a daisy-like flower grown in Africa. Both are short lived, and until a few years ago this was seen generally as a grave disadvantage. Spraying might have to be repeated again and again.

The highly expensive and toxic nicotine has become something of an also-ran among insecticides. There are some organic gardeners who extract it by boiling up old cigarette ends (an increasingly unrewarding pastime in this age of filter tips), but it is used chiefly in specialist enterprises where expense is no object – to protect house plants, for example. Pyrethrum, on the other hand, which is unstable in light and air and which therefore has been used mainly for arcane purposes like removing fleas from dogs, has taken on a new lease of life. Its low toxicity to mammals and its quick disappearance once it has killed the target pests are seen now as major advantages.

Scientists at the Government experimental station at Rothamsted have been trying to improve the natural pyrethrin molecule ever since 1948. By 1965 they had produced resmethrin and bioresmethrin, which were more toxic to insects than the natural compound, and even less toxic to mammals: indeed, they had the greatest margin of safety of any insecticide then known. But they were still unstable. They were esters, compounds of acid and alcohol, and both the acid and alcohol components were oxidized if exposed to light. Rothamsted then produced a series of alcohols which were ten to one hundred times more stable in light than natural pyrethrum and yet, with appropriate acids, were still insecticidal. The most promising of these compounds is up to one hundred times more effective against insects than DDT, but is only moderately persistent and therefore is less likely to accumulate in the environment, as DDT does. This kind of compound, a natural material improved by high-grade chemistry, harbingers a new generation of pesticides.

By comparison, the three outstanding groups of totally artificial insecticides – the organochlorines, organophosphorus compounds, and the carbamates – have an old-fashioned look, although they still fill several vital roles in agriculture and medicine. Their obvious dangers (in particular, their tendency to persist in the environment and to spread, so that even Antarctic penguins show traces of DDT) must be balanced against their equally obvious benefits. For example, the much maligned DDT, by reducing the range of malaria mosquitoes in the 1950s and 1960s, may have saved more human lives than any other chemical compound although, as we will see (p.36) its use was ultimately doomed.

DDT is the type-compound of the organochlorine insecticides. It was synthesized first in the nineteenth century, although it was not found to be insecticidal until the Second World War. It is not, despite adverse publicity, particularly toxic to man: indeed, ICI claim that people can safely handle it. But insects absorb organochlorine pesticide readily through the cuticle, whereupon it attacks their nervous systems. Other organochlorines still in use, though for increasingly specialized purposes, are dieldrin and aldrin.

The organophosphorus compounds, first discovered to be insecticidal in 1938, are highly variable. Some are too dangerous to be used, some are among the safest insecticides available, and some are taken up by plants so that the whole plant becomes toxic. Altogether, more than 90 of these compounds are now in commercial use. Like the organochlorines, they attack the nervous system.

In general, the organophosphorus compounds are less persistent than the organochlorines. For example, whereas dieldrin accumulated in the sheeps' fat when used in sheep dips (p.135), the organophosphorus compounds used now penetrate the skin but then are destroyed enzymatically. Thus dieldrin used to act as a systemic insecticide, while the organophosphorus compounds act only as surface poisons. Malathion, one of the best known organophosphorus compounds, is 3,000 times more toxic to insects than to mammals – precisely because mammals metabolize it to a

# Control of Malaria using D.D.T.

Areas affected by Malaria { ▨ Malaria eliminated 1939-1963
▦ Malaria still present 1963

non-toxic compound if they absorb it.

The carbamates are esters of carbamic acid. Again, they attack the nervous system. Carbaryl is the most widely used, and the new Pirimicarb is potentially extremely valuable, as it kills aphids but is harmless to bees and ladybirds. However, *Aphis gossyppii*, which attacks chrysanthemums and cucumbers, is already showing resistance to Pirimicarb (see p.39).

Exciting new compounds – exciting because they are highly specific and unlikely to be persistent – are insect-sterilizing compounds, various kinds of attractant, including pheromones, and compounds based on the hormones that control insect moulting. (See pp. 38 and 39 for control by sterilization and the use of pheromones.) Insect-moulting hormones include the juvenile hormone, which prevents metamorphosis, and ecdysone, which induces premature moulting. These should be highly specific, but such compounds are complex and synthetic analogues are expensive.

Fungi invade plant cells and therefore are difficult to attack. The 'surface' fungicides, which just remain on the plant surface, can be used only to prevent an attack. They are useless against established infection and they afford no protection to new growth. Surface compounds comprise copper-based materials, including the archetypal Bordeaux Mixture – a brew of copper sulphate and lime, used since the nineteenth century; elemental sulphur, which kills fungi (one reason why town-grown plants are particularly healthy) but which can also damage 'sulphur shy' varieties of apples and pears; and organo-metallic compounds, notably organo-mercury compounds, which can be wickedly toxic but are effective at very low concentrations. Used as a cereal seed dressing, organo-mercury fungicides have virtually eliminated bunt and covered smut. Other, modern, surface fungicides include dithiocarbamate and maneb, which has proved particularly effective against potato blight.

The past decade has produced several types of fungicide that are absorbed by the plant, to beard the fungal pathogen in its den. These 'systemic' fungicides include benomyl, which is used widely against foliage diseases and soil-borne pathogens, and ethirimol, which is applied as a seed dressing to barley. It is taken up by the germinating roots, and protects against powdery mildew. It finishes up in the leaves and not in the grain.

Herbicides may be total (killing everything) or selective (killing only the undesirables), but really the degree of selectivity depends largely on how the compounds are used.

One group of herbicides is based upon the plant hormones: indole acetic acid (IAA), which causes plant cells to elongate. 2, 4-D and MCPA both work by imitating IAA. However, whereas the natural hormone is metabolized after it has done its job, the synthetic analogues are not. They induce weak, spindly, and ultimately unviable growth.

Many types of herbicide are based on urea, including fenuron, monuron and diuron. These compounds can stay in the soil for up to a year, and when they are used in high doses (10 – 30kg per hectare) they are non-selective. If diuron is used in low concentration, however, it remains in the surface layers and kills only the shallow-rooted plants, so it can be used to clear the weeds from between, say, deep-rooted cotton plants.

The triazine compounds, simazine and atrazine, show much the same effect. At 2–5kg per hectare they can be used, selectively, to keep the shallow-rooted weeds from maize fields, and in low doses simazine serves to clear the way betweeen fruit trees and bushes, and in sub-urban rose beds.

Paraquat is lethal to all green plant tissue, but it is de-activated quickly in the soil through being absorbed on to clay particles, so it is useful for total weed control before planting a new crop and, indeed, is used to kill out old grass swards before direct drilling (see p.40). Paraquat is also used between rows of trees. Diquat is similar, but is less effective against grasses. It is used to destroy potato haulms, and for the pre-harvest desiccation of crops such as rice, barley, lucerne, sunflowers, oil seeds and rape, and to control aquatic weeds in lakes and ditches.

Finally, parallel to the many advances in pesticide chemistry, we now have a radically new approach to pesticide application. Conventional sprayers force pesticide through small holes under pressure. The result is a mist containing droplets that range in diameter from 6 to 700 microns. The smallest particles – about the size of sea fog particles – do not penetrate the layer of still air that surrounds all solid objects: they simply float away on the wind to constitute the particular kind of pollution called 'pesticide drift'. The largest particles deposit far too much pesticide in one place, leading to waste and to pollution.

The modern alternative is to distribute the pesticide by hurling it from a spinning disc, like spray thrown from a tyre. The disc is powered by a small electric motor (in some sprayers the motor runs off torch batteries held in the handle of the sprayer), and the edge is toothed. The pesticide is fed from a tube on to the centre of the disc, is thrown to the edge by centrifugal force, and then moves along the teeth to emerge as a fine filament which breaks almost immediately into small droplets. These can be blown on to the target in a turbulent airstream produced by a fan or, in simpler hand-sprayers, the wind alone will carry them into the crop. The particle size, which can accurately be controlled by adjusting the size of disc, the number of teeth, or the speed of rotation, is between 60 and 110 microns, which is the optimum size for maximum, even distribution.

Rotary 'atomizers' are used in many developing countries, although in Britain they are still somewhat experimental, despite the fact that the principle was applied first in the nineteenth century, in medicine. One difficulty has been to find suitable solvents for pesticides that are not soluble in water. In any case, water cannot be atomized effectively by spinning discs. So the pesticide 'active constituent' must be carried in some oil of appropriate viscosity. A further problem relates to the safety of the operator. Used correctly, sprayers of this type are much safer than conventional sprayers, but the solution used is far more concentrated, and with some pesticides this can pose problems for the worker who must change the reservoir when one tankful is used.

The problems are being overcome. Suitable oils have been developed, and a range of oil-based insecticides and fungicides is being

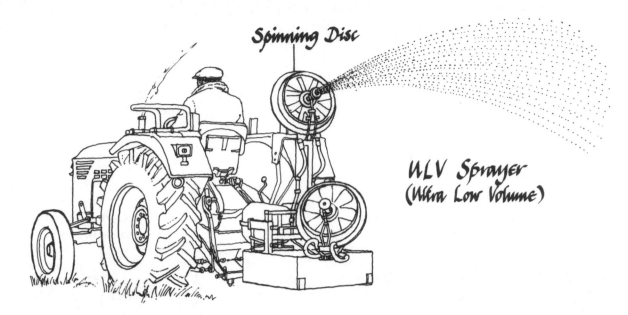

Spinning Disc

ULV Sprayer
(Ultra Low Volume)

marketed. At least one company (Ciba-Geigy) markets its products in containers that fit one sprayer model, so that the operator need only remove the cap from the container and fit the sprayer in its place.

The reduction in the quantity of pesticide needed is dramatic: between 1 and 10 per cent of that required for conventional spraying to achieve equal, or better, control. Because of the accuracy with which the pesticide can be placed, the solution does not drop from the plants to the ground to cause pollution in the soil and disturb populations of predators that spend part of their lives there. In the near future the huge barrels of pesticide, and the problems of disposal of empty containers and of drift, may be forgotten.

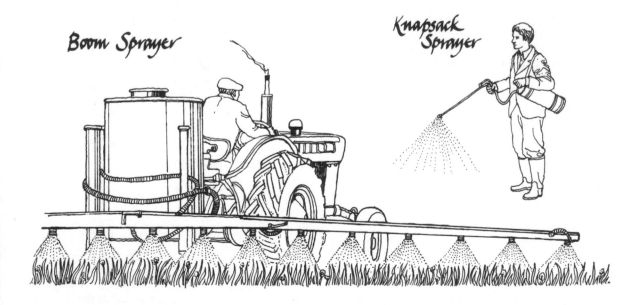

Boom Sprayer

Knapsack Sprayer

# Pest control

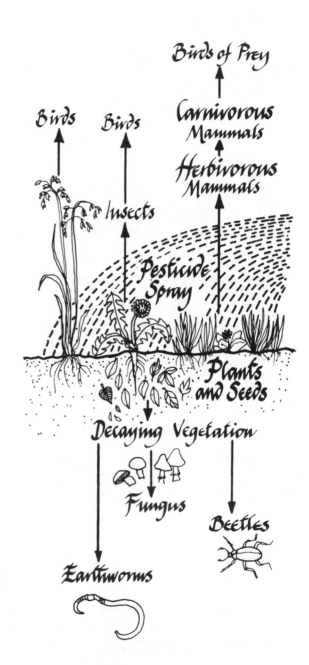

Twenty-five years ago 'pest control' tended to mean 'obliteration'. Farmers believed they could, and should, eradicate harmful insects totally by smothering their crops in the wonder-toys of organochlorine and organophosphorus. The World Health Organization spoke confidently of using DDT to eradicate the mosquitoes that carried malaria, and when that was done they would lay into other major vectors. In 1962 – to a chorus of abuse from industry and many academics – Rachel Carson published *Silent Spring*, which showed how disastrous this euphoric overkill was. 'Innocent' species, of insect and vertebrate, were being killed, and the creatures that normally kept the pest populations within reasonable bounds were being destroyed, so that the more pesticide was used, the more it needed to be used. Now, in 1977, we know not only that Miss Carson's arguments were indeed justified – for however 'harmless, DDT and the rest might seem in the laboratory, their gradual accumulation by the hundreds of tonnes in the environment is clearly undesirable – but also that the policy of overkill was foredoomed. As evidence we may note that the malaria mosquitoes, attacked so heavily with DDT in the 1950s, are now as firmly established as ever in Africa and are spreading rapidly in India and probably in the Middle East. This is partly because they are now largely resistant to DDT. Throughout the world some 200 species of insect pest are resistant to at least one standard insecticide.

However, to over-react to this initial setback by condemning all chemical control, to opt purely for so-called 'biological control' or for 'natural' pesticides, is as muddle-headed as the organic extremists' wholesale condemnation of artificial fertilizer (see pp.30 and 42). Mankind

The careless use of persistent pesticides may lead to their accumulation and concentration in food webs, and may be self-defeating. Insects on the underside of leaves may escape, but surplus pesticide that drips to the ground may depress predator populations.

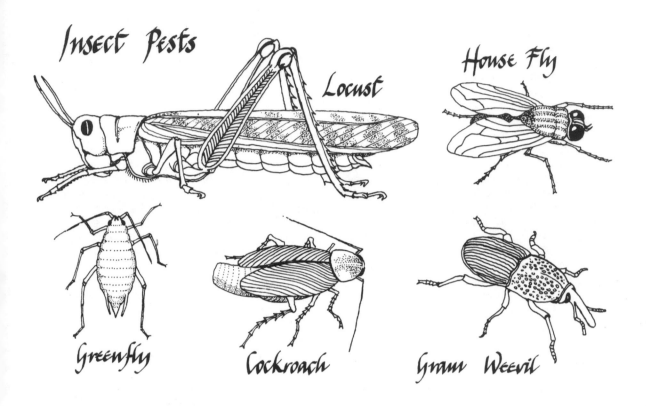

# Insect Pests

**Locust**

**House Fly**

**Greenfly**

**Cockroach**

**Grain Weevil**

loses 30 per cent of all crops through insect pest damage alone, plus an appreciable percentage from fungi, viruses, bacteria and weeds. True, too cavalier a chemical attack is dangerous and self defeating, but equally, many of the worst scourges can be controlled in practice only by modern pesticide. We should not talk of 'natural' versus 'chemical' pest control, but accept that satisfactory long-term control is impossible without profound knowledge of the individual pest's biology, and that modern chemicals are among the weaponry to be used against them.

In practice, there are three complementary approaches to pest or disease control.

The first is to reduce contact between host and pest. This means, above all, hygiene: keeping the fields free from trash (see p.41), stifling volunteer potatoes left over from last year (see p.66), operating herds and flocks of livestock on an all-in all-out basis (see pp. 129 and 157), rotating crops like potatoes, brassicas and carrots. Here, above all, we see the advantages of mixed husbandry and cropping.

However, before we condemn monoculture outright (monoculture is the growing of the same crop year after year on the same land), we may note that modern ecology offers several caveats. In particular, it seems that insect pests operate according to one of two strategies. Either they live permanently among their hosts, maintaining a fairly low level of infestation – like the codling moth in fruit – or else, like the fruit flies and desert locust, they work on a boom and bust principle. For most of the time they live at low-population, sub-pest levels and then spasmodically they break out in all-destructive swarms. The former kind of pest can be held partially in check by helping permanent predators (including birds) to establish themselves, but attack by the boom-and-busters must be met with insecticide. The main point, however, is that monocultures of vast areas are safer from the boom-and-busters than small patches are, just as endless tracts of Russia are safer from land invasion than is, say, Holland. Clear examples from Britain are rare, but maize for example suffers far less from bird damage when it is grown extensively than it does when grown in small plots.

The second approach to pest or disease control is to increase the resistance of the host. The vaccination of livestock is an obvious example, allowing suckling lambs or calves to take their dams' colostrum is another. A hot debate rages among pig farmers as to whether to operate germ-free herds – which are fine so long as they work, but are totally susceptible to any disease that does find its way in – or to allow constant, but tolerable, exposure to pathogens, so that the animals build up a resistance. Plant breeders are searching constantly for disease-resistant varieties, and many old types have faded out because of their susceptibility to mildew or black spot (soft fruits) or potato wart, or what you will. The search for rust-resistant wheats

(p.50) is never ending, because the rusts mutate, and always seem able to adjust to the new types.

Finally, we can attack the pest directly, and as insects are the subtlest and most elusive of pests we will confine discussion to them. There are four main stratagems: poison them, lure them to their doom, sterilize them, and encourage predators to attack them.

The last two methods illustrate the strength and weakness of what can be termed purely 'biological' methods of control. Sterilization involves rearing populations of male insects, sterilizing them in the pupal stage or as young adults, perhaps with chemicals but more usually with some kind of radiation, and then releasing them. Many female insects mate once only, and if they mate with a sterile male they produce infertile eggs. The aim is not to obliterate totally, but to reduce pest damage to within tolerable limits, though in fact small populations can be highly vulnerable (to predators, for example) and population reduction can lead inadvertently to extinction (as may be happening, on a different scale, with whales).

But there are plenty of snags. You need to breed a lot of males to make a worthwhile im-

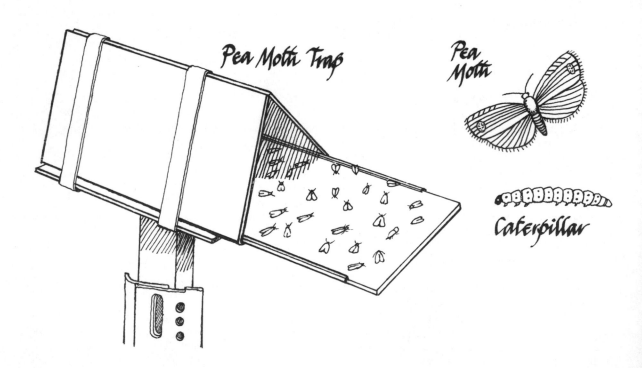

Pea Moth Trap

Pea Moth

Caterpillar

pact on the population. You need to release them at exactly the time – sometimes within a period of only a few days or even hours – when the females are ready to receive them. The technique does not work with species whose males migrate before mating, as many do. In agricultural practice the technique has proved useful against the screw-worm fly in the United States, and it is being tested in Holland against the onion root fly (which evidently is extremely rare in Britain), but its use is limited.

The second method – encouraging predator attacks on pests – is perhaps best stated the other way round: you should not destroy potential predators when attacking pests. Different insect species show different levels of susceptibility to particular insecticides, and some types (see p.33) will kill aphids, for example, without harming the ladybirds that feed on them.

However, attempts are made specifically to breed predators. For example, the Glasshouse Crops Research Institute at Littlehampton has been employing the winged parasite *Trioxys sinensis* to kill the aphid *Aphis gossyppii*, which attacks cucumbers. Again, this technique is tricky in practice. In particular, the predators cannot wipe out their prey without wiping themselves out. A healthy predator population is extremely useful for general pest reduction, but as a specific weapon it has limitations.

Finally, we may attack pests directly, with or without the aid of lures and traps. A technique described recently by scientists at the Government research station at Rothamsted, for attacking the pea moth *Cydia nigricana*, whose 'maggots' may destroy 20 per cent of the pea crop, shows modern pest control at its best. Note the specificity (only the pea moths are destroyed), the subtle use of chemistry (first to imitate the moth's airborne hormones – pheromones – and then to destroy it), and the profound understanding of the pest's biology. These show how naive is the rigid distinction between 'biological' and 'chemical' control.

Pea moths overwinter in the soil, as larvae. They pupate in early May, and the adults emerge in late May, June and July. They mate almost immediately, and the resultant eggs hatch in 9-16 days. The tiny larvae then quickly find and penetrate a young pea pod, where they live for three weeks. After that they emerge, drop to the soil, spin a cocoon, and rest up until the following year.

During the whole 12 months the insect is vulnerable to insecticide only in the 24 hours (or less) between hatching and entering the soil. To attempt to kill it in the soil by drenching the field with insecticide would be impossibly expensive and environmentally disastrous, and the non-feeding adults are hardly liable to be caught on the wing. But how can you catch the larva in its vulnerable period?

One method is to drench the flowering crop with long-acting insecticide (such as DDT) and hope for the best. Environmentally this is undesirable, especially as peas rely on insect pollination. A second method, now employed, is to send experts to see when there are moths or larvae about and then spray, but this is tedious and the moths are easily missed, and the experts can examine only a minute proportion of the whole.

However, to attract their mates, the females sit on a leaf with their abdomens raised and exude a plume of highly alluring chemical (a pheromone), which the males 'smell' through their antennae, and whose trail they follow upwind to the waiting virgins. Rothamsted scientists have found that the essential ingredients of these pheromone attractants are 12-carbon unsaturated acetates. They have synthesized these. The synthetic attractant is then put in traps among the pea plants, each trap having a sticky floor. The farmer examines the traps every day, as the peas flower. When, one day, it is full of male pea moths he knows that the eggs are about to be laid, and that the invasive larvae will be emerging after another 9 – 16 days. So, a week after trapping the males he sprays, with a relatively short-acting insecticide. The scientists reckon that if he repeats the operation three weeks later, he should have no trouble from pea moth.

Pest control such as this is effective, subtle, and should not offend environmentalists. Note how vividly it contrasts with the advice, still handed out by over-technological gardening manuals, to spray everything in sight at two-week intervals, willy-nilly, just in case a pest turns up. Note, too, that it furthers the principle of preventing disaster, which is always preferable to trying to recover from it.

We are entering the second generation of pest control, characterized by respect for both the biology of the pest and the integrity of the environment. We must control pests, and we cannot afford to eschew modern chemistry, but we need not create a 'silent spring'.

# Minimum cultivation

Ever since they began farming, men have attacked the surface of the soil with plough and harrow, to bury weeds and to prepare a crumbly seed bed. The virtue of such rigorous tillage has rarely been questioned. Indeed, the instruments of cultivation have become ever more subtle, and the beasts and machines that pull them, ever more powerful. But is all this effort really necessary? Wild plants grow well enough in untilled ground. Why can't crops?

Two scientists from the Rothamsted Experimental Station, B. A. Keen and E. W. Russell, made this point as long ago as 1937, when they told the Royal Agricultural Society: 'We can find no justification for operations beyond the minimum needed to get a seed bed and to check weeds until a crop is well established. Work in excess of this minimum, far from increasing the crop, appreciably diminishes it'.

So what does 'minimum cultivation' involve? First, you must make sure that the field is properly drained, which may mean installing a new drainage system, or simply breaking up heavy subsoil or 'pans' with a mole plough or a subsoiler (see p. 18). A fine tilth laid over a swamp or a brick is of little use.

Secondly, you must eliminate weeds, or the previous crop (if you are sowing a crop that follows on a ley), by spraying with a chemical such as ICI's Gramoxone.

After this you simply insert the seed with no more ado – what is called 'direct drilling'. The machines for this are of four main types. Triple-disc drills have one disc to cut a slot in the soil, with two behind arranged in a V that widen the slot and feed in the seed. Tine drills, with

*Direct Drilling*

specially strengthened tines, are especially useful on heavy soils to create an extra tilth. Rotary cultivator drills cultivate a narrow band of soil and place the seeds in slots behind the rotor. Single-disc and roller drills, which are particularly useful for drilling grass or brassicas into stubble and grass, have a single disc which cuts a slot for the seed, followed by a built-in Cambridge roller, which folds it in.

Forty years after Keen and Russell, minimum cultivation is still largely experimental, but it is catching on fast. It is favoured most for sowing winter cereals, but it has also been used widely for kale and fodder rape, and to sow catch crops or grass directly on to stubble. It has been used, too, on a small scale for sowing spring cereals and maincrop swedes and turnips, for putting new grass on old grass, and for oilseed and fodder rape.

The technique has three theoretical advantages, which do not always work out in practice. It should be cheap, not least because it saves tractor fuel, although the increased cost of the herbicide used may cancel this out. Secondly, and most important, minimum cultivation should be rapid. In extreme cases, as for example when sowing kale, swedes or turnips on a field that was previously down to grass, you can spray one day and direct drill the next. This means that cultivation can be timely. You can take advantage of a few fine days in autumn to get the wheat in (and in some years conventional cultivation may not be possible at all) and perhaps get barley away to a flying start by cashing in on a few bright days in early spring.

Thirdly, reduced cultivation might, in theory at least, increase yields, since a topsoil that is built up slowly by worms and weather might be better in the long run than one created by machine. In practice, though, the results of research seem to conflict with the experience of farmers. Experiments generally show reduced yields with minimum cultivation, not least because roots develop more slowly in untilled soil. Farmers, however, say that yields do not necessarily go down, and may increase. You can compensate for slower root growth by planting earlier, and yields improve year by year, presumably as the worm population builds up. This is an effect that would not show in short-term experiments.

There are also two powerful theoretical disadvantages. First, the spraying of weeds such as couch, which have underground rhizomes, may

Direct drilling can succeed only where soil drainage is effective. The topsoil must have a crumb-like structure through which water percolates down to the water table. 'Pans' must be broken up.

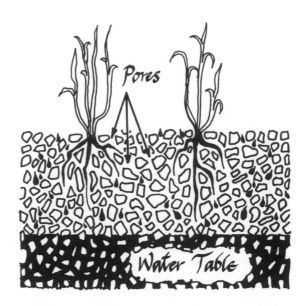

be ineffective. You will still have to use a rotary cultivator to bring them to the surface before you apply the herbicide. The cultivator will break the rhizomes, leaving short lengths in the soil. When these re-emerge the whole process will have to be repeated. In any case, to leave the soil surface covered with sprayed weeds or stubble ('trash') is bad farming. It provides an ideal breeding ground for slugs and other pests and diseases, and you cannot drill seed through dense mats of old grass. This must be sprayed and then allowed to decompose on the surface. So minimum cultivation does raise some problems of hygiene.

Secondly, the specialist machinery needed for direct drilling is expensive. Only the big farming companies can justify buying it. Small farmers must rely on contractors, but if they do that, they may sacrifice the timeliness which is the chief advantage of minimum cultivation.

Some agriculturalists believe that the day will come when conventional, plough-based cultivation is regarded purely as an emergency measure. Perhaps they are right, or perhaps it is that minimum and conventional techniques will continue to complement one another, as they do now.

# Organic farming

A few years ago, advocates of organic husbandry were dismissed by agricultural scientists as 'the muck and mystery school'. Since the steep rise in energy prices, attitudes have changed. Today organic farming methods are taken seriously and the only rigorous study comparing organic and conventional farms, in the American corn belt, has shown that in years when the weather is good the conventional farms are more profitable, but that in poor years the advantage lies with the organic farms.

Stated simply, organic farming (or biological farming, as it is known in most European countries) is farming without the use of artificial fertilizers or pesticides. As these products are generally energy intensive in their production (nitrogen fertilizer and most modern pesticides use hydrocarbon feedstocks as a source of organic chemicals as well as consuming fuel in the processes by which they are made), their cost to the farmer has reflected the general rise in fuel prices. Thus a farmer who does not use them has lower production costs per unit of land, and the gap between his costs and those of his conventional neighbour has widened. His yields are rather lower, but since the soil structure on an organic farm tends to be better than that on a farm heavily dependent on chemicals, the effects of the weather are felt less keenly and so yields are usually more reliable. In years when a conventional farm suffers from too much or too little rain the organic farm may out-yield it.

Small wonder, then, that with the future economics of agricultural chemical use so uncertain, the organic farmers have become 'respectable'. This change in attitude has made it possible for both sides of the 'organic v. chemical' debate to abandon the extreme positions that each had defended over the years. Both approaches to farming can now be examined more objectively.

It is far too simple to reduce organic farming to a mere avoidance of artificial fertilizers and pesticides. Organic farmers have always allowed the use of some fertilizer materials and some non-persistent pesticides, and most conventional farmers aim to return to their soil as much organic matter as they can. The real difference is more subtle. Organic husbandry has been defined by the International Institute of Biological Husbandry as the use of 'those techniques of soil care and cropping which result in the efficient utilisation of the sun's energy and of dependent biological processes for sustainable food production, through the utilisation of local resources alone'. 'Local' is taken to mean an area of balanced geographical and climatic resources, such as Great Britain. The aim of the organic farmer, then, is to develop a system that maintains and improves the fertility of the soil, so rendering farming more sustainable over long periods of time, that is self-sufficient, and that is guided by the working of natural biological processes.

The organic farmer must find ways to use efficiently the materials in his immediate locality. He can afford to waste nothing. So the organic farm is likely to be conceived as a total integral system, in which the waste products from one enterprise feed another. Livestock is almost certain to be incorporated to consume the grass that contributes by its root system to the structure of the soil, and to provide manure. Monocultural farming and even exclusively arable farming become very difficult to sustain.

So far as possible, pests, weeds and crop diseases are controlled culturally. By growing crops in a rotation, parasites specific to particular crops are prevented from accumulating, and weeds are removed more easily when they differ markedly from the crop they infest. Wild oats are difficult to control on cereal farms, for example, because they resemble the cereal crop very closely. They would create fewer problems in a rotational system. To prevent serious pest infestations, the organic farmer tries to maintain balanced populations of wild flora and fauna, which harbour pests but also their predators, so that a migration of pests into his crop is likely to be followed quickly by a migration of those creatures that eat the pest. Of course, the system is not wholly successful, but neither is chemical control. What is certain, though, is that the successful organic farmer must achieve a very high standard of husbandry. He must be, first and foremost, a very good farmer.

Interest in organic farming began in the 1920s, among a small group of people who were concerned at the speed with which farming was changing, and who feared that too little was known about the long-term effects of those changes. They believed that some relationship must exist between the way soils are treated and the quality of the crops grown. Since all flesh is grass, this must have implications for the health of animals and humans. Despite the fact that food substances ingested are broken down and restructured within the body, the idea remains plausible. So far no conclusive evidence has been found to demonstrate that the use of artificial fertilizers reduces the nutritional value of crops, but there is increasing acceptance of the idea that agriculture should be tailored more closely to the nutritional needs of consumers (see Sugar beet, p. 60). Nor has it been shown that the use of agricultural chemicals has any adverse effect on soils, provided that the availability of fertilizers does not encourage farming systems that omit the return of bulky organic matter to the soil – which sometimes it does. Similarly, criticisms of pesticide use are often criticisms of the misuse of potent chemicals, or the use of chemicals which have unpredicted side effects, rather than a more general disagreement with the principle of removing pests, weeds and fungi by poisoning them.

To a large extent, it is a matter of emphasis. Advocates of organic farming will argue that the agricultural research effort in all the industrial countries has, for many years, been weighted too heavily in favour of chemistry and high technology: that technological solutions have been sought to problems created by earlier technologies. If a similar investment were made towards research into organic methods the benefits might be greater, in that ways might be found to produce comparable yields – or greater ones – at less cost.

In 1946, in Britain, the Soil Association was formed to promote organic farming. In the United States the Rodale organization, which publishes a number of journals including the popular *Organic Gardening and Farming*, as well as books, has performed a parallel role. The Soil Association has a worldwide membership, but it is also affiliated to many similar organizations that have sprung up in most countries. Their activities are coordinated internationally by IFOAM, the International Federation of Organic Agriculture Movements, based in

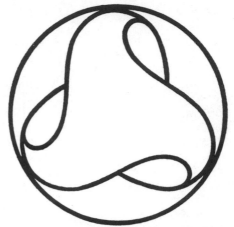

## THE SOIL ASSOCIATION SYMBOL OF ORGANIC QUALITY

France, and the collection of scientific information is now being organized by the International Institute of Biological Husbandry. Organic methods of gardening are promoted, in Britain, by the Henry Doubleday Research Association and the Good Gardeners' Association, both of which complement, and work closely with, the Soil Association (see p. 44 for addresses).

In order to protect consumers who prefer food that has been grown organically, and to guide farmers, the Soil Association has drawn up standards of husbandry which are summarized, in the words of the Association, as entailing the

Returning to the soil all animal and vegetable residues; handling manure so as to retain its full value by a system of rough composting; letting the soil feed the crops and avoiding the direct feeding with soluble minerals; avoiding the use of all chemicals liable to kill or lessen the activity of soil organisms; feeding the livestock as far as possible on the produce of the farm; the use of home-grown seed; practising mixed husbandry within the limits imposed by physical conditions and economics; minimal disturbance of the soil by cultivations, consistent with adequate weed control.

Standards based on these ideals are implemented by Organic Farmers and Growers Ltd, an organization formed to help market organically grown produce.

## Further reading

An Agricultural Geography of Great Britain by D. W. Gilchrist Shirlaw. Pergamon Press.

Annual Review of Agriculture, published each year by the Departments of Agriculture. HMSO.

Climate and the British Scene by Gordon Manley. Fontana.

Crop Production Equipment by H. T. Lovegrove. Hutchinson Educational.

Farming in Britain Today by J. G. S. and Frances Donaldson in association with Derek Barber. Pelican.

Farm Tools through the Ages by Michael Partridge. Osprey.

Pesticides and Pollution by Kenneth Mellanby. Collins.

Soil Geography by James G. Cruikshank. David and Charles.

Water, Soil and the Plant by E. J. Winter. Macmillan in collaboration with the Royal Horticultural Society.

## Information

**General:** Association of Agriculture, 78 Buckingham Gate, London SW1.

Crofters' Commission, 9 Ardross Terrace, Inverness.

Farm and Food Society, 37 Tanza Road, London NW3.

Ministry of Agriculture, Fisheries and Food, Land Use Division, Great Westminster House, Horseferry Road, London SW1.

National Farmers' Union, Agriculture House, Knightsbridge, London SW1.

**Pesticides:** Approved Products for Farmers and Growers published annually under the Agricultural Chemicals Approval Scheme by the Ministry of Agriculture and available free.

**Agricultural chemicals:** British Agrochemicals Association, Alembic House, 93 Albert Embankment, London SE1.

**Organic farming:** International Institute for Biological Husbandry, Longridge, Creeting Road, Stowmarket, Suffolk.

Organic Farmers and Growers Ltd, Longridge, Creeting Road, Stowmarket, Suffolk. Suffolk.

The Soil Association, Walnut Tree Manor, Haughley, Stowmarket, Suffolk.

**Regional:** At the Farmer's Service is a small booklet published each year by the Ministry of Agriculture, Fisheries and Food, and available free from MAFF (Publications), Tolcarne Drive, Pinner, Middlesex HA5 2DT, or from local offices of the Ministry, listed in telephone directories. The booklet gives addresses of local offices of the Ministry, and of the main government laboratories and experimental stations, as well as details of regulations, grants and price support mechanisms, notifiable diseases and marketing systems for all major products.

# PLANT CROPS

# Introducing the cereals

Since cereals are probably the oldest domesticated crops, and since they have been at the heart of agricultural effort for perhaps fifteen thousand years, it might seem absurd to suggest that only now is their full significance being appreciated. Yet twenty years ago, nutritionists implied that the protein in grain was of such low concentration, and of such poor quality, that it was better to regard cereals simply as a source of energy. Now we know that the zealots of the 1950s over-estimated man's protein requirements by a cool 300 per cent, that grain alone is an adequate source of protein, at least for adults, and that the 'protein gap' does not exist or, if it did, would be bridged most effectively by increasing the protein content of grain by a few per cent.

Worldwide, grain provides man with 50 per cent of his protein, and with more than 25 per cent even in carnivorous Britain. The chief defect in grain protein is the relative deficiency of the essential amino acid lysine, but in many cuisines grains are matched with pulses – chapatis and dhal in India, beans on toast in Britain – which are rich in lysine, and the two together counter each other's deficiencies.

Cereals are grasses. The grain itself is a 'caryopsis', a combination of fruit and seed. The husk, which manifests after milling as 'bran', is formed from the seed coat and ovary wall, fused together. Within the caryopsis there lurks the embryo of the next generation, with primordial root and shoot: rich in minerals, protein and energy. The embryo is removed when wheat flour is milled to make white flour, and is then called 'wheat germ'.

The nutritional importance of cereals lies chiefly in the endosperm, the food store laid down for the embryo. It contains starch, the prime energy source, some fat, especially in oats and maize, and proteins of varying concentrations. These latter largely determine the cooking, malting and storage characteristics of the grain. They do this in two ways. Proteins such as the gluten of wheat (see P.50) can display a whole spectrum of physical characteristics when heated or soaked, ranging from hardness, through plasticity, to stickiness. Secondly, the proteins include the biologically active molecules called enzymes; these determine, for example, the timing and readiness of

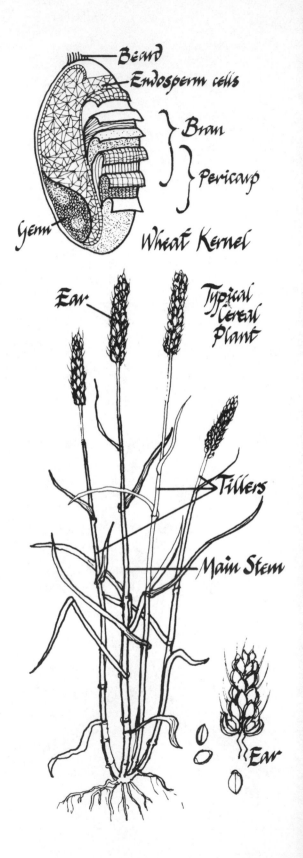

Beard

Endosperm cells

Bran

Pericarp

Germ

Wheat Kernel

Ear

Typical Cereal Plant

Tillers

Main Stem

Ear

germination, and the speed and extent to which the starch stores are broken down to form sugars. These enzymes in turn are under hormonal control. Plant breeders spend much of their time trying to influence enzyme and hormone content of grains, to produce types that will or will not germinate under particular conditions, that will or will not begin rapidly to break down their starch, and so on.

The whole cereal plant has the same basic structure as other grasses (see p.102). It has a short stem, throwing up vertical leaves, of which the 'flag' leaf is the principal. It produces side shoots from near ground level, known as 'tillers', and it throws up its seedheads only after the leaves have matured. Like other grasses, cereals can be grazed before seeding; indeed, lowland sheep farmers often use winter corn for an early bite: apart from feeding the animals it can improve the corn yield.

Wheat is the world's most widely cultivated cereal. Then comes rice, followed by maize, sorghum (millet), barley, oats and rye. The fate of this grain reflects the inequity that underlies the world's food problems. The poor and the rich people of the world split the total crop about fifty-fifty: 530 million tonnes each. But the poorer peoples include 70 per cent of the total world population. They consume about 480 million tonnes of their share directly, as grain. The rich peoples feed most of their share to livestock, and consume directly only 160 million tonnes.

Britain devotes about 3.7 million of her 19 million cultivated hectares to cereals, of which 1 million are down to wheat, 2.3 million to barley, and 230,000 to oats. The total yield is around 15 million tonnes. Of this, no less than 10 million is fed to livestock.

We import a further 8–10 million tonnes, of which half is also destined for animal feed. In all, barley contributes more than 7.5 million tonnes, wheat more than 3 million, oats 1.1 million and maize 1.6 million tonnes. Altogether we give almost as much grain to livestock as we ourselves produce. British pigs and poultry consume 8 million tonnes a year, and even cattle, whose agricultural *raison d'être* is their ability to thrive on fodder quite unsuitable for humans (see p.111), get through 5.3 million tonnes a year, with dairy cattle relying on cereal for a third of their feed.

Perhaps, as pressure on agricultural resources increases, and as the nutritional qualities of

cereals are acknowledged more widely, we might see baking coming back into its own. Perhaps it will discover, or rediscover, the use of maize, rye and barley flour, and reawaken interest in oats, whose high fat content is a nutritional bonus. We need, too, a temperate cereal, perhaps a modified wheat or barley, that would cook as easily and deliciously as rice. A fresh emphasis on grain's potential as food rather than feed would be the main step towards a self-reliant Britain.

# World Distribution and Use of Cereals

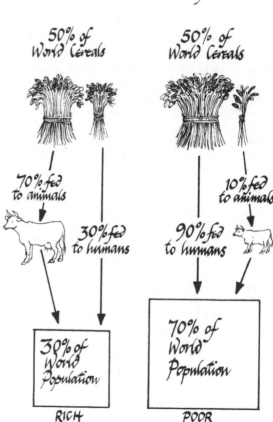

# Cereals: general principles

In general, cereal yields are related directly to the growing season. You cannot sow too early in spring, because the ground will be too frosty or too wet; you cannot harvest too late because the rate of loss and deterioration in the field after ripening is rapid, and the threat from autumn winds and rains, that can destroy the greater part of the crop, grows as the season wears on. So cereal growing in Britain is intrinsically tense. Timeliness is all.

Despite this, farm advisers are forever remarking on the casualness with which many farmers approach cereals. Thus average cereal yields increased by about $2\frac{1}{4}$ per cent per year from the early 1950s to the early 1970s – wheat going from less than 2.5 tonnes per hectare around 1950 to 4.4 tonnes in 1973, and barley from 2–2.1 tonnes to more than 3.75 tonnes in the same period – but in recent years the increase has stopped. What is worse, the present mean of around 4.4 tonnes per hectare conceals a range (both between farms and within farms) of 2.5–6.9 tonnes per hectare.

Many modern varieties can yield about 20 per cent more than those of a generation ago, and with the magic ingredient of 'tender loving care' we should be able to increase present yields by at least another 30 per cent, which means a further 5 million tonnes, equivalent to half our import. It is a matter of increasing the productivity of the poorer farms to that of the average, rather than expecting still more from the top farmers. To say that we need better husbandry is to imply that we need more husbandmen, and that is one of the key messages of this book.

The present shortfalls in cereal husbandry probably have two main causes: first, the work is inevitably concentrated in spring and autumn, and so is liable to be hurried; and secondly, the farmer all too easily neglects his cereals in summer, when he should be on hands and knees looking for leaf disease or 'roguing' wild oats (see p.49), and in winter when he should be getting rid of pests like the wheat-bulb fly.

To some extent the work load may be spread by sowing some cereal in autumn and harvesting it in mid-summer. Most wheat in Britain is autumn sown, and is then called 'winter wheat'. In Europe and the United States most wheat is winter wheat, but in the harsher climates of Canada and the USSR, where the young plants could not survive the cold winter, wheat is spring sown and is harvested later. Barley is less often winter sown, oats are sown in autumn only in the south, and the extremely hardy rye is often autumn sown, and is then grazed in spring before being allowed to grow on to produce a crop.

Cereal growing has seen three major revolutions in Britain since the Second World War: the increase of agricultural chemistry, with pesticides, herbicides and fertilizers; the rise of the machine – particularly the now ubiquitous combine harvester, of which there were only 100 in Britain in 1938; and, perhaps consequent upon these innovations, the end of the concept of 'rotation'.

To take the last first, it used to be axiomatic that cereal should not be grown on the same plot for more than one, or at the most two, seasons in succession. Now, on some land, it seems that wheat and barley at least may succeed themselves or each other indefinitely: some fields have carried barley for twenty or more successive years. 'Break crops' – of potatoes, legumes, sugar beet, vegetables or, increasingly, of short-term grass – still have their part to play in adjusting fertility and interrupting disease cycles. But they do not always lead to an increase in subsequent cereal yields, and the benefits they bring are generally short lived. Typically, yields of winter wheat or spring barley fall to a low point three to five seasons after a break, and then stabilize or pick up. Sometimes the cause of the initial drop can be identified – increase in the fungal root disease 'take-all' for example, or in grass weeds – but usually no reason can be found.

As for machines, the combine has made many of the old and picturesque processes like threshing and field drying redundant, but it has increased the need for post-harvest drying. However, the modern trend of harvesting cereal while it is still young and moist, drying it later with warm air, has greatly reduced (or should do so) harvest and post-harvest losses which in the old days could sometimes take most of the crop.

Correct fertilization is crucial. Too much nitrogen is wasteful and may be harmful, as it can produce over-long straw that is mechanically weak. Under the weight of a ripe, heavy ear, a sudden squall, with a strong wind and heavy rain that is common in late summer, can cause it to fall over ('lodge'). Although a modern com-

'Lodging' in a cereal crop

bine can cut within a few inches of the ground there is a danger of damaging the cutting blades with stones if they are set too low, and, in any case, some of the seed will have been knocked from the ears and lost irretrievably. If the grain is wet and the soil warm, the seed may germinate, so ruining it completely. Lodging causes heavy losses. When calculating the quantity of nitrogen to apply, the farmer must remember that previous breaks of beet or potato may leave a soil rich in nitrogen. Some nitrogen must be applied with each crop. Phosphorus and potassium, in general, can be added at three-year intervals.

Despite modern herbicides and pesticides, weeds and leaf diseases such as fungal rusts and various viruses are the cereal farmer's chief enemy. Black grass, capable of reducing yields by 11kg a hectare, now affects around 240,000 hectares, mostly in the south-east. Worst of all are wild oats, which can reduce yields by 25–30 per cent. They are spreading rapidly westwards from their eastern stronghold, and now affect some 800,000 hectares. In all cases control is by cultivation and herbicide combined: it still pays to take out small infestations of wild oats by hand (roguing). Each oat left to seed can produce 20 the following season: a 90 per cent reduction in the number of wild oat plants can be made good in a few years.

Weeds of Cereal Crops

Shepherd's Purse   Black Bindweed   Wild Oat   Ragwort   Couch Grass   Charlock

49

# Wheat

Cultivated wheats are of four main kinds: emmer, the primitive type that was a great stand-by in the Iron Age, and is still grown in a few countries; rivet, cone, or English wheat, once the principal wheat of the south of England but now superseded and lingering only in a few countries as feed; durum wheat, grown mainly in warm, dry climates, and used for pasta; and most important of all – and the only kind significant in Britain – the many varieties of bread wheats. Britain grows about 4.5 million tonnes of bread wheat on one million hectares: about 60 per cent of our total supply.

In truth, though all our wheats are designated 'bread' wheats, only a proportion is actually used for bread making. Bakers believe that British people like puffed-up, spongy loaves. Flour that can sustain such a structure is termed 'strong' – and, indeed, the dough made from it is physically tough. The 'strength' comes from the proteins (see p.46), so millers demand wheat with a high protein content, which in actual terms means 10 per cent protein on a 14 per cent moisture basis, or 11.6 per cent in the dry matter. They also demand, incidentally, a low content of the enzyme alpha-amylase, which tends to break down starch into sugar during bread making.

These pernickity requirements face wheat growers with a dilemma. In general, high-protein varieties yield less heavily than low-protein types, not least because the total bulk is determined mainly by the starch content. A plant that diverts its energy into protein production has less to spare for starch, and so it will be smaller and weigh less. Millers in fact pay more for wheat than do feed merchants, but the grower must decide whether the premium justifies opting for quality rather than bulk. Many growers fall short on both counts. Five tonnes a hectare should be possible almost always: eight tonnes a hectare are common.

## Cultivation

The fact that most British wheat is autumn sown – and winter wheats can out-yield spring wheats by 25 per cent – simplifies cultivation.

The secret is to get in early. Cultivation may be easy in September but well nigh impossible after a sticky October. A rough seed bed will do. The land is ploughed soon after harvest, then left briefly to weather, after which it is merely stirred with cultivator and harrows (see p.22).

The rough clods left by such treatment help protect the young crop in January and February, when they themselves are broken down by frost.

The aim is merely to establish the plant, so that it can withstand the winter and get away to a flying start in spring. You want a few tillers set by winter-time, but not too much leaf. So you may apply phosphorus and potassium when sowing winter wheat (this is not necessary every year, see p.30) but only a minute amount of nitrogen – not more than 25–35 units a hectare (a fertilizer 'unit' is a measure of the nutrient element contained in a fertilizer, so that units of nitrogen, phosphorus, etc. are measures of the weight of the elemental substance; one unit is equal to 1 per cent by weight of a 1-cwt bag of fertilizer: 1.12lb, or 795 grammes). More would produce over-lush growth and then be leached away by the winter rains.

Apply the bulk of the nitrogen, say 375kg per hectare of 34.5 per cent ammonium nitrate, in spring, to provide just over 250 units of nitrogen in total. A split application, 125–250kg early in spring with the rest at the end of May, is better than an all-in-one dose. The late boost of nitrogen can increase the size of the flag leaf which, by its photosynthesis, contributes most to the final yield.

## Wheat breeding

Recent years have seen two major trends in wheat breeding: first, the perennial pursuit of disease-resistant, and particularly rust-resistant, varieties; and secondly, one of the most exciting enterprises of recent years, the development of semi-dwarf varieties at the Plant Breeding Institute, Cambridge.

Brueghel's roisterous harvest scenes depict wheat the height of a donkey. Well into this century the favoured varieties stood up to 1.4 metres tall. Farmers and scientists alike believed that wheat needed to be tall if it was to yield heavily.

Now we know this is not so. The many genes that affect height, or straw length, do not necessarily influence grain yield. Indeed, very tall varieties in theory yield less heavily, because

# Types of Wheat

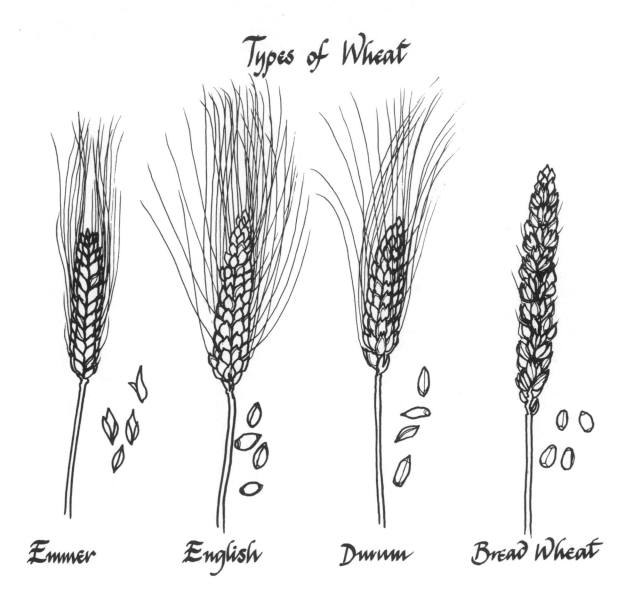

**Emmer**     **English**     **Durum**     **Bread Wheat**

they divert too much energy into straw and because they cannot be fertilized heavily without growing too tall to stand up. Since the Second World War breeders have rearranged the genes in the old varieties to produce successively shorter types, like the still popular one-metre-tall Capelle-Desprez.

The quantum advance came when the American breeder O. E. Vogel introduced the extraordinarily short Japanese wheat Norin-10 to the United States. This is a variety whose lack of stature depends not merely on gene arrangement, but on specific dwarfing genes. Vogel 'borrowed' these genes to produce the semi-dwarf wheats of the Green Revolution. The Plant Breeding Institute has also borrowed them, together with other genes from unrelated dwarf types like Minister Dwarf and Tom Thumb, to produce a new generation of semi-drawfs suitable for growing in Britain. By the early 1970s the new semi-dwarfs were out-yielding standard varieties by 10 per cent. They became available commercially in 1974. The names of the latest types are included in the lists of recommended crop varieties issued by the National Institute of Agricultural Botany, and obtainable through regional offices of the Ministry of Agriculture, Fisheries and Food.

# Barley

Barley differs from other cereals in having three flowers at each node in the ear. Primitive barleys (as discovered, carbonized, in Neolithic and Bronze Age remains) are generally six rowed. In most modern types, however, the outer flowers of each triad are sterile or male, so the ear finishes up with only two rows of seeds.

Britain produces 8–9 million tonnes of barley each year, of which more than 2 million are malted and the rest goes for feed. Of the malting barley, about half is used for beer, around 40 per cent for whisky, and the rest mainly for vinegar. Malting barley fetches a higher price, and British and Continental brewers favour British barleys. Leading maltsters have suggested that by 1980 Britain could profitably use half its barley crop for malting. This would not be mere frivolity. Kenneth Blaxter, one of the world's leading agricultural thinkers, points out that beer provides an admirable way of storing barley, and that a self-reliant Britain could reasonably produce more of it.

However, maltsters are even fussier about barley than millers are about wheat. In particular, in contrast to millers, they demand a low protein (or nitrogen) content. Malting begins with the barley's germination and the breaking down of the starch. The higher the protein content, the less starch there is, and too much nitrogen in the grain can produce cloudy beer and generally reduce brewing efficiency.

Barley's dual function at first looks like versatility, but in practice this splits it into contrasting crops, thus raising two problems. First, barley used for feed should ideally have a high protein content. Secondly, barley intended for malting must be fertilized very carefully. It must be given enough nitrogen, at the right time, to maximize yields (there is a difference of 2.5 tonnes a hectare between the national average yield and the top yields) but not so much that surplus nitrogen, mainly protein, accumulates in the grain.

## Cultivation

In practice, most British barley is spring sown, which usually means February to April, but in favourable districts and years may be as early as January. Sowing must be particularly early on sandy soils, to allow time for good roots to form

Barley

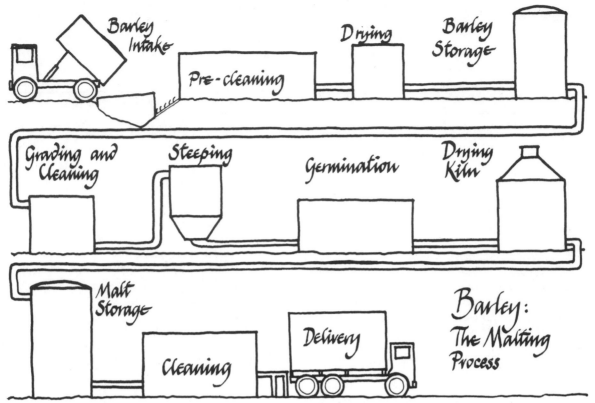

Barley: The Malting Process

Malt is made from barley grains that have been kept moist and warm long enough for them to germinate. They are then dried

by the summer. A month's delay in drilling from mid-March to mid-April reduces potential yield by up to 1.25 tonnes a hectare. Spring-sown crops require carefully prepared seed beds.

Plough early in autumn, leave the land in furrow to let the frosts do their work, then after the New Year watch for the frost and dry weather that makes the top 5–8 centimetres friable. Then disc harrow to form a tilth and follow with harrows and drill. Note, though, that because barley is spring sown it is best grown on light land that warms up quickly. Medium loams and light soils over chalk are ideal. These should not be over-cultivated: one or two passes with the cultivator is often enough and on light soils the drill itself may do all the cultivation needed. Soil varies from field to field and from day to day. You must acquire a feel for its particular needs.

Now for fertilization. The nitrogen requirement depends on the previous crops. From 170 to 200 units a hectare should be ample for malting barley, which cannot usually follow potatoes, sugar beet, or newly ploughed leys because of the high nitrogen residue these crops leave behind; 75 units should be applied as the barley is sown and the rest – for malting barley – must be applied before the three-leaf stage. If it is applied later it winds up in the grain, and so reduces malting quality. If it is applied all at once, with the newly sown seed, some will be lost by leaching.

Good malting barleys have a low dormancy, and therefore germinate easily. This means that they tend to germinate in the ear, before harvesting, so the timing of harvesting is crucial. On the other hand the earlier the harvesting, the greater the need for post-harvest drying, and if barley is heated above 43°C during drying its enzymes are destroyed and it will not germinate, so it cannot be used to produce malt.

Cultivating and preparing malting barley is exacting. Do it well, and nothing should be beyond you.

# Maize

Maize is bringing a sub-tropical aspect to ever-increasing areas of Britain. It is the only cereal to originate in America and, indeed, before the Old and New Worlds became one, it was the only cereal the native Americans possessed. Whether it was first domesticated – not later, probably, than 4000 BC – in Central America and spread south to the Andes, or in the Andes and spread north, is not certain.

It is known, however, that Columbus brought maize to Europe, from whence it has spread all over the world. A remarkable series of hybridizations undertaken in the United States earlier this century has increased yields several fold, and put it into the big league of world crops. Maize is a staple food in parts of South America and southern and eastern Africa, and a major feed crop in the United States and, increasingly, in Europe. In addition, variants of this most versatile grass – the sugary sweetcorn and the hard popcorn which bursts when it is heated – are delicacies, and the grain, roasted and pounded, is the basis of cornflakes.

Fully grown, the maize plant may grow to a height of 2.5–3 metres. At the top, the male flowers form 'tassels', while below, on the stem, the female flowers at first bear great beards of 'silk' – the styles, designed to catch the wind-blown pollen – and later swell to form the 'cobs', usually one or two per plant, with the seeds arranged in rows.

Attempts have been made to integrate maize into British agriculture since the nineteenth century, but the great spread northwards from Italy and the south of France got under way after 1945. France has been the pace-setter; her maize-growing area has increased from 240,000 hectares in 1965 to more than 2.8 million in 1974. Britain has had to wait for suitable temperate varieties, but she, too, has increased cultivation from about 400 hectares in 1965 to more than 20,000 by the mid-1970s. The crop has become more attractive as feed since the cheap barley of the 1960s became a thing of the past.

Maize has still not lived down its sub-tropical origins. It does not grow if the temperature is below 10°C and it needs a long season. Indeed, to produce forage maize, where the whole plant, immature cobs and all, is smashed for silage, requires an 'accumulated heat' of 728°C between May and October, and grain suitable for

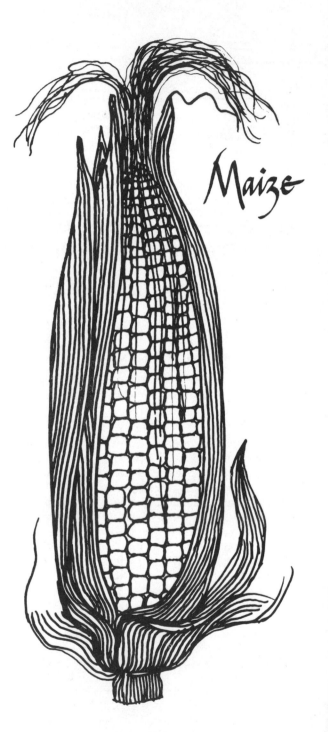

*Maize*

Wild Maize    Teosinte    Tripsacum

The three New World grasses involved in the development of domesticated maize

Farmers who can grow maize may expect up to 10 tonnes of dry matter per hectare. The protein content, at 8–10 per cent, is less than that of barley and considerably less than dried grass, but the high energy content and total mass make the crop highly attractive for feeding to cattle, both dairy cattle, when maize silage is supplemented with protein, or beef, when it may be supplemented with urea.

Maize also fits conveniently into the farming year. It is harvested and sown late, so the peaks of activity are spread, and because of the late sowing – seeds may simply perish if put in before the end of April – weeds, particularly wild oats, can be dealt with first. On suitable land, and in favourable seasons, farmers can please themselves whether they crop early (late September) for silage, or wait for the grain to develop by the end of October.

Several factors militate against small-scale cultivation. First, harvesting, either for silage or for grain, requires specialist machinery. Secondly, rooks are very troublesome until the crop is about 30cm high, and they do most damage to small, isolated patches. They can be deterred by fixing black nylon thread, around waist high, at 10–40 metre intervals – two men can cotton a hectare in about $2\frac{1}{2}$ hours. It is possible, however, that large-scale cultivation will encourage the spread of maize diseases, notably stalk- or foot-rot, caused by fungus.

separate harvesting, with a 40 per cent moisture content, needs accumulated heat of 762°C. Grain maize, in general, can be grown only to the south of a line from The Wash to the Bristol Channel, and the crop is not recommended at all above an altitude of 120 metres. It also prefers a deep, loamy soil and it requires heavy fertilization – although this can be an advantage, as the crop can soak up heavy doses of slurry.

A maize crop. In America, this is 'corn'

# Rye

Rye *(Secale cereale)* is evidently the newest of the Old World cereals – Pliny describes it as a novelty. Indeed, it is probable that it was domesticated almost by accident after an inauspicious start as a weed of wheat. As knowledge of wheat cultivation spread into regions where wild rye thrived, the rye benefited from the cultivation and dominated the crop until farmers abandoned wheat and cultivated rye instead. At all events, it has competed with wheat and barley as a bread grain ever since, although its importance has been declining for some time. By the mid-eighteenth century the English and Welsh got three-fifths of their bread from wheat, and only 15 per cent from rye, with barley (12 per cent) and oats (11 per cent) well on the way out as cereal staples. The 400,000 hectares of rye being grown in the eighteenth century had dwindled to 40,000 by the end of the nineteenth, and apart from a modest increase during the two World Wars, it has declined steadily ever since to around 6,000. It would hardly fill even that modest area were it not for its value as a winter catch-crop.

Yet rye, like oats, deserves a better deal. The grain has roughly the same total protein content as that of barley or wheat, but unlike wheat it lacks the elastic protein 'glutenin', so rye dough is not spongy (see p.50). However, the heavy black bread it makes – in a specialist form it is called pumpernickel – is still favoured, and rightly, in northern and eastern Europe for its robust, nutty flavour. Indeed, until 1957 the West Germans grew more rye than wheat. Perhaps the East Germans still do.

Rye meal produces the hard breads, and rye flakes find their way into breakfast cereals. In addition, in Canada and the United States the grain is malted to make rye whisky, in Holland it is distilled to make gin, and in Britain some of it is fed to livestock. Rye starch, incidentally, has been used widely for glue.

Rye straw is as desirable as that of oats, and for the totally opposite reason: it is almost devoid of nutritional value, and so can be used safely for bedding horses. It also grows to a spectacular 1.5–2.5 metres in length (that is, height), it is practically solid in cross-section, it is wiry and weather-resistant, and therefore is favoured for thatch. Indeed, at times rye has been grown exclusively for its straw. Obligingly, it yields two and a half times more straw than grain, by weight.

Its immense height means that rye cannot be manured heavily, or risked on very fertile or wet, heavy land, as it would be likely keel over. But because its extensive roots enable it to tolerate drought, it is grown, almost always, on light, sandy soils. Indeed sometimes it is raised in winter specifically to stabilize such soils. Mostly

*Rye straw used for thatching*

it is grown in the high-sunshine, low-rainfall, arable areas of south-east England, and often as a break crop between wheat and barley. In some ways rye may be too accommodating for its own good. For example, although evidently it prefers mildly acid conditions, with a pH of around 5.5, it is sometimes required to grow in extremely acid soils, below pH 4. It does not do well under such conditions, but the wonder is that it survives at all.

## Cultivation

Rye is generally sown in the autumn; if you can get it in by the end of the summer, or in early autumn, well and good, otherwise October will do. On the light soils that rye prefers, the weather should not hinder cultivation. The only delay might be caused by the presence of previous crops.

On such light lands, cultivation is minimal. You need merely to clear the way for the crop's wide-ranging roots. Above all, this means avoiding plough pans. The crop needs little or no nitrogen – which would cause lodging – but it does like 75–150 units of phosphorus and potassium to the hectare, applied at the time of sowing. Farmers sometimes apply 25–30 tonnes of farmyard manure per hectare to very light soils before sowing rye, just to improve the soil. In such cases, no artificials are needed.

## Rye for forage

Rye's final merit – indeed, often the sole reason for growing it – is its value as a forage. This is comparable to the value of the forage brassicas (see p.96). If you get it in by mid-summer it may allow some grazing in November, and this will stimulate spring growth. Alternatively, it may be strip grazed by cattle (usually dairy cattle) in spring. The optimum height is around 20–25cm. In practice, though, grazing begins at 15cm and lasts for a fortnight, with the optimum height occurring some time during this period. Then again, sheep may graze the crop in March, when it is 10–12cm high, after which it can be given 75 units of nitrogen and cattle may be turned on to the aftermath in April or May. In some cases cattle have been allowed on to rye in early March. One way or another, rye's superior hardiness should give you an earlier bite than grass would, and the earlier you can get the beasts on to fresh pastures, and away from concentrates, the more you should save.

Rye

# Oats

From the beginning of agriculture – or, according to the archaeologists, for at least 5,000 years – oats have enjoyed an ambivalent status. On the one hand the notorious weed *Avena fatua* (wild oat) is still very troublesome in Britain (see p.49). On the other hand oats are a useful, and sometimes invaluable, source of grain and forage. The Greeks expressed the dilemma: they grew them as green fodder and hay for horses, and cursed them as pests at the same time. *A. fatua* itself is still cultivated for grain, green fodder and other purposes in south-east Asia. Pliny, in the first century AD, thought oats were merely a degenerate form of barley. All in all,

the hardy and versatile oat is an inevitable pollutant of wheat and barley, and a successful competitor. As one authority put it, 'oats forced themselves on the early cultivators'.

The British cultivated oat is *Avena sativa*, which apparently derives from *A. fatua* and two other species – including *A. sterilis*, which is still grown for fodder around the Mediterranean. The first British carbonized remains date from 400 to 250 BC in Wiltshire, Somerset and Dorset. Probably we acquired the crop from Europe.

Oats deserve far better treatment than they get. Like rye, they are out of favour. Before the Second World War we grew 540,000 hectares in England and Wales, 300,000 in Scotland, and 100,000 in Northern Ireland. As grassland was ploughed up during the war, to increase our self-reliance, the total area probably increased to around 1.4 million hectares. Now, in the whole of Great Britain, we are down to 200,000 hectares. The proportion eaten by humans seems to be falling, too: before the war it was 10 per cent, and by the 1960s it was 7½ per cent. The French, who grow oats widely, consume directly only 0.2 per cent.

Yet the oat has a high nutritional value and an interesting cuisine. At around 10.5 per cent, its protein content tends to be higher than that of barley, and its carbohydrate content, at 60 per cent, is 10 per cent less. Its outstanding features are its high oil content – sometimes more than 5 per cent, as against 1.5 per cent in barley – and its high crude fibre content, which, at more than 10 per cent, is two and a half times higher than that of barley.

Both the high oil and high fibre contents raise problems, as does the protein content of barley (see p.52). Theoretically, oil is a valuable nutritional asset, which livestock farmers at least recognize. The millers, though, prefer a low oil content, as otherwise the flour they prepare for human consumption is difficult to store. Indeed, it is the lip-ase (fat-digesting enzyme) on the outer coat of the oat kernel that breaks up the oil in stored meal, and so produces the characteristic flavour, or 'nip'.

Livestock farmers, on the other hand, do not approve of the high fibre content, which reduces overall digestibility, although modern nutritional theory suggests that humans eating a typical Western diet could do with more fibre. The fibre is used at present, among other things, as a filter in breweries, as deep litter in poultry houses, and to make paper. It is also a source of

Oats

furfural, which is used as a raw material in the manufacture of nylon and fungicides.

As human food, the oat kernel, after milling, is the basis of porridge, oatcakes, black puddings and haggis. With its high nutritional content, its flavour, and its obvious 'meat extending' ability it deserves a wider following than it receives. Only the Scots, it seems, have really explored its potential. The oat husks and oat dust left after milling are a useful feed, and the final product of the mill, the meal seeds or 'sids', are the basis of the Scottish beverage 'sowan', a jelly-like gruel that is mixed with milk or syrup and is justifiably favoured for invalids.

Finally, oat straw is outstandingly nutritious. Cut young, it contains 3 per cent crude protein, 2 per cent oil, 40 per cent carbohydrate, and is about one-third crude fibre. The total tonnage of straw, per hectare, will slightly exceed that of the grain.

## Growing oats

Oats tolerate a wide range of soils and partly for that reason they have tended to be pushed to the margins. Indeed, *Avena strigosa*, an ancient cultivated species known from the Bronze Age, was cultivated formerly in north and west Scotland, on the poorest alkaline soils. Oats do seem to prefer slight acidity, around pH 5.5, and will grow at a pH as low as 4.4 (which barley will not), but they will not tolerate extreme acidity. In areas of high rainfall they prefer light, medium soils, though they will do well in heavy clays or silts if the rainfall is low. A combination of high precipitation and high field capacity produces over-long growth, and lodging. In a cool and consistently humid climate they grow slowly, but the grain fills better and more evenly. In other words, they like Scotland, and it is just as well that the Scots, hitherto at least, have liked them.

In the south of England and Wales oats are sometimes sown as a 'winter' crop, often after barley or wheat; they do very well after beans, particularly when these are harvested early, leaving the oat crop plenty of time to become established before the cold weather. If they follow a crop that leaves nitrogen behind – early potatoes, or beans – they need no fertilizer when they go in, and a modest 75–100 units of nitrogen per hectare in spring. If they are slotted into a mainly cereal rotation, they will need 50 units of nitrogen in the autumn to start them off (plus 75–125 units each of phosphorus and potassium) and another 125–150 of nitrogen in spring.

Most oats are spring sown, however. Since they are the only cereal that is favoured consistently in high-rainfall areas, they are often the first crop after grass. Sometimes two oat crops follow a grass ley. Sometimes they follow swedes or turnips. Oats have their own arcare vocabulary. When they follow roots they are called 'Redland oats'; in Scotland when they follow another oat crop they are termed 'Yaval oats', and so on. But oats, unlike barley or wheat, must not be grown too often on the same land. They will be plagued by cereal root eelworm.

Fertilization for spring oats again depends on what they follow. Nitrogen requirements, for example, may vary from 0 to 50 units per hectare when the crop follows a grass–dover ley in a high-rainfall area, up to 125–150 units when the crop is in a mainly cereal rotation in a low-rainfall area, with phosphorus and potassium adjusted accordingly. In areas of extreme acidity you need lime, but this should go on a previous crop, as limed oats can become deficient in manganese.

Winter oats should be sown as early as possible – leaving the soil rough, as described for wheat (see p.50) – but in practice this usually means the first two weeks in October. November is too late. If the crop becomes too lush in autumn, 'winter proud', it can be grazed down in the spring, though only on light land or you may create a quagmire.

Spring sowing also, as with barley, should be as early as possible: in February on light soils. High-altitude, marginal hill farmers, who sometimes have to wait until April or even May, suffer accordingly. In one study, oats sown in late March yielded 3 tonnes per hectare, whereas the May-sown crop gave only 2 tonnes.

In a more austere world, this nutritious and tasty grain deserves revival.

# Sugar beet

Sugar beet is the only non-cereal crop that is grown extensively in Britain for human food but is not grown in gardens, although it belongs to the same species (*Beta vulgaris*) as the beetroot, seakale beet or Swiss chard, and spinach beet.

Sugar beet is both a superb and profitable crop, and a nutritional disaster. To its credit, it is a useful arable break, it is able to tolerate a wide variety of soils – anything that is not heavy clay or light sand – it requires thorough cultivation, which benefits other crops in the rotation, and it yields between 22 and 70 tonnes (and occasionally more) per hectare, of which 15–20 per cent is sugar. In addition, the pulp, after the sugar has been extracted, is a valuable feed, and the leafy tops have as much feed value as an entire crop of oats. After all, beet is a member of the *Chenopodiaceae*, which also includes Good King Henry, much favoured by leaf-protein enthusiasts (see p.184) and Fat Hen, now an agricultural weed but probably cultivated as a leaf crop in the Iron Age. It is small wonder that Britain's farmers grow about 200,000 hectares of beet, mostly on holdings of around 10 hectares, thus producing between 600,000 and one million tonnes of refined sugar, about a third of our total 'requirement'.

On the other hand, sugar, which now provides Britons with about one-fifth of their calories, is heavily implicated in dental caries, one of affluent man's most common afflictions. Although calorific, sugar is not particularly filling, and so it makes perhaps the greatest single contribution to obesity, as well as, according to Professor John Yudkin and others, contributing directly or indirectly to coronary heart disease, which is by far the biggest killer of Western man. In addition, in contrast to starchy foods like cereals and potatoes, sugar provides energy without protein, so that high-protein foods become necessary to restore a proper energy–protein ratio. Paradoxically it is the sugar-eating Westerners, and not the cereal eaters of poorer countries, who 'need' meat. Certainly we can do without sugar. Until the nineteenth century it was a luxury in Britain, and although the sugar beet plant has been known since pre-Christian times, and it is 200 years since sugar was first extracted from it, it was hardly grown in Britain until the 1920s, when the government encouraged its cultivation to alleviate agricultural depression.

Taken all in all, though, we believe sugar does have a place: to provide sweet sauces for meat, in fruit and other preserves, and, of course, in beer, where it assists a remarkably simple way of storing barley (see p.52).

## Cultivation

Even though sugar beet is exclusive to farms (although gardeners could grow small quantities and eat the root, cooked in the same way as turnip or swede) gardeners can learn a lot about first principles from its cultivation.

As with the potato, sowing time is crucial. Mid-March is favoured, and every week's delay after this loses 1–2.5 tonnes per hectare. Sowing time is critical not, as with the potato, because of danger from frost damage, but because beet is a biennial which forms a sugary root in its first winter and produces seed the following summer. If it is cooled too early in its growth – simulating its first winter – it is liable to produce seed ('bolt') in its first year, and never form a useful root. So growers who sow early are advised to use modern non-bolting varieties.

Harvest time is also critical. November is the ideal time, because the sugar concentration falls after this, even though the weight of the root may increase into December. In practice, harvesting begins in October, so as to stagger the work for the refining plants. Harvesting was a back-breaking job until it became mechanized, for the roots must be dug from the ground and the tops chopped off. Nowadays a single machine (see p.28) lifts the beets, tops them, and feeds them into a trailer or lorry.

Although the beets are large – 30–45cm long – trials show that cultivation deeper than 20cm brings little benefit, so illustrating the modern gardening concept that it is the top few centimetres of soil that are the most important.

Irrigation is almost mandatory. In a dry season every centimetre of water gives up to 250kg more refined sugar.

Fertilization, too, is critical. Beet likes a lot of

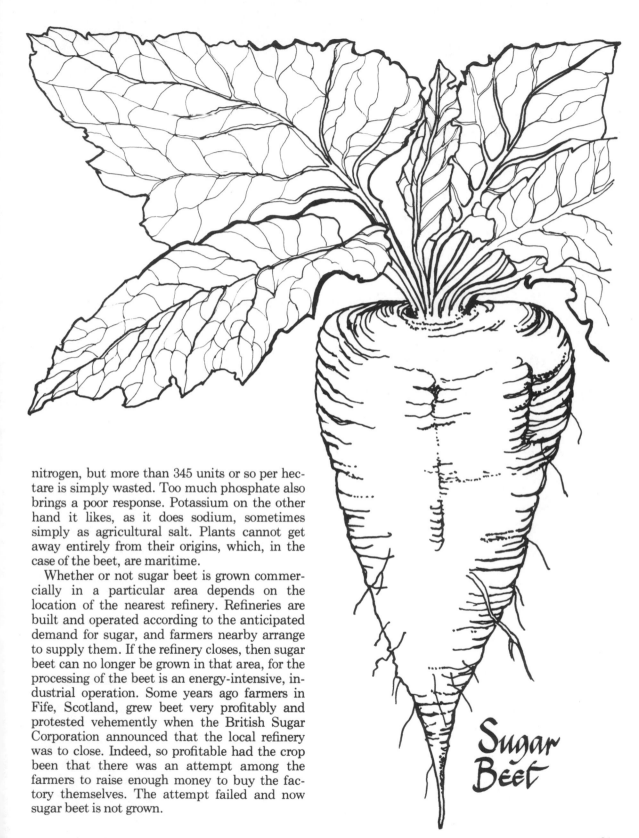

Sugar
Beet

nitrogen, but more than 345 units or so per hectare is simply wasted. Too much phosphate also brings a poor response. Potassium on the other hand it likes, as it does sodium, sometimes simply as agricultural salt. Plants cannot get away entirely from their origins, which, in the case of the beet, are maritime.

Whether or not sugar beet is grown commercially in a particular area depends on the location of the nearest refinery. Refineries are built and operated according to the anticipated demand for sugar, and farmers nearby arrange to supply them. If the refinery closes, then sugar beet can no longer be grown in that area, for the processing of the beet is an energy-intensive, industrial operation. Some years ago farmers in Fife, Scotland, grew beet very profitably and protested vehemently when the British Sugar Corporation announced that the local refinery was to close. Indeed, so profitable had the crop been that there was an attempt among the farmers to raise enough money to buy the factory themselves. The attempt failed and now sugar beet is not grown.

# Flax and hemp

When we think about agricultural self-sufficiency for Britain, we tend to think exclusively of food production. This is reasonable enough, up to a point, but the land also produces important non-food crops: the raw materials for the manufacture of industrial starches and alcohols, for example. It also produces fibres and industrial oils.

To a large extent the traditional fibre and oilseed crops have been replaced. The place of linen was taken first by cotton, and then by cheap man-made fibres, including rayon, which is derived from wood. Wood pulp has come to dominate the paper industry. Petroleum has provided more and more of our lubricants.

The trend could be reversed, and already it shows signs of stabilizing. There are some uses, for example, in which linseed oil is superior to other oils – in paint manufacture in particular. Man-made fibres are no longer as cheap as they were since the rise in oil prices, and cotton producers are charging more and insisting on selling us finished cloth, rather than the raw material for our own mills. Much the same thing is happening to the wood-pulp industry, and there is good reason to wonder how much longer the forests of the world can satisfy our appetite for paper.

Although it is sensible to think of increasing the area in Britain that is producing timber, conifer plantations may not be the best or most versatile source of fibres. Being annual crops, flax and hemp can out-yield even the fastest-growing forest many times over, and they can do so within the farming system, so that the quantity produced can be varied from year to year rather than from generation to generation. The fibre itself has more uses. It makes yarns, ropes, cloths and, when these first products are of no further use, it can be recycled to make high-quality paper. Even today, the best paper is made from linen, and hemp paper is said to be superior to wood pulp for printing and binding.

In the Common Market as a whole, about 50–60,000 hectares are sown to flax and about 4,000 hectares to hemp, each year. In Britain we are not permitted to grow hemp, of course, but we do produce a few thousand hectares of flax, almost all of it for oil.

The words 'flax' and 'hemp' are used to describe a range of fibre crops, many of them tropical, that botanically have nothing to do with true flax, *Linum usitatissimum,* and true hemp, *Cannabis sativa,* both of which grow in a temperate climate.

## Flax

Flax is an inconvenient crop in some ways, and because the whole of the plant is used it can exhaust land rather quickly. It must be grown as part of a rotation, and should not return to the same land more than once every seven years.

As with so many other crops, two different enterprises are involved that are not really compatible. If the aim is to produce oil, you want a short-strawed, heavily fertilized variety; if the product is to be fibre, the plant should be long strawed, and not fertilized heavily.

Varieties tested at the National Institute of Agricultural Botany include Linda, which has long straw, Vitagold and Bionda, with medium straw, and Linott, Antares and Noralta, which produce short straw. Seed yields were in the order of 17kg per hectare, or rather less. The Common Market average yield of straw is about 8,500kg per hectare, containing perhaps half that amount of linen fibre.

## Cultivation

Flax prefers a loamy soil, but it can be grown successfully on a wide range of soils, and climatically it will tolerate most of what the British weather can do to it. The best fibre flax prefers moist conditions, however, and traditionally has been grown in Ireland and parts of Scotland.

It should be sown on well-prepared, firm seedbeds. The seed is very small, and so soil preparation is more important than for, say, cereals. There must be no weeds.

For oilseed production, you need to apply per hectare about 150 units of nitrogen, about 80 units of phosphorus, and about 85 units of potassium at sowing, with a further top-dressing to bring the total nitrogen up to about 170–200 units per hectare. The soil must not be acid (the pH should be between 6.5 and 7.0), so some lime may be needed.

If you are growing for fibre, reduce the amount of nitrogen.

The seed should be sown not more than 4cm below the surface, drilled at the rate of about 80kg per hectare, or broadcast at a higher rate.

Sow as soon as the ground is ready – as early in the year as possible, and anyway before the end of April. The plants will emerge about ten days later, and must be kept free from weeds until they become established. Harvesting should be possible for oil by early September, and for fibre a little before then.

Once the plants are about 10cm tall they can be left to themselves. Fibre flax grows to a height of about one metre, with a pale green stem producing small leaves over its whole length, and small blue or white flowers.

As the crop ripens it will turn golden in colour,

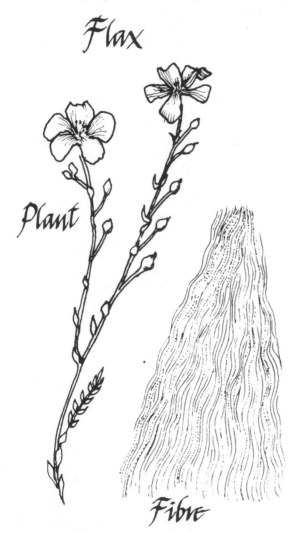

Flax

Plant

Fibre

the flowers will be replaced by seed pods, and these will become dry and brittle. Each roughly spherical pod contains a number of seeds.

The fibre crop should be harvested before the seeds are fully ripe, and the plants should be taken whole, roots and all. Traditionally they were pulled out by hand. Flax produces only shallow roots, so this is less arduous than it may seem. Cutting the stem damages the fibre. The seed is not necessarily lost, however, for the first stage in fibre processing involves drying the harvested plants, which also allows the seeds to mature. They are then removed before the fibre goes to be retted.

The oilseed crop is cut. It is a tough plant that may cause problems in a combine harvester if the crop is not approached carefully, and the settings on the combine adjusted correctly.

The oil is extracted by crushing.

### Hemp
If the commercial growing of hemp for fibre becomes legal, the procedure is similar to that for flax. The much larger hemp seed is sown (drilled or broadcast) on to a firm, well-prepared seed bed, to a depth of about 3cm and at a density of 80 to 90kg per hectare. Sowing should be as early as possible, and the plants grow to a height of 1.5–3 metres. They are harvested when the flowers are in full bloom, either by pulling by hand, or by cutting as close to the ground as possible. The emerging crop should be kept free from weeds, but once it is established no further attention is needed.

The subsequent method of processing hemp fibres is identical to that used for flax.

### Nettles
It is unlikely that anyone will wish to grow stinging nettles as a farm crop, but if they are allowed to grow to their full height – of up to 2 metres – they, too, provide a fibre that can be extracted in the same way as flax and hemp fibres. Nettle fibre can be spun and woven into a coarse cloth and then, presumably, recycled as paper.

# Introducing the potato

No vegetable, fruit, or Malvolio has ever been more notoriously abused than the potato. Condemned by the dietician as 'stodge' and shunned by the slimmer, in fact it is a fairly low-energy food that could be a major source of high-grade protein and that is already, in Great Britain, the most important single source of vitamin C.

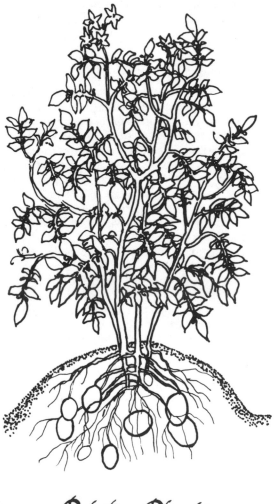

*Potato Plant*

Potatoes are a modest energy source compared, say, to cereals, because they are 80 per cent water. The average Briton's 170-gram daily intake provides only 138kcal, about one-twentieth of the daily energy needs. Poor Irish people of the nineteenth century had to eat about 3.5kg of potatoes a day to meet their energy requirements. Potatoes go well with fat, however, and potato chips have more than three times the energy content of boiled potatoes, partly because of the added fat and partly because of the loss of water.

It may make sense to cut down on chips and potato crisps when slimming, but clearly cutting down on potatoes generally is to strike yourself a severe gastronomic blow while barely affecting your calorie intake. It would be far better to double your (boiled) potato intake and cut out something else.

The quality of potato protein has been alleged to be almost as high as that of eggs. Of the eight essential amino acids it is mildly deficient only in methionine. Indeed, 1.4kg of potatoes a day (a fairly heroic intake, but not amazing) would provide your daily protein needs – without making you fat. A Canadian study showed that only soya beans, producing 380kg of usable protein per hectare, produced more protein per unit area than potatoes, which averaged 280kg. Beans (150kg), peas (140), and spring wheat (120), lagged far behind. Green leaves, such as cabbage, would outstrip even soya in protein yield per hectare (see p.184), but cabbages contain far too much fibre and water to act as a worthwhile protein source for humans, unless, of course, the protein is extracted before consumption.

The vitamin C content is about 30mg per 100g when the new potato is first lifted, but falls during storage to about 8mg per 100g in spring. Boiling destroys or leaches out some of the vitamin, but 60 per cent evidently survives even this treatment and potatoes supply Britons with 30–90 per cent of their daily vitamin C requirements. They also supply useful amounts of B vitamins and a respectable list of minerals. In short, the potato is one of the finest staples conceivable. If it were reinvented, it would be hailed, rightly, as a wonder food.

It did not start that way. The first types, cultivated high in the Andes perhaps 5,000 years ago, contained glycoalkaloids which were bitter and, in large amounts, toxic, but from them developed spontaneously a strain in which the chromosome number was doubled. These

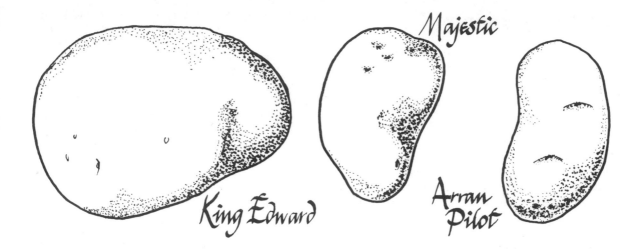

King Edward

Majestic

Arran Pilot

'Andigena' potatoes were a great improvement on the wild types and, in great variety, are still cultivated today.

It was Andigenas that the Spaniards (and probably not Drake or Raleigh, despite the legends) first brought to Europe in the sixteenth century. They did not do well. They were not adapted to the long days of northern latitudes and so were grown only in parts of southern Europe, they yielded poorly even there, and, in any case, they were long and narrow, with deep eyes.

Selection in the eighteenth century produced the northern-adapted, high-yielding Tuberosum series, which became a staple for the working poor in the nineteenth century, as they were cheaper than grain (whose price was kept high by the Corn Laws) and they could be grown in the wetter, western parts of the British Isles, where cereals would not ripen. By 1900 varieties had been produced that could still pass as 'modern'.

The genetic variation within the stocks was small. All the modern European varieties had been derived entirely from the original sixteenth-century stocks. Without a good variety of genes to work on, it is difficult to improve crops by breeding. This is why some potato varieties have lasted for about fifty years, while cereals are often superseded in a decade or less.

In order to increase the genetic base scientists at the Scottish Plant Breeding Station in Edinburgh, and elsewhere, are now recreating a totally new strain from the original Andigena types. In a few years, varieties from this 'Neotuberosum' series should be available commercially – the first quantum advance in potato breeding since the eighteenth century.

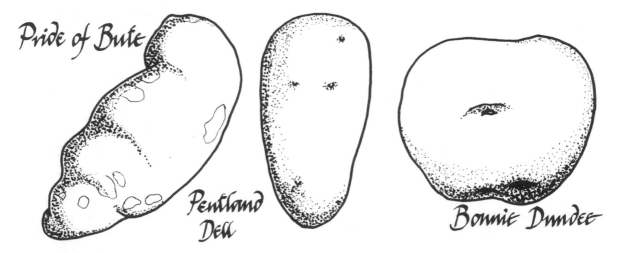

Pride of Bute

Pentland Dell

Bonnie Dundee

# Potato growing

Potatoes are tubers, swollen underground stems that serve the plant as storage organs. Yields are highly variable, which is a great embarrassment to the professional grower, but they reflect, directly and simply, the growing conditions. They like a well-dug, fertile soil, commensurate with a yield that in maincrops may be 17.5–37.5 tonnes a hectare, or 7.5–25 tonnes for earlies. They hate to be dried out, they like as long a growing season as you can give them (although earlies and second earlies are picked young) but are susceptible to frost. They are prone to a range of diseases, with the degree of susceptibility varying markedly from variety to variety, and they turn green and toxic if they are exposed to the light. All the intricacies of cultivation derive from these simple principles.

The farmer may provide potatoes with 25–40 tonnes of farmyard manure per hectare, and supplement this with 750–1500kg of artificial manure – for example, 250kg ammonium sulphate, 250kg potassium sulphate, and 500kg of superphosphate.

For the gardener this means growing on soil heavily manured or fed with compost the previous year for the avaricious spinach, onion, lettuce or tomato, and applying 80–100 grammes per metre or row of a general fertilizer, such as John Innes base.

The farmer sows about 2–3 tonnes per hectare of 'seed' potatoes (not literally 'seeds', but tubers about the size of a hen's egg), and the gardener sows them about 10cm deep, 30cm apart, in rows about 60cm apart for earlies, or somewhat wider spacing for maincrop. In each case the aim is to provide a complete canopy of green as early in the season as possible, to catch all the sun that's going, but without crowding underground.

Sowing time is critical. East Anglian farmers aim to sow maincrops during the first week in April, and reckon that every week's delay after that costs them 1–2.5 tonnes per hectare in yield. Earlies are got in as soon as the soil is dry enough, but to increase the length of the actual growing season commercial growers and gardeners alike are advised to sprout or 'chit' the seed before planting: stand the seed in trays, with the eyes uppermost, in a light, cool but frost-free shed or greenhouse. They can be planted when the shoots are a centimetre or so in length – they should not be allowed to become long and straggly before planting. The gardener can afford to tend his crop more carefully than the farmer. For example, he can cover the newly emerging leaves with bracken or straw if necessary, to protect against frost.

'Earthing up' is a common practice: either drawing up the soil around the newly emerging plants, or planting them in shallow ditches and pushing the soil in on top. The purpose, besides giving some protection against frost, is to keep the emerging tubers out of the light and so prevent them from greening. The danger of creating such a large surface area is to increase the chances of drying out: bone-dry soil drawn over the plants may slow their growth critically. Farmers like a sunny May and a wet June, and are thinking increasingly in terms of irrigation: 2.5cm of water per hectare can increase the yield by 2.5 tonnes.

Hygiene is the key to continued success with potatoes. A rotation is essential, particularly to prevent the build-up of eelworms, whose eggs, once introduced, may remain in the soil for up to seven years. Viruses are also a menace. Farmers sometimes save their own seed, but even so they regularly import seed specially guaranteed to be virus-free, and gardeners are certainly advised to do this. Blight, the notorious fungus *Phytophthora infestans,* cause of the Irish famine of the 1840s, can be controlled by spraying in July with one of the modern fungicides based on copper or tin. The main source of infection, at least on farms, is the 'volunteer' plants allowed to regrow from the previous season, and these must be eliminated. Blight is endemic over most of Britain, but it does not attack every year or in every area. It is more likely in cool, wet seasons.

Farmers are obliged to grow for the market, which increasingly means raising varieties with a high dry matter and sugar content for potato crisps or small uniform varieties for canning. The joy of gardening is to experiment – in the case of potatoes with a range of shapes from spherical (Bonny Dundee or Angus Beauty) to sausage-shaped (like Pride of Bute), with colours that range from the bright red Duke of York to the deep blue-purple Arran Victory or Pride of

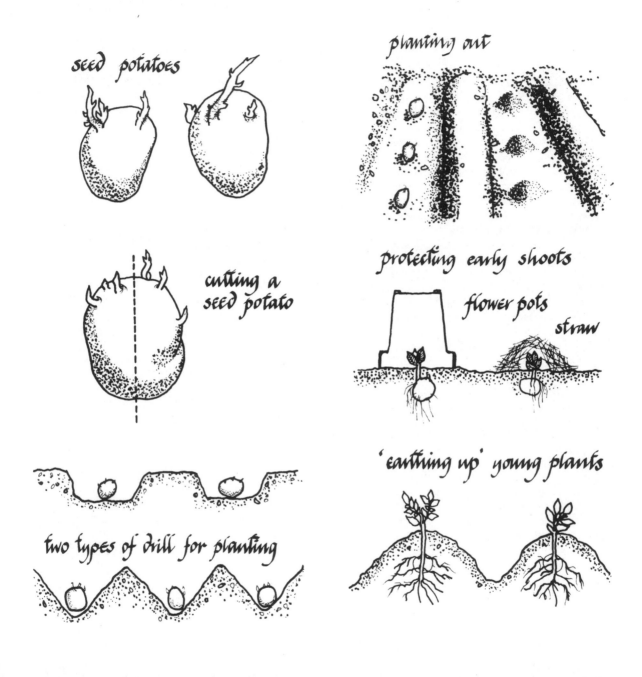

seed potatoes

planting out

cutting a seed potato

protecting early shoots

flower pots

straw

two types of drill for planting

'earthing up' young plants

Bute, and with textures, from the waxy Sefton Wonder or Russet Conference to the floury Golden Wonder and, again, Pride of Bute. The National Institute of Agricultural Botany recommends which types to grow. It would be irresponsible to stray far from their list without good reason, for they tend to recommend the types least susceptible to disease. All the same, it would be useful if gardeners were to complement the commercial growers by keeping the more exotic types alive, both for their own pleasure and for the benefit of posterity.

# Vegetables

## General principles

Plants need air, water and nutrient for their roots, and light and space for their growing tops. They do not like competition from other plants, although they may benefit from proximity in various ways (see p.71). Some can withstand frost, but all require a warm soil for maximum growth: a warm soil is far more important than a warm atmosphere. All are more or less susceptible to attack by a host of roundworms, insects, mites, fungi and viruses.

Within the context of those basic principles, gardening practice varies infinitely. For example, the old-fashioned recommendation always to double-dig – that is, to remove one spit (one spit is the depth of the blade of a spade or the tines of a fork) of soil and then turn over the exposed subsoil – is now giving way to the suggestion that you should cultivate as little as possible. But a heavy clay soil, particularly if it is low-lying, is liable to stay waterlogged and cold unless you break up the subsoil, and perhaps introduce bracken or twigs 30cm or so down to make a crude drainage sump. You should use the weather to help you cultivate. Dig roughly in the autumn and allow the winter frosts to break down the lumps to a fine tilth. But if your soil has a poor structure – which means primarily that it is deficient in organic matter – and if you are subject to heavy winter rains, then exposure could do more harm than good. Winter ground-cover which is dug in as green manure in spring may be preferable.

At different times a vegetable plot requires three basic treatments: the introduction of organic matter, such as farmyard manure or compost (but bear in mind that the former is a potent fertilizer and the latter, generally, is not); application of fertilizer; and application of lime, since fertilizer and organic matter tend to make the soil acid. The different kinds of treatment favour different kinds of crop, and these preferences form the basis of the Royal Horticultural Society's recommended three-course rotation.

The first year, after applying manure, you may grow peas, beans, onions, lettuces, leeks,

## Double Digging

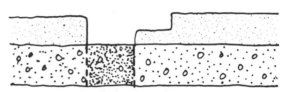

Mark and dig out a trench about one metre wide and one spit deep

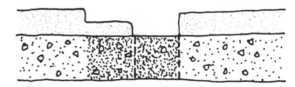

Divide this trench into two half-width trenches, dig a second spit from the front strip and remove the topsoil completely

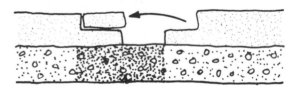

Fork over the exposed subsoil, then dig a second spit from the rear strip and place the soil in the front strip

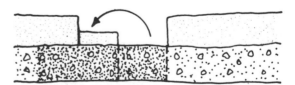

Move back half a metre, dig out one spit and put the soil into the 'step' in the front. Fork over the exposed subsoil

Remove the second spit from the new strip, put the soil over the forked subsoil, and continue working back

tomatoes, spinach, spinach beet and celery, and follow these as they are cropped with carrots or beetroot.

The following year you grow potatoes, carrots, beetroot, parsnips and swedes, with onions, spinach, lettuces and cabbages following on in the autumn.

The third year you add lime, which suits the brassicas: cabbages, brussels sprouts, cauliflowers, kales and broccoli. You can spare yourself over-energetic digging this last year, as brassicas tend to favour a well-packed soil.

In theory, the whole plot is divided into three, with each section in a different year of the cycle. In practice, you may find it convenient to grow certain crops, particularly runner beans whose supporting canes or trellis can be made permanent, in the same place each year. This is permissible, but carrots, brassicas and potatoes especially must be moved on from year to year, or their pests build up. Commercial carrot growers often own no land at all. They simply move the whole growing operation from area to area, renting fields as they go, mainly to outpace the dreaded carrot fly.

As we stress elsewhere (see compost, p.80, soil-less culture, p.72) the key desiderata of air and water are difficult to reconcile. Soils tend to be waterlogged or arid. The spongy texture of organic matter helps to resolve this conflict, and a valuable space-saving method making full use of this fact is the 'Biodynamic/French Intensive' system that has been pioneered in California.

In this, as much organic matter as possible is mixed into the top 30cm of soil, and then the ground is contoured in a series of raised beds, 1–2 metres wide and of indefinite length. This creates a loose, airy texture for the roots and increases the surface area, which gives you more room to plant in and helps to raise the soil temperature by increasing exposure to the sun. Yields per unit area are said to be four to twenty times greater than is achieved by commercial farmers.

Garden laid out according to the R.H.S three-course rotation

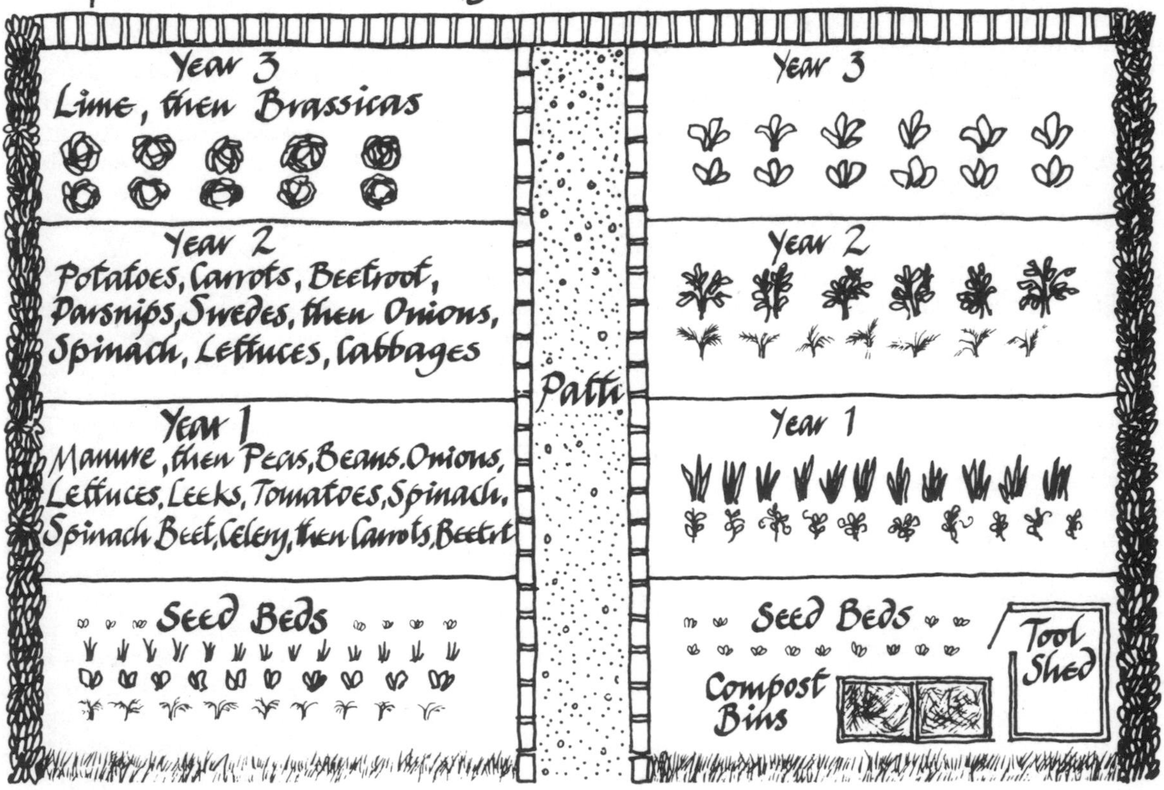

Year 3
Lime, then Brassicas

Year 2
Potatoes, Carrots, Beetroot, Parsnips, Swedes, then Onions, Spinach, Lettuces, Cabbages

Year 1
Manure, then Peas, Beans, Onions, Lettuces, Leeks, Tomatoes, Spinach, Spinach Beet, Celery, then Carrots, Beetrt

Seed Beds

Path

Year 3

Year 2

Year 1

Seed Beds

Compost Bins

Tool Shed

# What to grow?

Amateurs grow vegetables for three reasons: for cheap food, to produce rare delicacies that are not easy to buy, and for the combined satisfactions of the experimental scientist, the craftsman and the aesthete. Different crops and varieties suit different ambitions.

Limited space can be used most economically by growing crops with a compact habit, those that grow extremely rapidly, and those that grow at odd times of year – through the winter, say, and finishing in June. Modern varieties are contributing on all fronts.

Cabbages are notoriously space-consuming. For compactness you can hardly better the pointed, rapidly growing Hispi. Tom Thumb is a compact lettuce that can be grown at 15cm intervals, and the Chinese cabbages, particularly the pointed Pei-Tsai, yield an astonishing concentration of crisp, nutty, lettuce-like leaves in October or November from a sowing in July. Both the neglected corn-salad or lamb's lettuce and New Zealand spinach (unrelated to true spinach or spinach beets) are grown to produce a continuous sward that can be culled at will, and are space-saving in a different way. An ingenious choice of varieties will also allow 'intercropping'. Try mixing the autumn-sown early peas Feltham First and Feltham Advance in the same row (or swathe). First matures ten to twelve days earlier than Advance, so the two together give a longer season. Two rows of beans between three of peas is another space-saver, while the herb savory, intercropped with broad beans, is claimed to save the beans from blackfly.

Rapid growth is the hallmark of Hispi cabbage, Chinese cabbage, radishes and many varieties of turnip including the F1 Tokyo Cross which, so the Ipswich seedsmen Thompson and Morgan claim, produces 'tasty fresh turnips' within a month.

The urge to extend the growing season, and to produce crops in the paradoxically lean month of June, has quickened interest in autumn-sown, over-wintering varieties. The new carrot, Frebund, is said to be the best for autumn sowing in frames, or outside during January, for June cropping. The round-seeded pea, Sleaford Phoenix, is said to excel Meteor, perhaps the most famous of the autumn-sown peas. Most exciting of all are the hybrid onions from Japan, like Imai Yellow or the flatter-shaped Senshyu, to be sown outdoors in the last two weeks of August for cropping in midsummer the following year. Thompson and Morgan also claim to be extending the season with their bush tomato Sub Arctic Plenty, whose seedlings are said to withstand several degrees of frost. Another notable newcomer is the leek Abel, ready to eat in autumn and lasting for several months after that.

But why stay within the range of traditional English vegetables? Courgettes were once exotic; now they are an easy standby. Peppers (capsicums) and aubergines – the former allowed to sprawl but the latter requiring careful staking and pinching-out – can be grown like tomatoes, though they prefer continuous cover. The asparagus pea, sown fairly thickly to produce a dense, protective leaf-canopy, produces pods that are delicious if picked an inch long (try them with scrambled eggs). Kohlrabi, cultivated as a greenhouse special in Germany, grows freely in Britain, but its swollen, turnip-like stems should be eaten when golf-ball, not tennis-ball, sized as is usually suggested. The peculiar Manchurian squash, or vegetable spaghetti, is grown like marrow, but is more versatile.

Present crops offer far greater possibilities than most gardeners – or professional growers – appreciate. Colin Bowcock, grower and gardener at Willaston, Cheshire, specializes in pushing vegetables to their limit. He has produced lettuce weighing 11kg, a parsnip 2.6 metres long weighing 4.5kg, a leek over 2 metres high weighing more than 4kg, an onion with a 48cm circumference, and – *pièce de résistance* – a potato plant from a single set, carrying 360kg of tubers, and an autumn cabbage weighing 43kg. Mr Bowcock achieves such results by using giant vegetables to their limit. He has produced a lettuce weighing 11kg, a parsnip 2.6 metres long frames, fed continuously with foliar feeds and finally – like a patient in an intensive care unit – with a drip feed. This is far too extravagant for normal purposes, but it illustrates a vital point:

that great husbandry can transform our conception of what is possible.

## Growing for yield

Prize-winning vegetables are grown in isolation. The reduction in yield as plants are forced to compete for sun and nutrient is dramatic, and if it is too great cabbages fail to heart, turnips fail to swell, and tomatoes will not ripen the miniscule fruits they produce. All crops require early thinning: the weak aetiolation among crowded seedlings may never be fully outgrown.

On the other hand, maximum yield per plant does not necessarily imply maximum yield per unit area. Unless you are growing for the show-bench, you must squeeze in more plants and sacrifice a little individual yield. In fact, this is not all to the bad. Many crops are better if eaten small. Some, like young lettuces, may benefit from the transient shade and cooling offered by adjacent plants. Fruiting may be far better in slightly inspissated stands than among scattered plants. Thus pollinating bees have no love for isolated runner beans on windy allotments, but they will linger amongst dense stands, and wind-pollinated sweetcorn benefits from close companionship.

The modern need to maximize yield per area has produced three major trends: greater interest in dwarf, fast-growing varieties; renewed interest in the ancient cultivatory techniques of broadcasting, catch-cropping and intercropping; and a tendency to allow vegetables into the herbaceous border, making a virtue of necessity.

Broadcasting can be employed profitably with carrots, small beetroots such as Little Ball, spinach, radishes, parsnips, turnips and onions. You scatter the seed on the surface about 1cm apart each way – mixing the seed with sand may help you achieve this – and then scratch it into the soil with, for example, an old fork. You thin early – leaving the sturdiest seedlings – until the plants are the critical distance apart. For carrots, depending on variety, this may be 5–10cm each way. The result is a pleasant swathe of plants, with the roots practically touching underground and the leaves forming a dense, weed-excluding canopy on top. Hoeing is difficult, however. Do not make the swathes more than 60cm wide, to allow for hand weeding. Peas and beans may also be broadcast. Peas should be about 7.5cm apart on the bottom

of a 5cm-deep, flat-bottomed 'trench', beans 15–20cm apart, about 7.5cm down.

Catch-cropping means utilizing the odd weeks between main crops: beetroots or turnips picking up the autumn sunshine after the early potatoes, Chinese cabbages grown between potatoes and autumn-sown broad beans and peas, radishes here, there and everywhere. Like most roots, radishes *must* be grown fast or they become fibrous.

Intercropping – different crops mixed and alternated in the same plot – complements catch-cropping. Lettuces happily occupy the rows between beans or onions, being removed before the main crop comes into fruition. Courgettes may cover the ground between tomatoes. White- and red-flowered varieties of runner bean may share the same screen – a wise move, as white-flowered types seem to fruit in years when red ones fail.

Finally, the urban grower should not ignore the aesthetic delights of vegetables. Globe artichokes and runner beans – cultivated in the eighteenth century exclusively for their flowers – have obvious beauty, but the exotic luxuriance of courgettes, Swiss chard or red cabbage should not be despised. Broadcast swathes of lettuces and beet can form the basis for the most Italianate of formal gardens, with permanent dividing paths being both useful and aesthetic. The only rules are to avoid shade in general and trees in particular, but low, tightly clipped dwarf hedges can be used to separate beds.

# Vegetables without soil

Soil is marvellous stuff, but it does have many disadvantages. It is heavy, it tends to be too dry, wet or cold, it is reluctant to hold on to nutrients, and it creates ideal conditions for pests of all kinds.

So why bother with it? Why not bring nutrients, air and water, possibly warmed and certainly free from pests and diseases, directly to the roots?

This is the thinking behind the variety of techniques that constitute soil-less culture, or 'hydroponics', techniques that are still experimental, but that have been adopted by many professionals and that have much to offer the amateur.

The simplest form of soil-less culture is the peat bag, with fertilizer already included, so that all that is needed is water. Manufacturers have improved the medium so that its earlier tendency to be powder-dry or bog-wet (and waterlogged) has been largely eliminated. High cropping-rates, and the possibility of growing exotic plants like capsicums and aubergines on balconies where soil would be too heavy, or in greenhouses where the build-up of diseases is a perennial problem, may more than make up for the high capital cost. Onions can reach show standard in peat bags, and celery such as Greensnap, or lettuces such as Salad Bowl, have grown well in bags outdoors. No tools are needed, and the peat can be recycled for future crops: eventually it should end up on the garden.

Various kinds of aggregate – including vermiculite, better known as an insulator – have been used instead of peat, but the ultimate is to use no rooting medium at all. Here the 'Nutrient Film Technique', or NFT, developed by Dr Allen Cooper at the Glasshouse Crops Research Institute in Sussex, reigns supreme.

NFT requires sloping channels, which may be practically horizontal or vertical, down which there flows a layer of dilute nutrient solution less than one millimetre thick. The plants sit with their roots in the channels, and eventually form a dense mat of high tensile strength, so the plants need no more support than they would if they were planted conventionally.

The technique is infinitely versatile. The channels may be custom-built polythene gulleys such as those used, sometimes four tiers deep, in commercial Californian greenhouses. They may be formed simply from the grooves in corrugated asbestos, as on the farm of one Queensland lettuce grower. Plastic laid directly on the ground (whose rockiness, infertility or slope is of no consequence) may be used to raise a crop of grass in the desert. Water must be supplied, of course, but the major causes of water loss – drainage and surface evaporation – are eliminated. The nutrient solution is introduced at the top of the channels. The surplus collects in a covered sump at the bottom, and then is pumped back to the top to be recycled.

Obviously, the concentration of nutrients must be maintained constantly, but this is far

Peat Growing Bags on a Balcony

simpler in theory than maintaining soil fertility. In the soil you must not only add at least minimal amounts of each nutrient, you must add them in the right proportion: excess potassium may interfere with the uptake of magnesium, for example. When they are suspended in weak solution the individual nutrients do not compete in this way, so it is necessary only to ensure that each nutrient is represented adequately. You can forget about the proportions. In any case, Interlates Ltd (see p.108) supply suitably balanced solutions.

Soon perhaps we will see NFT channels, pumps and nutrients supplied in kit-form for the amateur, either to make the maximum use of greenhouse space, as in California, or else to create intensive cropping systems on balconies or flat roofs. On roofs NFT could be a winner, for soil weighs nearly 800kg per cubic metre and the run-off of surplus water can cause problems. NFT equipment is available for commercial nurseries (see p.108), but the principles are so simple that the enthusiastic amateur should have few difficulties in building his own system.

# 'Nutrient Film Technique' (NFT)

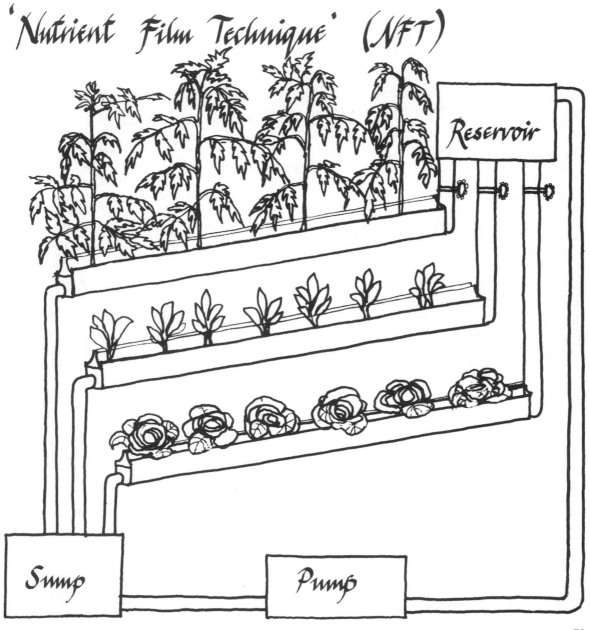

# Vegetables month by month

**January:** This is the month for planning and ordering seeds, and at the same time checking to see whether any seeds left over from last year can be used. Parsnip seeds must be sown in the year starting from the time they were packeted. Turnip, swede, broad and runner bean, pea, parsley, salsify, and spinach seeds will remain viable for three years. The leaf brassicas, mustard-and-cress, lettuce, leek and carrot seeds keep for four years. Radish, beetroot, spinach beet and onion seeds keep for five years. Marrow and cucumber seeds keep for seven years and celery for six.

The preparation of beds for spring sowing should be well advanced, but you must not work the soil when it is frozen or when it is very wet.

Broad beans can be sown in the south of England and Wales and rhubarb crowns can be divided (a clump of rhubarb will crop for 15 years or so).

The kit of essential tools for the garden or allotment vegetable grower

**February:** Lime the soil if necessary – but not the ground that is to grow potatoes. Use about 750g of lime per square metre.

Plant shallot sets and sow parsnips and radishes together. The radishes will grow quickly and mark the rows of slow-germinating parsnips without competing with them. Early seed potatoes can be put in trays for chitting (see p.66).

**March:** Continue working the seedbeds to a fine tilth whenever conditions are dry enough.

Sow lettuces, radishes, carrots, early peas and onion sets. If the broad beans have not been sown, they can be sown now. Sow summer cabbage, brussels sprouts, broccoli, kale, cauliflower and, in the south of England, leeks, into seed beds for later transplanting. The lettuces, radishes, carrots and peas should be sown in succession, at weekly or fortnightly intervals, to provide a constant supply of fresh vegetables later.

As soon as seeds have germinated and the young plants have formed true leaves, you should thin them, leaving the strongest and trying not to damage them as you remove their weaker neighbours. Make sure that the soil is

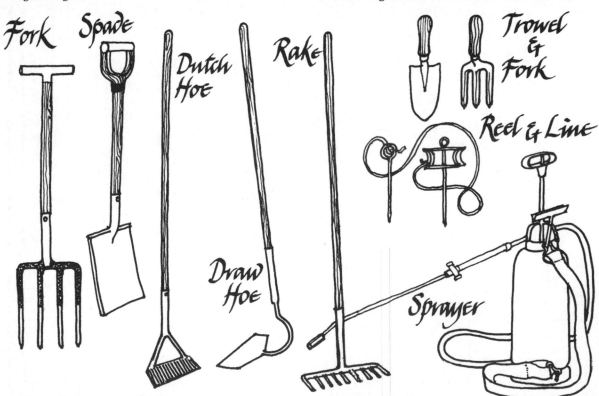

Fork  Spade  Dutch Hoe  Rake  Trowel & Fork  Reel & Line  Draw Hoe  Sprayer

drawn up round the young carrots that are left to help hide them from carrot fly.

**April:** Plant early potatoes, spinach and spinach beet, salsify, kohlrabi, summer turnips, swedes, more early peas and a first sowing of maincrop peas, more broad beans and, later in the month, beetroot. Winter cabbage can be sown in the seedbed, and the leeks may be ready to come out of the seedbed and into their final positions. Make a hole for each leek about 15cm deep and the width of a broom handle, drop in the plant, add a pinch of soot, fill the hole with water, and leave it at that. The leeks will grow to fill the space available to them.

Begin weeding, and concentrate on the plants that develop slowly, like the brassicas, and the thin ones, like leeks and onions. They are less able to compete with weeds than crops that throw out luxuriant foliage quickly, such as peas or parsnips.

Protect emerging peas from bird and rodent attack. Mice have been known to burrow the length of a row of peas, eating the lot without ever surfacing, so the first the gardener knows about it is that his young plants wither and die. You can soak peas in kerosene (paraffin) to deter mice without harming the seed or crop. Black cotton or plastic netting will keep the birds away, but if you use netting support it far enough from the ground for it to remain clear of the pea vines. If they become entangled in it, harvesting will be difficult. Provide some kind of frame for the pea vines, about a metre high. Broad beans require no support.

The first sticks of rhubarb may be ready to eat, and also some early lettuces and radishes.

February: Lettuce, Radishes, Carrots

April: Lettuce, Tomatoes, Carrots

June: Tomatoes

October: Winter Lettuce

Use a cloche or frame throughout the year to extend the season for some crops and to give others an early start

Globe Artichoke

Globe artichokes are large, attractive plants that can be started from seeds sown under glass in February and transplanted in May, or by planting offsets in April. The plants will produce a few heads in their first year, more in their second and third, and then yield will decline gradually. The plants should be replaced after four or five years

**May:** Sow the last of the maincrop peas, the summer spinach, French and runner beans – in succession – and, towards the end of the month, endive and outdoor tomatoes and maize (sweet-corn). Continue to transplant seedlings from the seedbeds to their final positions as soon as they are ready, i.e. large enough to survive (leeks the size of small spring onions, brassicas with leaves about 5cm long). The outdoor tomatoes should go in a sunny, sheltered spot, and they will need sticks for support. The French and runner beans will need strong support: the easiest way of providing this is to build 'wigwams'. Use four canes about 2.5 metres tall (with about half a metre sunk into the ground) to mark out the corners of squares of about one metre a side. Bend the tops of the canes together and fasten them. Sow four bean seeds around the foot of each cane, so that the climbing plants each have ample soil, but they twine together as they climb, and the weight (which can be considerable) is distributed. Wigwams look attractive and make economical use of canes.

Continue with the weeding and hoeing, and earth up the potatoes as you go.

You should be harvesting rhubarb, spring cabbage, lettuces, radishes and broccoli.

**June:** All the brussels sprouts and leeks should be in their final positions by the end of the month. Sow more beetroot, winter carrots, more French and runner beans, lettuce, endive and more peas.

When the broad beans have flowered, and pods form and start to fill at the bottoms of the plants, pinch off the plant tops. Watch out for blackfly, and if they appear, use a soap and water solution in a spray gun to knock them from the plants.

If there is a risk of potato blight (see p.66),

Early peas thrive if they are sown thickly, and they then smother out invading weeds. You can broadcast them into trenches, rather than drilling them in rows

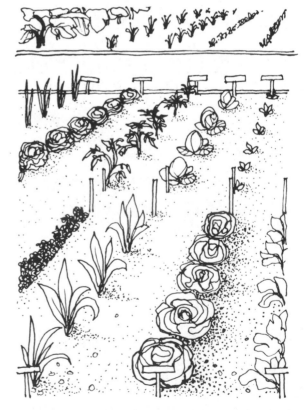

Short rows often produce more than long ones, probably because they are managed more intensively

76

spray the potatoes and tomatoes (which are also susceptible) with a copper fungicide such as Bordeaux Mixture.

Early potatoes can be lifted, the first of the spring onions will be ready, and the early peas. Shallots will be ready by the end of the month. If you are growing and harvesting asparagus, stop cutting in June and allow the plants to grow again.

**July:** Sow more carrots as space becomes available. In the north of England and in Scotland, sow spring cabbage for harvesting next year, and spinach, so they can establish themselves before the end of the growing season.

Feed tomatoes and marrows with a liquid manure (such as seaweed) if they look weak or the leaves are discoloured.

The early potatoes will be ready now if they were not ready in June. The broad beans and peas will be ready, and the dwarf beans and carrots will still be appearing from their successional sowings, as will lettuces and radishes.

**August:** Sow more spring onions for eating through the winter, and in the south of England and Wales sow next year's spring cabbage. You can still sow more lettuces and radishes.

If cabbage-white caterpillars attack the brassicas, use an insecticide against them. Cucumbers and marrows may need some supplementary feeding, and so may the tomatoes if they have not begun to ripen.

Harvest the onions. As soon as the tips of the plants go yellow, work along the rows bending down the tops sharply, at right angles, parallel to the ground, and loosen the roots. After a few days the tops will wilt and shrivel. When they are dry the onions are ready to remove.

Being aromatic, many herbs help keep away insect pests, while attracting bees. They are best grown in their own plot, however, to avoid interfering with cultivation of annual vegetables

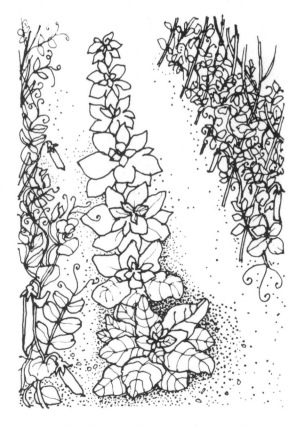

Intercropping (for example, a row of spinach between two rows of peas) makes economical use of space

**September:** Sow turnips and move the spring cabbage from the seedbed to its final position. Be careful when moving young plants, especially in the north, for there can be early frosts in September.

Earth up the leeks. This blanches the part beneath the surface and so increases the edible portion of the plant.

Lift the maincrop potatoes, onions if these were not ready in August, tomatoes, runner beans, marrows, lettuce, carrots, radishes, turnips and some cabbage.

**October:** As the crops are harvested, fork over the beds ready for the next crop. Remove all weeds and crop residues, except for the roots of legumes, which still carry their nitrogen-fixing symbionts (see p.31).

Towards the end of the month you can sow some broad beans, but make sure that the seeds are labelled 'for autumn sowing'. The advantage of autumn sowing is that the plants get an early start in the spring and set pods before they can be attacked by their principal pest, the blackfly, whose life cycle is governed by day length. You can sow winter lettuce, but if there is a risk of frost protect them with cloches.

You will still be harvesting carrots, beetroot and turnips, and you should remove the last of the spring and summer cabbage.

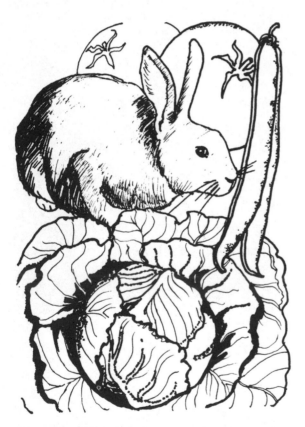

Most vegetable varieties have been bred to be small, because what family can eat a cabbage weighing 40kg? There have always been enthusiasts who grew giants, however, and the UK champion cabbage grower has yields of over 1,300 tonnes per hectare, and has records for a 4kg leek, a 5kg cucumber, a 4kg parsnip, more than a tonne of potatoes from six 'seeds', an 11kg lettuce and a dwarf bean over 43cm loing

Young brassicas can be protected from birds with netting placed over wire hoops

**November:** Continue to prepare seedbeds, adding compost just forked lightly into the surface.

Sow new rhubarb crowns, and begin to force old ones. Start blanching endive and seakale.

Begin lifting parsnips and swedes.

**December:** Continue preparing beds when the weather permits, and check that tools and implements are clean and in good condition.

You should be harvesting cabbages, brussels sprouts, cauliflowers, swedes and parsnips.

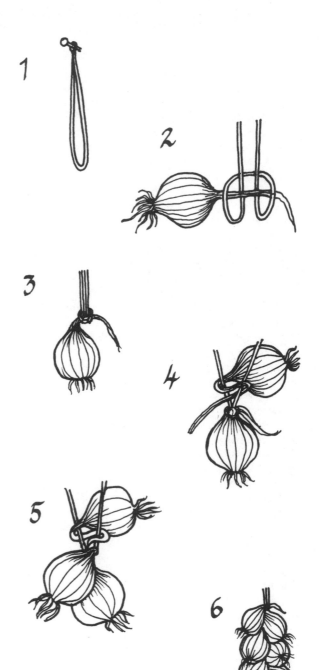

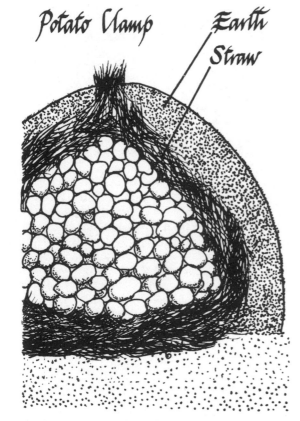

Potato Clamp — Earth — Straw

Carrots should be stored between layers of sand. Potatoes go in a 'clamp': cover the potatoes with straw, allowing some to stick up vertically for ventilation, then put earth over the straw. Turnips should be stored, but parsnips, swedes, salsify and, except in very cold winters, beetroot, keep well in the ground

Onions can be stored in any cool, dry place, or they can be made into 'strings', starting with a one-metre length of strong string tied to make a loop and hung over a nail

# Garden compost

Compost is the residue left after organic material has been decomposed by bacteria and fungi. Physically, it is rather light, crumbly at least when dry, and dark brown in colour. Chemically, being an organic mix, it is too complex to analyse, but its chief constituent is carbon. Although it will generally contain a wide range of trace minerals, its nitrogen, phosphorus and potassium contents are sometimes far too low for it to qualify as a fertilizer. Its role in the soil – a vital one (see p.30) – is to maintain structure: air and water-holding capacity. The biology of compost heaps is extraordinarily complex. It involves successions of activity by hundreds of types of bacteria, fungi, and the fungus-like actinomycetes. Which types are present, and the metabolic pathways that each pursues, will vary from heap to heap, depending on what you put in it, and the prevailing physical conditions. But though the events are complex, there is nothing mystical about them. Composting does not deserve the sneer of 'muck and mystery', nor does it benefit from incantations or infusions of arcane herbs – or, indeed, from most of the commercial preparations and apparati that are supposed to help things along. Although the ecological details of each heap may be infinitely variable, the basic principles are childishly simple and, if you follow them, you will make good compost.

Chemistry first. Organic material, the raw material of the heap, consists mainly of carbon, with some nitrogen, and a water content varying from almost zero (straw or hair) to almost 100 per cent (cabbage leaves or urine). Decomposition occurs when bacteria and fungi feed on this material. For decomposition to occur at a maximum rate, and to a maximum extent, the ratio of carbon to nitrogen must be optimal. So you should try to balance high-nitrogen materials – such as hair, fresh grass cuttings, and excrement of all kinds – with high-carbon materials, such as straw or dead leaves. If the heap is too rich in nitrogen (too many chicken droppings, for example) then some of it will simply be jettisoned into the air as ammonia, and wasted. If the heap is poor in nitrogen, decomposition will be too slow: leaf mould can sit around for months.

Thermodynamics next. In general, decomposition can take place by aerobic processes, which require oxygen, or anaerobically. Aerobic decomposition is rapid, relatively non-smelly (since aromatic compounds either are not formed at all or are broken down rapidly), and generates tremendous heat. Anaerobic decomposition – characterized by the rotting vegetables that sometimes lie around in street markets – is slow, smelly, and (perhaps because activity is so slow) does not generate heat. In practice, in almost all heaps, both anaerobic and aerobic processes will take place together, but obviously aerobic processes are preferable.

So how do you tip the balance towards aerobism? First, you include some material with structural strength – such as straw – to keep the texture open. Wet vegetables simply form a squash. Then, you do not make the heap too big: higher than 1.5m will crush the bottom material, though the heap can be as long as you like. Thirdly, you turn the heap regularly to mix it and to ensure regular infusions of air.

But you must also help the heap to keep warm. If it is too small, or too wet, or too exposed, it will be too cold for rapid aerobic decomposition. The heat gained by covering a small heap should more than compensate for the theoretical loss of ventilation, for in a well-made heap air should be trapped already.

That is all there is to it. If you have too little nitrogenous material – if your heap is all dead leaves, for example – put on some cheap nitrogen, such as ammonium sulphate or the contents of the chamber pot. If it is too dry, water it. Do not bother with those patent preparations for decomposing bacteria, because bacteria are highly specific and if the ones you introduce do not suit your particular pile of rubbish they will die, while the ones that do suit your heap will find their own way to it. We are not talking now about precision. Composting is not that serious. It is not high science, neither is it theology. It is like good cooking: you need a 'feel' for what is required, built by experience upon simple principles.

### The compost bin
Most amateur gardeners today make compost by some variant or adaption of the Indore method, devised by Sir Albert Howard when he was working as an agricultural scientist at the experimental station at Indore, India. In our climate it helps to keep the heap warm if it is contained in a box or bin (it is also tidier), and ideally you need two of these bins side by side,

constructed so that the front can be removed in order to facilitate emptying the contents.

For the small garden a convenient size is one metre high, wide and deep. Make six upright posts from squared timber (about 50mm square) 1.5m long, and sink them into level ground so that 1m of each projects above the surface. Nail planks sawn to 1m lengths to the uprights to make three partitions – one at each end and one in the centre – and planks sawn to 2m long to make the back. Use more 50mm squared timber to provide additional uprights along the front to make slots into which planks will fit. These uprights need not be sunk into the ground. Planks sawn to 1m long fit into the slots to make fronts for both bins. All the wood must be well creosoted.

Stand bricks on their edges in the bottom of both bins, a centimetre or two apart, to allow air to enter the compost heaps from below.

Begin the heap by covering the bricks with tough, woody weeds or hedge clippings. Then add a 20cm-thick layer of vegetable matter. Cover this with nitrogenous material. If you use animal manure, add a layer about one centimetre thick; if you use more concentrated nitrogen, add just enough to colour the surface. Then dust this with slaked lime to counteract the heap's natural acidity. Add a second 20cm layer of vegetable matter, nitrogenous material, lime, and so on until you reach the top. Sprinkle the heap with water if it is dry, cover it, and wait for it to heat up.

It should heat and then cool. As it cools, remove the planks from the front and turn the heap into the second bin, so that the top goes to the bottom. Water again if necessary and let the heap heat for a second time. When it is completely cold it should be ready for use. The process will take longer in winter than in summer. In winter, make sure the heap does not become too wet. Polythene is not very good for covering: water condenses on the underside and runs back into the heap, damping and cooling it. If the site is not too windy, corrugated iron sheets, laid at an angle, will drain away surplus water.

Any organic material will decompose in time, but woody material rots much much more slowly than most other vegetable matter. Newspaper will rot more quickly if you tear it into pieces. Leather will rot. Large animal bones will not – but they may attract rats. Anything that does not rot at the first composting can be added to the next heap. If the heap does not heat, add urine to provide more nitrogen.

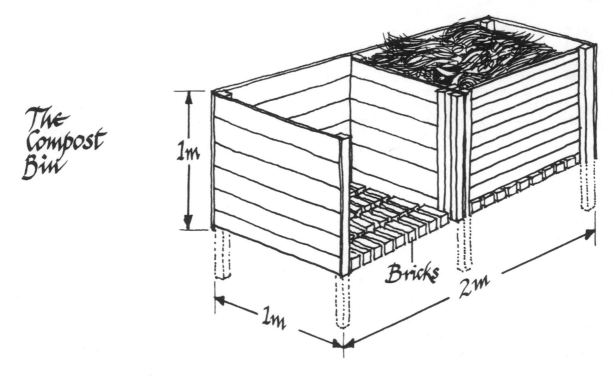

The Compost Bin

1m

Bricks

2m

1m

# Tree fruits

who are also growing apples, as among a random mixture of varieties, all growing in a small area, it is likely that your tree will find a companion. However, nurserymen will help you choose compatible varieties.

Apple trees bear fruit either along their branches, or at the tips. Tip bearers, such as Beauty of Bath, Bismark, Blenheim Orange, and Worcester Pearman, do not require pruning except to clear away dead wood.

### Apples

Apples can be grown anywhere that is sheltered from cold winter winds, on deep, fertile, loamy soil. If your soil is not fertile it is worth waiting a few years until you have improved it before planting apples.

Cultivated apples are produced by grafting varieties bred for particular characteristics on to the roots of an entirely different kind of apple tree, grown purely for its roots. An almost endless list of combinations is possible, including trees that produce two or more varieties of apples.

Depending on the space you have available, you can grow standard trees which grow to a height of 6 metres or more, semi-dwarfs (about 2 metres), or dwarfs (about 1.5 metres). Dwarfing is achieved mainly by choice of rootstock, and this also determines the rate of growth. On poor or chalky soils choose Malling VII, Malling 26 or Malling Norton 106, all of which produce fruit quickly. If the aim is to crowd as many trees as possible into a small space, then choose the most dwarfing rootstocks: Malling IX for good soil, Malling VII (only semi-dwarfing, though) for poorer soils.

Having chosen a root, you must choose the top, which determines the variety. Avoid Cox's Orange Pippin if you are north of the Midlands, because it was developed in southern England and it is not hardy.

Plan for groups of varieties, rather than single varieties. Apples are not self-fertile, which means the blossom must be cross-pollinated (by insects) with another compatible variety that is in blossom at the same time. Some varieties, such as Bramleys, are triploid, and need two pollinating varieties. Some nurseries have produced what they call 'family trees', which are two or more compatible varieties grafted on to the same root, so that a single tree becomes self-fertile. The compatibility problem may solve itself if you live in a town among other gardeners

**Planting:** Clear the ground of all weeds before you buy the trees: they should go into the ground as soon as possible after you buy them, any time between November and March, provided the ground is not frosty or too wet. If they cannot be planted immediately, unpack them and store them in a trench filled with straw, allowing plenty of room for the roots.

Dig a hole for each tree and space the holes 2.5–3 metres apart for dwarfs, 3–4.5 for semi-dwarfs, and 3.5–5.5 for standards. Bramleys can be grown only as standards because of the size and weight of individual apples.

If any roots are broken, nip them off cleanly with secateurs. It takes two people to plant a tree. First drive in a stake beside the hole, then put the tree in the hole and have one person hold it upright while the other fills in with earth, shaking it about to make sure no air pockets are left. The hole should be filled level with the surrounding surface, but make sure that the soil is below the small bulge on the tree stem that marks the place where the upper part of the tree was grafted on to the rootstock. If you bury this bulge, the upper part of the tree will produce roots and a dwarf will 'un-dwarf' itself. Finally, tie the tree to the stake using a proprietary tree tie or an old nylon stocking, but not string, which can cut into the bark. Tie the tree at the top, middle and bottom of the stake, and leave a big, fat knot between the tree and the stake. Last of all, mulch the surface with straw, leaf-mould, compost, or some mixture of them.

**Pruning:** The purposes of pruning are to make the tree neat and its fruit easily accessible, and to make sure that light and nutrient reach those parts of the tree that are producing fruit.

If the tree was not pruned when you bought it (ask the nurseryman at the time) cut back the longest shoots by one-fifth and the shorter ones by one-half. Always cut back to just above a bud

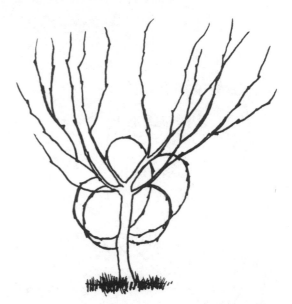

Vigorous young tree before pruning and festooning

Same tree after pruning 5 shoots forming a festoon

that points away from the main stem. Twelve months later repeat the process. Remove any broken shoots or branches and keep the centre of the tree open.

You can retard the growth of the tree by festooning long shoots – bending them over and tying them lower down – or by cutting them. If you cut less than one-quarter of the full length of the shoot, the effect will be invigorating, but more than that will be repressive, and the closer the cut is to the main stem the more repressive it will be. You can prune in summer or in winter, but summer pruning is more repressive. Seal cuts until they heal (Sellotape, or pieces of polythene used like bandages, will do). If you remove leaves from a tree that is growing vigorously you will force it to produce more fruit buds.

Select the longest and strongest branch. The shoot that grows from the end of this branch is the leader. Each winter cut back the leader to one-third of its length, remove completely any shoots that grow in towards the centre of the tree and broken or overcrowded shoots, and cut back

other shoots as repressively as you wish. If you prune in summer, cut back the leader to three-quarters of its length, side shoots to two-thirds, then in winter remove the whole of that year's growth plus one bud of the previous year's. An alternative is to remove about a quarter of the leader in May, and in July to cut back every side shoot that is thicker than your little finger, leaving only the leaves at the base plus two more leaves further out. In winter cut back all the new growth to leave two leaf buds.

Do not prune tip bearers at all.

**Cordons:** Apples can be grown as cordons, rather like vines. Use posts and galvanized wire to make a support, as with vines, and carry the leaders horizontally or diagonally away from the short main stem, supported by the wires. This method produces a tree that is easy to manage and that is displayed attractively. Remove shoots that grow away from the wires to achieve a flattened effect.

**Problems:** Scab, which produces unsightly

Invigorating

More Invigorating

Twisting

Depressing Tip

Repressive

Bending

More Repressive

Most Repressive

Repressive Practices

patches on the skin of apples (without affecting their eating quality) and canker, which produces debilitating growth on the tree bark, are both caused by fungi, and can be controlled by careful pruning to remove infected parts.

The apple sawfly (*Hoplocampa testudinea*) may invade, leaving its larvae inside the apples. Wait until the following year and spray with an insecticide about a week after the blossoms have fallen.

If you tie sacking around the main stem of the tree, close to the ground, in early summer, and remove and burn it in autumn, you will help to control a number of pests that migrate from the soil, including codling moth, and if you use a proprietary grease to make a wide greaseband around the tree after the sacking is removed, this will also help.

Serious infestations of insect pests have to be dealt with by spraying, however.

## Pears

Like apples, pears grow on trees produced by grafting, in this case on to a quince rootstock. For rich soils choose Quince C rootstock, for poor soils Quince A.

Some pears are self-fertile, others not, but even the self-fertile varieties benefit from cross-pollination. The nursery from which you buy trees will sell you compatible varieties. Probably the most popular pear is Conference, and this is compatible with Williams Bon Chrêtien, usually shortened to 'Williams' but known in America as 'Bartlett', where it is the pear most often used for canning. It can be used as either a dessert or cooking pear. The true connoisseur always chooses Doyenné de Comice, however. Unfortunately, it grows well only in southern England, it does not crop regularly, it is susceptible to scab but hates the lime-sulphur sprays most often used to control scab, and, all in all, it is not the easiest of trees to grow.

**Planting and pruning:** Plant pear trees in the same way as apple trees, allowing them at least 3.5 metres of space each. They like nitrogen, do not like grass growing around their roots, and do not like any competition.

They stand up to heavy pruning better than apple trees do, and are pruned in the same way. They cordon well and fruit more heavily when cordoned.

Thin the pears by removing the smaller, weaker fruits, but check first that the large ones are not damaged by pear-midge maggot, which will leave a small hole on the surface marking its point of entry.

Standard insecticides will deal with minor insect pests and there are no major ones. The only serious disease is fire blight, caused by a bacterium (*Erwinia amylovora*). First the blossom turns black and then the leaves; finally the bark turns dark grey, and if you remove a piece you will see dark brown damp cankers beneath it. There is no cure, and all infected trees and shrubs must be destroyed by law.

## Plums and damsons

Plums prefer a deep, well-drained, rich, loamy soil and they are heavy feeders, appreciating an autumn dressing of compost or fertilizer. They blossom early, which makes them susceptible to frost damage, so do not plant them in a frost hollow.

Some varieties are self-fertile, others not.

**Planting and pruning:** Plant in winter, allowing 3.5–4.5 metres between trees, and if you intend to shape the tree do not prune more than is necessary, apart from removing dead wood, and never prune in winter, because of the danger of fungal infection in the slow-healing wounds. Remove dead wood as soon as possible, however, because it may be attacked by silver-leaf fungus *(Stereum purpureum)* which will infect adjacent live wood. Apart from wasps, plums have few pests.

## Peaches

If you grow a peach tree from a stone it is very unlikely that the tree will produce any fruit, because it will be a variety bred for a Mediterranean climate. There are varieties that fruit in our climate. Peregrine produces a large fruit in mid-August, Rochester fruits at the end of August, Duke of York produces a red fruit (inside and out) in July, and Bellegarde fruits in September.

**Planting and pruning:** Plant the trees against a south-facing wall, 3.5–4.5 metres apart. Plant in winter and wait until spring growth begins before you prune. Peaches will grow well in most soils, but they prefer a rich, loamy soil, and they are heavy feeders so need a dressing of compost in autumn.

Prune the trees in their first spring by cutting all the shoots to half their length. If any of the shortened shoots begin to die back at the tip, cut away the dead part a little at a time until you expose live wood. Thin the fruit each year, as with pears. No further pruning is necessary, but you may remove shoots that cross one another or grow inward.

Spray in spring and autumn with a copper fungicide (Bordeaux or Burgundy Mixture) to prevent leafcurl fungus *(Taphrina deformans)* and use insecticides to deal with any infestation of peach aphis *(Myzus persicae)*.

## Nectarines

The nectarine is a smooth-skinned peach and, like the peach, it is self-fertile, although it does benefit from cross-pollination. Nectarines are grown in the same way as peaches, but their

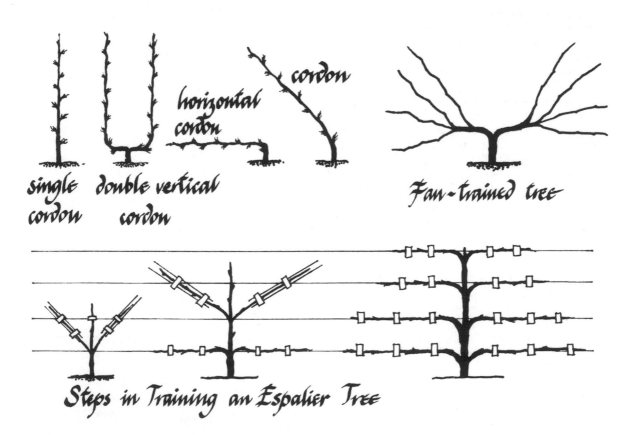

single cordon   double vertical cordon   horizontal cordon   cordon   Fan-trained tree

Steps in Training an Espalier Tree

thinner skins make them more vulnerable to attack by birds, wasps or other pests. The most popular varieties are Humboldt, which ripens in late August, and Lord Napier, which is a little earlier.

## Apricots
Apricots will grow well only in southern England, and prefer a rich, fertile, well-drained soil. Plant them against a south-facing wall and treat them as you would peaches. The most popular varieties are Hemskerk, whose fruit ripens in August, and Moorpark, which is a little later.

## Cherries
There are two self-fertile cherries, Morello and Late Duke, both used for cooking. The remainder fall into twelve pollen groups, and each variety must be pollinated by a member of another group, and even then there are some incompatibilities. So the trees must be chosen with great care.

**Planting and pruning:** If you grow cherries against a wall it will be easier to hang protective netting over them to deter the birds, but you will need wires fixed to the wall on to which the trees can be trained, and it is simpler to fix the wires before planting.

Allow plenty of room for the roots, put some compost into the holes and some lime, and space the trees at least 6 metres apart.

Do not prune in winter. In June remove any shoots that have died back, and shoots that spring from the base of the tree. No other pruning is needed.

Cherries are susceptible to die-back, which is controlled by removing affected parts. A greaseband will keep away climbing pests such as caterpillars and ants, and a copper spray will prevent leafcurl.

## Medlars and quinces
Both trees are self-fertile, and can be grown as bushes or trees. As trees they can grow to a height of about 8 metres, with a weeping habit. They prefer rich, loamy soil (quinces are more particular about this than medlars, and quinces also like a moist habitat) and they can be grassed all round.

Allow at least 6 metres between trees, and prune them only to achieve an attractive shape.

They have few pests or diseases, but those

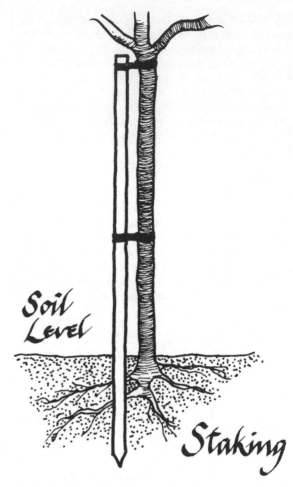

*Soil Level*

*Staking*

that occur are the same as the diseases and pests of apple trees, and can be treated in the same way.

## Almonds
These can be grown in the same way as plums or peaches, but be careful to plant edible sweet almond trees and not the very poisonous bitter almonds.

Almonds (the Common Almond, *Prunus Amygdalus* and the sub-species *P.A. macrocarpa* and *P.A. dulcis* are edible, the rest are not) are usually grown on their own roots, but they can be grown on plum stock and in America they are often grown on peach stock.

Pruning is minimal, consisting only of shaping the young tree and removing all dead wood.

Pests and diseases are the same as those of the related plum and peach, the most disfiguring being peach leaf curl, which can be controlled with Bordeaux mixture or a lime-sulphur spray.

### Walnuts

Walnuts do not produce nuts until they are about eight years old, and the timber is at its peak after 120–150 years. Walnuts are self-fertile and grown on their own roots. They can be cultivated as bushes, half-standards or standards – which will grow to a height of about 18 metres and a span of about 9 metres. Plant them carefully, see that they grow straight, and in the mid-summer of the third year pinch off the tips of the strongest shoots. Repeat this each year for a further five years. It accelerates fruiting and causes the tree to fruit lower down.

### Cob nuts and filberts

These grow wild, but they can be cultivated as extremely slow-growing bushes that will take a century to reach a height of about 2 metres. Cultivated bushes are grown from suckers taken from close to the root of established bushes, or formed by layering shoots from adjacent bushes.

The sucker is cut down to a height of about 45cm and the shoots that grow from it are reduced to three, spaced evenly around the stem. The next year these are cut back to leave two buds on each, so producing six new shoots. The same procedure is followed a year later, making twelve shoots which form the leaders of the formal bush. They are pruned severely to produce tough, thin branches. In later years pruning consists of removing dead wood and cutting back side shoots, keeping the leaders of equal length.

### Designing an orchard

Most orchards are planted in fields of irregular shape, so the first step in making the best use of the space available is to survey the field and mark it out in rows, as a grid.

Allow one pollinator to eight trees of the main variety, with the pollinator adjacent to all of them. Grow blocks of the same variety rather than mixtures, for ease of management.

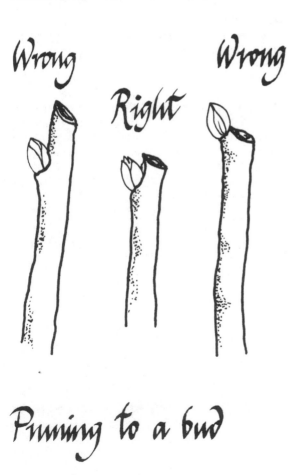

Pruning to a bud

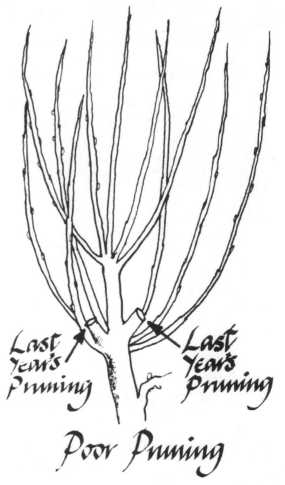

Poor Pruning

# Soft fruits

## Gooseberries

Gooseberries prefer some sunshine and good drainage, but otherwise they will grow almost anywhere. The plant is a bush, but it can be trained against a fence or wall. Its long history as a competition crop has led the gooseberry into a maze of genetic by-ways so that there is a very long list of possible varieties. The most popular commercial gooseberry is Careless, which spreads wide and low and crops heavily.

**Planting and pruning:** Prepare the ground well, removing all weeds, and apply generous amounts of compost, manure or leafmould. Plant the bush so that the lowest branches are about 15cm above the ground, and remove roots that may be growing upwards. Allow about 2 metres between bushes. Once they are planted do not dig around the roots – use the hoe for weeding.

After autumn planting, prune the bush so that its branches all grow upwards. Later it can be cordoned or shaped in an 'umbrella' or 'stoot' form.

**Problems:** A lime-sulphur spray will control the most serious fungal disease, American gooseberry mildew, and also the gooseberry red spider mite *(Bryobia praetiosa),* but sunshine, adequate nutrition and pruning will help prevent disease.

## Raspberries

The raspberry *(Rubus idaeus)* is native to Britain and grows wild. It likes cool, moist soil, but not frost, and when choosing cultivated varieties make sure they are resistant to virus diseases to which raspberries are prone.

**Planting and pruning:** Plant canes in November, 40–45cm apart, in trenches that have a good layer of compost or manure in the bottom. Fix a wire fence or 'box': strands of wire joining two sets of posts set about 30cm apart with the canes between them.

Cut the canes back to about 30cm in length and in February cut weak canes to the ground and remove any dead wood from the top of the others. In subsequent years, after harvesting, cut to the ground all the canes that bore fruit that year.

## Blackberries

Cultivated blackberries are larger and sweeter than their wild relatives. They will grow anywhere.

**Planting and pruning:** Plant in late autumn, about 2 metres apart, and no deeper than they were in the nursery – there will be a mark on the canes to show the soil level. Prune them back to about 20cm. In subsequent years, prune by cutting away all old growth each autumn, and tie the new growth to a fence or wall.

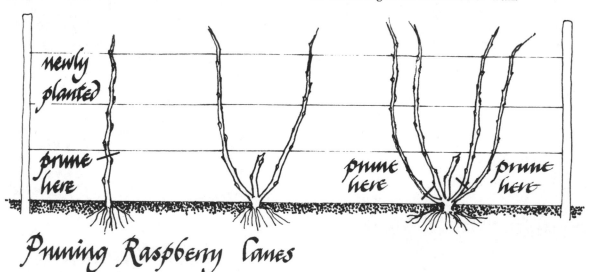

Pruning Raspberry Canes

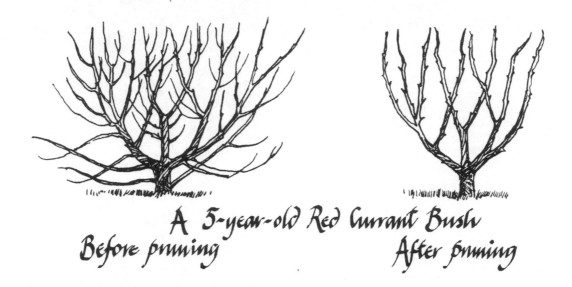

A 5-year-old Red Currant Bush

Before pruning

After pruning

## Loganberries

The first loganberry was discovered in 1881 as a sport in the California garden of a Judge Logan. Loganberries are grown in the same way as blackberries. The veitchberry, a blackberry–raspberry cross, the boysenberry, said to be a loganberry x blackberry–raspberry hybrid, the Japanese wineberry, the nectarberry and the Worcesterberry, which is related to the gooseberry, are all grown in the same way as blackberries.

## Blackcurrants

Blackcurrant health drinks are made from the fruit of the Baldwin variety, which ripens late and with a high vitamin C content, but there are many other varieties, some of which crop more heavily.

**Planting and pruning:** The plants grow as bushes and need about 1.5 metres of space all round them. They prefer a sheltered site, a good dressing of compost or manure, and no weeds. After planting in late autumn or early winter, cut the bush back to about 3cm above ground level.

Prune to build up a framework of strong, short, old branches low down on the bush, with younger canes growing from them. Each year cut away old wood that is producing no new shoots, as well as shoots that hang downwards.

**Problems:** Blackcurrants are prone to big bud and reversion, two serious diseases. Big bud is caused by a mite and shows as swollen buds in winter and spring. Removing the affected buds will stop the activities of the mite, but too late to prevent it transmitting the virus that causes reversion, which is fatal after a few years. There is no cure, but the virus disease can be avoided by buying only virus-free plants. The larvae of the currant, or magpie, moth *(Abraxas grossulariata)*, which are loopers with black and white markings and a yellow stripe down each side, can be controlled with an insecticide. A shoot borer can cause foliage to wilt in hot weather. The remedy is to remove the foliage, find the hole by which the borer entered, then cut back until you remove the invader, and burn the cuttings.

## Red and white currants

There is a range of varieties of red and white currant, ranging in flavour from acid to not-very-sweet. The currant bushes are similar to those of the blackcurrant, but they are pruned differently.

**Planting and pruning:** Plant in autumn or winter and allow about 2 metres around each plant. Add some potassium if the soil is not fertile, and a good dressing of compost anyway. Avoid very wet situations.

Grow the bushes on single main stems with the branches held well above the ground, and remove at once any suckers that appear at the base.

For the first few years after planting, build up the main framework of the bush by halving the length of the leaders and cutting back side shoots to two buds each winter. Once the bush is established little further pruning is needed, but in June cut back all side shoots to about 10–12cm. This will increase yields.

Red and white currants are prone to most of the same pests and diseases as blackcurrants, and they are dealt with in the same way.

## Strawberries

Cultivated strawberries were introduced to Europe from America, and they are less hardy than the native wild varieties. The name has nothing to do with 'straw' – it comes from the Old English word 'streawian', from which also comes 'strewn'.

Unlike other fruits, strawberries form part of the vegetable rotation, seldom lasting for more than about three years. Often they are destroyed finally by virus disease. There are remontant, or 'perpetual-fruiting' varieties, but even these succumb in the end and in any case they should be kept apart from other varieties. Remontants and the 'rollerberry' fruit for longer than most strawberries, and there is a long list of varieties of them and of more conventional types.

**Planting and husbandry:** Strawberries like a rich, loamy soil and an open, sunny site. Prepare the ground, remove weeds, especially perennials, and apply a generous dressing of compost.

Plant in August, although remontants can go in rather later. Strawberries have shallow, spreading roots, so the centre of the plant will be higher than the root tips when you plant them.

If you are planting in rows, allow about 40–45cm between plants and about 75cm between rows. If you want to make a bed, allow 30cm between plants and 30cm between rows, staggering the plants in the rows. The plants will send out runners, which will root, and each two rows will produce a mat about a metre wide.

The plants will produce some fruit in the summer following the one in which they were planted, they will crop heavily the summer after that, then they will begin to decline and in the fourth year you should remove them, burning them and any straw you used as a mulch to suppress weeds.

*Strawberry Plants growing in a barrel 20 plants to a sq. metre*

This mulch is applied in the spring following planting, it goes between the rows, and it needs to be 5cm thick. Between planting and mulching keep the rows well hoed.

Traditionally, strawberry growers remove all the runners before they root, but there is no clear evidence that this improves yield.

Clean up the beds each autumn, removing the old straw, dead leaves and any surviving weeds.

**Problems:** Protect the plants with netting to keep away the birds, and use an insecticide to deal with aphids – but make sure that it is one that will break down and disappear before you eat the crop.

If the roots are too dry your plants may suffer

from mildew, and if the roots are too wet they may be attacked by grey mould *(Botrytis cinerea)*. Both fungi can be killed by dusting on flowers of sulphur.

## Figs

Figs have been grown in the south of England since medieval times, and they will produce fruit there, but that is the limit of their geographical range and you should not attempt to grow them except in the south.

When you buy a fig tree, be careful that it does not turn out to be a castor oil plant! The two look very similar when they are small and many a gardener has been encouraged by a less than scrupulous nurseryman to make this mistake. In fact, though, figs can be propagated very easily from cuttings, by layering, or by planting suckers. If you have a piece of ripe wood, plant it in a warm, moist corner and leave it to grow for two years before planting it out.

**Planting and pruning:** Figs prefer a poor soil. Given plenty of nutrient they produce a lot of rank growth and no fruit. The first essential for good cropping is to prevent the tree from forming a tap root. Dig a hole about a metre square and 60cm deep. Line the hole with bricks or concrete (or use a tub), and make sure that the base is covered completely with a 30cm-thick layer of broken brick or stone, packed together. This will allow drainage, but inhibit root growth. Fill the rest of the hole with soil and a little lime, and plant the tree. If you are planting several trees, allow 3.5–4.5 metres between them. It does no harm to move the trees every four years or so – rough treatment improves the crop!

Prune the trees vigorously, removing suckers and any unwanted growth, and train the branches against a wall in a fan shape, with 30cm or so between them.

Fig trees sold in Britain are self-fertile (ones grown in the Near East are not). If the tree fails to fruit, the chances are that you have not treated it severely enough and it is growing too much foliage. When it does fruit, the figs will form in three layers, at the top, middle and bottom. Some of the figs will be fat and healthy, some will be tiny, and the others will be somewhere between. The big figs will ripen. In a warmer climate, the medium-sized ones will

ripen later to give a second crop, but in Britain they will simply divert resources from the first crop, so you should remove them. The tiny figs will become next year's crop, so they should be left alone.

**Problems:** There are no diseases or pests of figs in this country, but if the trees are to be left outside through the winter, they may need some protection. You can make a little roof for each tree, out of straw, to keep off the worst of the rain and snow, or you can free the branches from the wall and wrap each one in straw bundles. Put 30cm or so of litter around the base of each tree.

If the trees are in tubs, these can be brought inside and taken out again in spring.

*Fig leaves and fruit*

# The home vineyard

Grape vines were introduced to Britain by the Romans. After the Roman occupation the vineyards were managed largely by the monasteries, and when the monasteries were dissolved most of them went into decline. Perhaps it was our northern preference for ales and beers that prevented wine drinking from becoming really popular, or British vineyards really commercial.

Be that as it may, there is no scientific reason that inhibits the production of wine in this country, and indeed in recent years some commercial vineyards have been established and are doing well. The Pilton Manor Vineyard, near Shepton Mallet in Somerset, for example, was planted in 1966 and 1968, on a site that had accommodated a vineyard in medieval times. Production from the 6-hectare plantation is now in the region of 5,000–10,000 bottles per hectare of one particular grape variety grown there, and 7,500–17,000 bottles per hectare of the other. Pilton Manor Vineyard is open to the public (see p.108), and you are invited to see the vines growing and to taste the wines.

The Pilton wines are white: there is a general agreement that British soils and the British climate are better for white wine production, but it is possible to produce red wines, at least for private use. Commercially they might be difficult to market against French and Italian wines.

## The site
Grape vines are tough and hardy. They will withstand winter frosts and snow, but during the summer they need plenty of sunshine. They will grow on a wide range of soils, provided these are – or can be made – slightly alkaline. The pH should not fall below 6.5. The soil should be well drained.

The poorer the soil, the fewer the grapes that will be produced, but the higher will be their quality. On very fertile soils, the vines produce luxuriant foliage that does not contribute to grape yields. So if you are lucky enough to be able to comb the country for an ideal site, try to find a stony or gravelly soil on a limestone base, with a low organic-matter content, which will force the vines to root deep; never give them any nitrogen as fertilizer or other manure. The Pilton Vineyard is sited on stony topsoil overlying limestone which, in turn, is over clay and finally blue lias, and the pH ranges between 7.0 and 8.0.

The vineyard should be on a slope, if possible, and facing south, south-east or south-west. The Pilton site faces south and the gradient is about 1 in 10. In general, the vineyard should not be too high above sea level: 50 metres is probably ideal, 100 metres could be too high.

## Varieties
The Pilton Vineyard grows Riesling-Sylvaner (also known as Muller-Thurgau), which produces a hock-type wine, and Seyve-Villard 5/276 grafted on to Telekii and Kober 5BB rootstocks. Seyve-Villard crops heavily with yellow grapes.

These are both fairly standard vines and they

*Riesling*

92

will grow more or less anywhere in southern England and the Midlands, and on sheltered sites further north.

A better white wine variety for the north might be the Madeleine–Sylvaner cross, which ripens early. Siegerrebe is also an early ripener, producing a grape with a muscat flavour more suited to heavier dessert wines, or for blending with other grapes to improve their flavour.

If you want to try black grapes, Seyve-Villard 18/315 has been tested widely and is grown on a considerable scale in France, Seibel 13053 produces Beaujolais-type wines, and the Canadian vine Brant produces many bunches of small, black grapes that can either be eaten or used for making an indifferent wine that can be blended with other wines to improve their colour.

Then there are the dessert grapes, such as Black Hamburg, Muscat Hamburgh (in southern England only) and Excelsior, which yields pale yellow grapes. Some of the dessert varieties can also be used for making wines. All in all, there is a wide range of varieties available, and having taken advice (see p.108) on which are best for your area, you should experiment.

At present you can grow any vine you like anywhere in Britain. For commercial production at least, this situation may change as the British wine industry is brought into line with those of its Common Market partners. The French Appelation Contrôlée regulates which varieties can be grown where, and the day may come when the system is extended to this country.

As a rule of thumb when choosing varieties, the further north you are, the earlier your crop will need to ripen.

## Laying out a vineyard
If the site slopes, you may wish to terrace it, though this is not strictly necessary. Plant parallel to the contours of the slope, so that each row receives its share of sunshine. If the site is level plant rows that run north and south, so that the sun shines along them and the front rows do not shade the rest.

Stake out the rows, with strong, well-seasoned, weatherproofed endposts sunk 60cm into the ground and standing 2 metres above it, and brace them well. Stretch 3mm galvanized wire between the posts in two strands, one about 45cm above the ground, the other about 90cm. Every metre along the rows insert a cane to sup-

port the young vines. The rows themselves should be about one metre apart.

If you have a south-facing wall, vines can be planted at its foot – about 2 metres apart – and they will cover the wall in a few years. If you have a greenhouse, vines can be planted along the sides, so that as they grow they are trained up the walls and towards the centre (*not* from the centre outwards).

Plant the vines, and if the supplier has not pruned them for you cut them back to leave just three buds.

From now on, on no account dig or fork the ground or you will damage the vine roots. Weeding must be limited to the hoe or small hand fork.

When you plant, place the vines into holes large enough to accommodate their roots without cramping, and if the soil is not especially stony or gravelly, put some broken clay pots in the hole to help drainage. Some compost or well-rotted manure in the hole will help the plants to get started, but make sure the roots do not come into direct contact with it.

The young vines may take some time to recover from the shock of being transplanted, and they may look dead. If in doubt, scratch the bark with a knife. If you see green beneath the surface, then life is present.

## Training and pruning
If you leave vines alone, just tying the new growth to supports to prevent it from trailing, they will produce luxuriant growth and good crops of grapes. The grape quality will not be of the best, however. To grow really good wine grapes you must restrict production by inhibiting the plant. This means pruning.

There are two important principles. The first is that for best results each vine should have only one main stem. The second is that fruit is produced on last year's new growth.

Young vines must be allowed to form strong roots. In their second year they may produce fruit, but it is wiser to nip the bunches off as soon as they begin to form, so that the plant goes on growing roots. If the vines have made poor growth in their first year, prune them back to three buds once again.

The buds you have left will produce shoots. Tie these to the cane and encourage them to grow upwards.

At the end of the first year's growth, choose the two strongest shoots and bend them down to

**1**

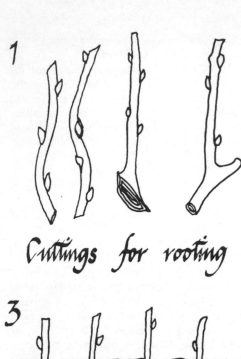

Cuttings for rooting

**2**

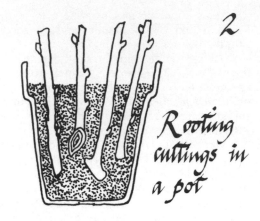

Rooting cuttings in a pot

**3**

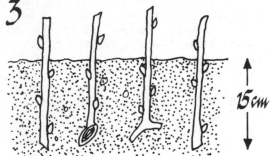

15 cm

Rooting cuttings out-of-doors

**4**

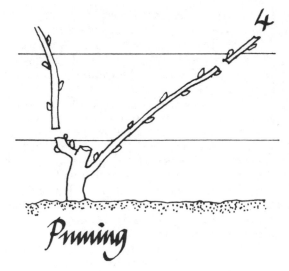

Pruning

**5**

Tying

**6**

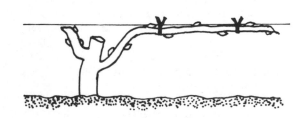

Double Guyot system

the lower wire, and tie them there, one on either side of the centre. Cut off the third shoot to three buds.

In the summer, pruning is aimed to prevent the production of unwanted foliage, and it is achieved by pinching off the growing canes when they are about 75cm long, and then using the garden shears to remove unwanted side growth.

Each winter, established vines are pruned by untying the two shoots on which that year's fruit was produced, and cutting them off at the base. Their place is taken by two of the year's newly grown canes, and the third is removed to three buds. Thus the lower wire is always used to support the fruiting canes, and the upper wire supports the new growth.

Cloches can be used to encourage fruiting, and they can be placed over the fruiting canes, which are only about 45cm from the ground.

Vines can be grown to any shape, of course, simply by training them and removing unwanted growth. The method of training them along wires, which we have described, is called the Double or Dwarf (or Single, if the vines are reduced to a single growing cane, rather than two) Guyot system, and it is the one most widely used commercially. Single and Double Guyot systems are used at Pilton. The purpose of the double system is to safeguard against damage to the fruiting cane, in the belief that half a crop is better than no crop.

Prunings can be used to raise replacements for old or damaged vines, or for sale. Pick the stoutest of them and put them in a pot of moist (but not wet) loam and sand – several will fit in one large pot – or into an outdoor trench containing loam and sand.

### Diseases and pests
Mildews (powdery and downy) are the most common fungal diseases of British vines. They can be prevented by a winter wash and a spring and summer spray of copper sulphate (Bordeaux Mixture).

Black spot (Anthracnose) can damage vines grown in gardens or against walls, especially in warm, wet weather. Prevention involves a winter tar wash of the dormant vine, and spraying the surrounding soil with a fungicide (or Jeyes' Fluid) to kill the over-wintering spores.

There are no insect pests specific to outdoor vines grown in Britain, and an ordinary insec-

ticide can deal with attacks from woodlice, which occasionally damage young vines, and with red spider mite.

Birds can steal the fruit, and so can wasps. The most effective, but laborious, way of keeping both of these from the crop is to tie each bunch of grapes in a perforated polythene bag. If this is impractical, then loose netting will keep out the birds, and half-filled jars of a syrup solution placed between the rows by the foot of each pair of vines will keep the wasp population within limits.

Rabbits can damage young vines, so if rabbits are a common local pest, put wire mesh around the plants.

### Wine from your own grapes
The sugar content of British-grown grapes may be rather low for wine making. You can compensate for this by adding sugar for strength and to mask the acidity. To obtain a final alcohol content of 18 per cent by volume, you may need to add about 200g of sugar per litre. If you are using a hydrometer, fresh juice with an SG of 1050 will need 200g of sugar per litre, with an SG of 1100, 75g per litre, and with an SG of 1130 it will need no sugar. If you do not use a hydrometer, then add sugar a little at a time until fermentation ceases and the flavour of the wine is as you like it.

Use only fresh, ripe, undamaged fruit, and no stalks. You will need 1–1.5kg of grapes for every litre of wine. For white wine (using black or white grapes) put the fruit in a bag made of calico or sacking, and press gently several times. For red wine you do not need the bag: the skins of black grapes give red wine its colour. Leave the skins in the fermenting juice for one or two days to make rosé wine, or for up to ten days for red wine. The skins must not float on the surface for long, and must not dry out, so use a disc of heavy hardwood that fits loosely in your fermenting crock and has 5cm holes drilled in it, to push the skins down daily.

Use natural (wild) or bought yeast, and ferment the juice as you would to make any other kind of home wine.

### Two crops . . .
Finally, remember that grapes are only part of the edible crop produced by vines. The leaves make a delicious vegetable.

# Forage brassicas

Grass is the ideal feed for livestock in spring and early summer, but after June its nutritional value falls dramatically (see p.106) and in a conserved form, as hay or silage, it has severe drawbacks. For example, while good grass fed to dairy cows can provide maintenance plus 18 litres of milk or more (see p.122), silage made from the very same grass will give you maintenance plus only one quarter the yield of milk. Therefore the conserved grass must be supplemented with concentrates, which mainly means cereals. These are no longer cheap, and although they may give dairy farmers good value for money their use for fattening steers or lambs is less and less easy to justify. In order to supplement the conserved forages, to give his beasts the desirable 'succulence', and to reduce his cereal bills, the farmer turns mainly to the

genus *Brassica* of the family *Cruciferae*: cabbage, kale, rape, turnips and swedes.

Kale and cabbage both belong to the extraordinarily versatile species *Brassica oleracea*, which also includes the savoys, brussels sprouts, broccoli, cauliflower and kohlrabi. Kale is renowned for its hardiness: it is the most reliable crop for a hard winter. Forage varieties include the thousand-headed, which can give enormous crops and may be cropped two or three times. It is particularly good for fattening sheep and lambs. The marrow-stem kale, imported from France, has stems like kohlrabi, growing to 120cm high. The leaves are often fed in the autumn, and the stems saved for winter. There are various hybrids, including 'rape kale', a hybrid of rape and kale.

Rape, like the swede, is one of the species *Brassica napus* and has been cultivated since ancient times. It comes in giant or dwarf strains, and in addition to its role as forage, rape is a valuable source of oil. This could be an immense asset in a more self-reliant Britain, for vegetable oils and fats are the single most important agricultural commodity that we find difficult to

Turnip

Rape

Swede

Cabbage

Kale

grow. The area sown to oilseed rape has been increasing rapidly over the last few years.

The related swede, *Brassica napus napobrassica*, is one of agriculture's many botanical enigmas. It is known only from the seventeenth century and it may have originated as a hybrid of *B. oleracea* and *B. rapa* (the turnip). Although it resembles the turnip, anatomically it is dissimilar, as the swollen 'root' also includes the base of the leafy stem, which is why the top of a swede is ringed with leaf scars.

Finally, there are turnips, *Brassica rapa*, which have been known in Europe since prehistoric times. They may be round, flat, cylindrical, yellow, or white. Sometimes they have a purple or green top, and sometimes not.

Together, the brassicas can span the entire season. You can plant cabbages around February to produce a crop in August, or transplant them in July to give a bite in the following January or February. The highly versatile kale can go in any time from March (when it will give you a crop in August) until August, when it should yield some spring keep – if you can keep the wood pigeons at bay. The giant rapes are planted mid-season, and the dwarf varieties are used for late sowing on cereal stubbles, but as they are not so hardy as kale they should be eaten before Christmas. Swedes go in during May or June, and give a crop which can last from after the following Christmas until May; turnips usually go in later than swedes and often, like the 'stubble turnips', they follow the cereal harvest, to give a crop the same autumn. The particular variety of swede or turnip that you plant depends on whether you harvest them mechanically in autumn, or leave them to stand the winter and perhaps fold cattle or sheep on them. In this case you need frost-hardy varieties, which generally means those high in dry matter. The high dry-matter types may not yield as highly as the low dry-matter ones, but the feed value per hectare may be greater.

For a number of years the forage brassicas went out of fashion, because of their high labour requirement. The braird (newly emerging plants) needed to be hand-thinned, then the crops needed to be hoed, and, finally, they had to be lifted. Thomas Hardy's *Tess of the d'Urbevilles* will give you an insight into the disadvantages of root brassicas.

However, mechanization has put paid to all that, and enthusiasm has revived. Modern seeds with their high germination rate can be precision-drilled, so no thinning is needed. Pre- and post-emergent herbicides have done away with hoeing, and without the need to hoe plants can be sown closer together, so you get more per hectare. Harvesting, too, is now done by machine.

## Cultivation
Cultivation is straightforward. In general, besides taking kindly to organic manure the brassicas respond particularly to phosphorus and potassium. Thus swedes and turnips need only about 150–200 units of nitrogen per hectare, but will take 500–550 units of phosphorus and 185–250 of potassium, while even the leafy kale responds to 250–370 units of potassium. Swede and turnip are prone to boron deficiency, which causes heart rot. You can get special boronated fertilizers.

The seedbed itself – cabbages are sown first in a small seedbed and then planted out; the other brassicas are sown in situ – should be shallow. The top should be well worked to a tilth about 10cm deep, overlying firm soil beneath. How you achieve this depends on the time of year you sow, and on whether you farm in a wet or dry district. For spring sowing in a wet district, for example, you would probably need to begin with two passes of the plough, mainly to help drying, before you cultivate. In a dry district, a pass with the cultivator followed by the disc and zig-zag harrows (making each cultivation shallower than the preceding one) should do the trick. Of course, direct cultivation (see p.40), particularly following a cereal crop, cuts out the need for such preparation.

## The future for brassicas
The forage brassicas deserve their revival. Trials at the Rowett Research Institute, Aberdeen, have shown that swedes can replace silage-plus-barley for fattening steers, and kale and rape have earned high reputations for fattening lambs. In addition, these crops are admirable catch-croppers. Kale, particularly the hybrid types, or dwarf rape or 'stubble turnips' can go in after the cereal harvest, and all types may follow a crop of winter rye, grown for an early bite (see p.56). Finally, the ability of the brassicas to soak up vast amounts of slurry or farmyard manure can solve the springtime disposal problem.

# Forage legumes

The leguminous plants that are grown for forage – that is, to be grazed or conserved, leaf, stem, seeds and all – include some of agriculture's quaintest botanical relics, raise some of the knottiest agronomic and physiological problems, but also may contribute more protein and sheer bulk than any other crop. The total area sown to them is falling dramatically year by year, yet with appropriate research these plants could make a very substantial contribution to agricultural self-reliance.

The odd vestiges of an earlier agriculture include the Birdsfoot Trefoil, *Lotus corniculatus*, which was known in Britain before the sixteenth century and which grows widely but is seldom cultivated today; and the Greater Birdsfoot Trefoil, *L. uliginosus*. The main question is not whether such plants show outstanding merit, but whether *potentially* they have merit. Would the present highly variable types respond usefully to breeding? They might. Under highly marginal conditions, on dry soils of low fertility, and provided that it were not grazed heavily, *L. corniculatus* might be a useful replacement for white clover. The Greater form, *uliginosus*, often out-yields white clover in upland conditions and has been studied in breeding programmes in North America. This could be a valuable crop for the Scottish uplands (breeders please note!).

The lupins (*Lupinus* spp.) were originally poisonous. In common with many legumes, they contain alkaloids that act as natural insecticides. Low-toxin varieties have been available since the 1920s, however, first of the yellow lupin (*L. luteus*), then of the blue (*L. angustifolius*) and white (*L. albus*). They can be grown on sandy, acid soils of low fertility (although the blue and white types prefer higher fertility), and that is an asset in itself. Their agricultural future lies with their seeds, as sources of protein and oil. Lupins have an indeterminate habit and their shoots dry slowly, which makes it difficult to preserve the whole plant.

The Yellow Trefoil or Black Medick *(Medicago lupulina)* has had a chequered career. It has been cultivated since the fifteenth century, and at one time it was used to fatten lambs. It can grow on land that is too poor to support clover or lucerne, and it has been used in eastern England as a break crop between sowings of red clover. It does not suffer the clover pestilences of *Sclerotina,* the rot fungus, or clover's particular species of eelworm, but medick does not do for hay, and it is no substitute for red clover in terms of yield or quality. The 66 tonnes of it grown in Great Britain in 1974 was only 5 per cent of the amount being traded twenty years earlier.

Although we can live without medick, Britain's neglect of the related *Medicago sativa* – lucerne – is a sad loss. American farmers call lucerne by its Moorish name, alfalfa, and they grow more than 10 million hectares of it. We grow only 17,000 hectares: a desirable area, according to some experts, would be nearer 250,000 hectares.

Lucerne probably originated in the Near East and Central Asia, and was one of the first forages to be domesticated, some 9,000 years ago. Its long, fast-growing taproot makes it particularly tolerant of drought. Indeed, in trials at the Plant Breeding Institute in Cambridgeshire, only maize and sainfoin stood up to dry conditions better. However, it can also grow in areas having up to 1,000mm of rain a year.

Unfortunately, lucerne is difficult to make into hay. The stems, which in modern varieties can be a metre long, need good weather to dry, and the dried leaves are brittle and drop easily. If it is to be ensiled it must be wilted and needs additives, because although rich in protein it contains little soluble carbohydrate. So most British lucerne is dried artificially and thus is confined to big enterprises (see p.106). What is more, in common with clovers, lucerne contains soap-like compounds called saponins, which foam up in the rumen of the animal, preventing the escape of the gas that is produced in massive quantities by fermentation. The result is 'bloat', which, as Thomas Hardy described in *Far From The Madding Crowd*, can rapidly prove fatal.

All the same, a breeding programme to overcome such problems – or careful management to circumvent them – seems well worth while, for lucerne can give the highest yield of dry matter, and of protein, of all British crops, yet does not need fertilizer nitrogen and actually benefits subsequent crops (see nitrogen fixation, p.31).

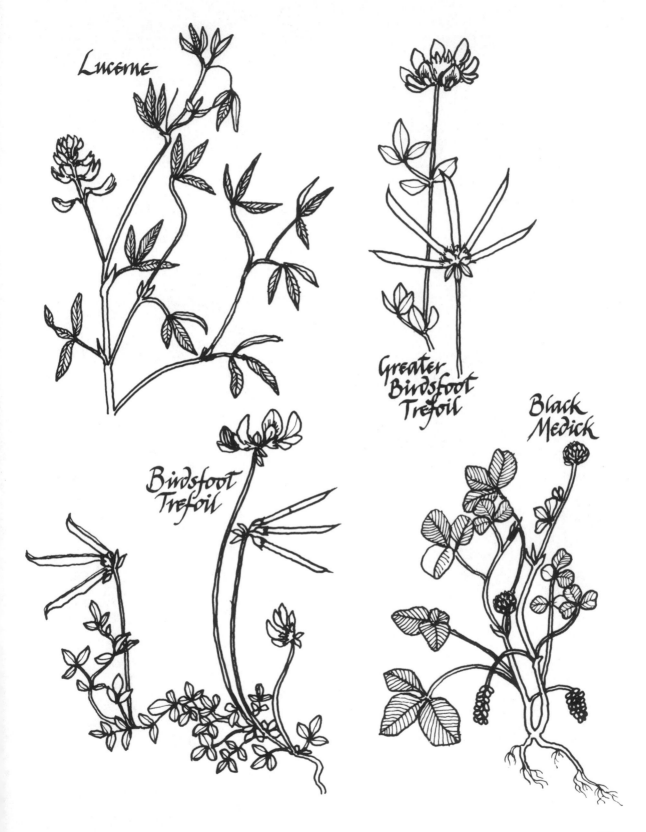

Lucerne

Greater
Birdsfoot
Trefoil

Black
Medick

Birdsfoot
Trefoil

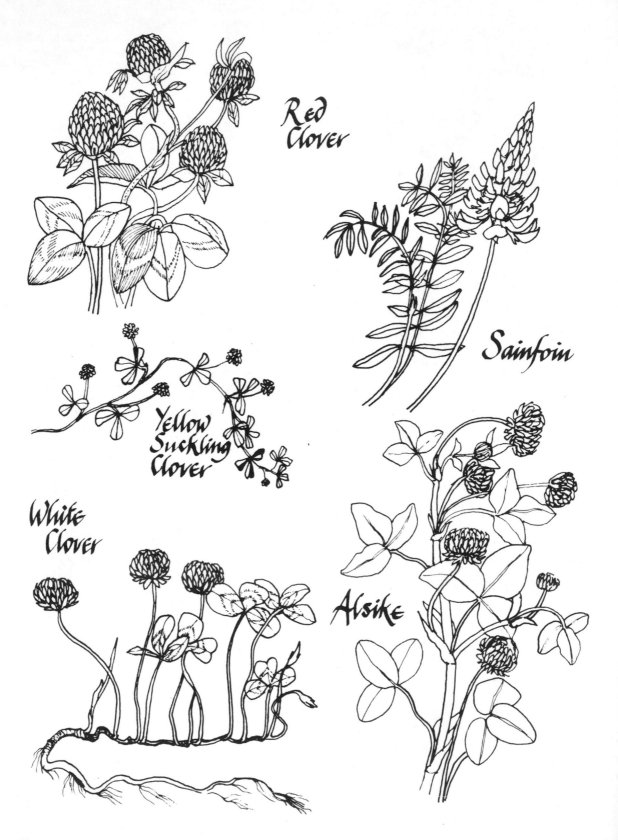

Red Clover

Sainfoin

Yellow Suckling Clover

White Clover

Alsike

Sainfoin, *Onobrychis viciifolia*, has been used in leys for more than 300 years, but its use has declined some two-hundredfold in the last 25 years. With its extensive root system it stands up to drought well, and traditionally it is associated with areas of chalk and low rainfall. Racehorse owners and breeders have favoured sainfoin as high-quality grazing or hay, and stock certainly seem to like it. But its role in feed may be rather subtle. Ruminants tend to ferment protein in their rumens, along with everything else. This makes it difficult to give ruminants a high protein diet. Sainfoin is rich in tannins, however, and tannins tend to protect protein from such fermentation, so that it passes through into the animal's intestine and is digested properly. So sainfoin may help ruminants to make the most of high-protein feeds. It might also help to reduce bloat, because it does not foam. However, the yield of sainfoin is rarely more than two-thirds that of lucerne, and unless it can be raised this ancient crop has a precarious future.

This brings us to the clovers. There are five main types, all belonging to the genus *Trifolium*.

The first, the yellow-suckling clover, *T. dubium*, is an annual, common in Europe, and tolerant of acid. It has dropped right out of favour and use.

The alsike clover (*T. hybridum*), by contrast, enjoyed a vogue in long leys towards the end of the nineteenth century and some of its popularity has persisted. In 1974, British farmers sowed as much alsike seed (by weight) as they did that of lucerne, trefoil and sainfoin together. It is an erect perennial that can live for three to five years, but although it probably tolerates poor soils better than red clover, it seems to have no clear advantage over it. Perhaps farmers know more about this crop than the scientists do; or perhaps, yet again, folk-lore is prevailing.

The great merit of the crimson clover, *T. incarnatum*, is its rapid germination after light rains, which means that it can be used as a catch-crop after cereals, or to fill in the gaps in a failed red clover crop, particularly in non-acid soils in the south. Even so, the crimson too is only just hanging on to its agricultural niche.

By contrast, red clover, *T. pratense*, is a valuable source of hay and seed on many an eastern counties arable farm. It was introduced in the seventeenth century and played a big part in the Norfolk four-course rotation and in the six-course rotations on the heavier lands of Essex. There are three main types, masquerading under a confusing catalogue of names, that come into flower at two-week intervals. The earliest flowerer is used mainly for hay, and the latest flowerer stands up best to grazing. New tetrapoloid forms (that is, forms in which the chromosome number has doubled to give four sets instead of the usual, diploid, two) are now being used more and more.

The most important clover by far, however, is the white clover, *T. repens*. It is the most widely sown legume in mixtures, and often it is indigenous. It could have particular potential in the hills. Because of its creeping habit via stolons it stands up well to grazing, since only the leaves are removed. If it is combined with grass it can produce as much protein as an all-grass sward that has been fertilized with 150–300kg of nitrogen per hectare. However, some hill soils seem to lack the essential symbiotic bacterium, *Rhizobium trifolii*, that fixes the nitrogen. The yield of clover can be increased substantially by inoculating the soil with suitable fungus strains. White clover does have its drawbacks. It does not set seed readily in Britain, so we tend to have to rely on seed imported from New Zealand. It is difficult to establish, it needs good management, and it is susceptible to disease, particularly *Sclerotina*, but it is another crop that could repay research.

Finally, legumes that are grown normally for their seeds might find another role as forage plants. Winter, horse, tick and broad beans might all prove useful, and peas, too, might yield more protein per hectare as forage than as 'grain'.

The forage legumes deserve a revival. Well-managed lucerne or red clover can out-yield well-fertilized grass, and the white clover, or even trefoil, could open up great areas of hillside. There are many problems, but none that should prove insuperable.

# Introducing grass

Grass supplies our sheep and cattle with two-thirds of their energy and an even larger proportion of their protein; grass management, of greater or lesser intensity, is the single most important component of our agriculture and the greatest influence on our landscape: much of Britain would be wasteland if it were not grassland, and those arable farmers who have abandoned grass breaks have often lived to regret it. In any reasonable scenario for British agriculture, grass must play a major role.

Grass has achieved its enormous universal significance because of one small anatomical accident, albeit an accident strongly favoured by evolution. Its vegetative stems – those bearing leaves ('blades') as opposed to those (the straw) that bear the seed heads – are extremely short; or at least, in the case of the creeping species like the bents or couch, lie beneath or close to the soil surface. Thus the growing tissue that produces the new leaves lies within a centimetre of the ground. (Most other plants stand more or less upright, with their growing tissue well above the surface.) So when grass is grazed it retains its potential for growth, whereas most other plants would either be killed or severely set back. More, a grass blade that is left to reach maturity simply dies, and tends to inhibit new growth. So grass not only tolerates grazing (or cutting, the mechanical equivalent) but positively gains by it, since no leaf is allowed to become moribund. If grass is not grazed or mown it always gives way to other species – to reeds followed by scrub, perhaps, or to heather followed by bilberry – and is ultimately replaced by forest. But so long as it is grazed, replacement species are kept at bay. The beautiful downlands of the south-east, or the rough moors of the north and west, owe their existence to deforestation and subsequently to a thousand generations or more of sheep or cattle.

Britain has about 150 grass species, of which fewer than 20 (some of which are now marketed in several varieties) are agriculturally useful. The ideal agricultural grass grows quickly, has a long growing season – perhaps from March to November – is easily digestible, with a relatively low fibre content, is palatable (which means, among other things, that it must not carry the wicked cutting edges that characterize so many

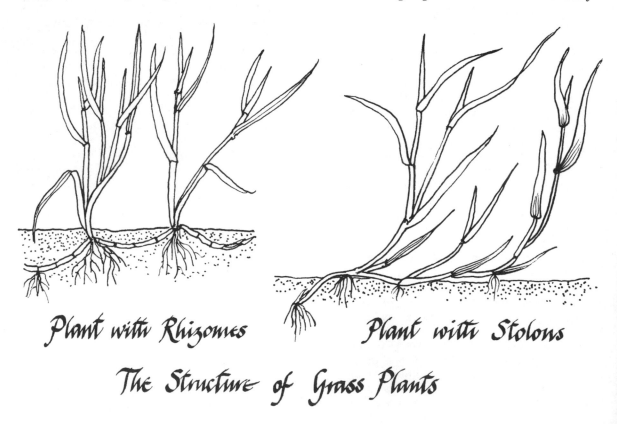

*Plant with Rhizomes*    *Plant with Stolons*

*The Structure of Grass Plants*

species), is high in energy and protein, and is appropriately hardy. These qualities are in marked contrast to those required in a suburban lawn, which should be slow-growing and mechanically tough. In practice succulence has often to be sacrificed for hardiness, and some of the most productive agricultural species, such as Italian ryegrass, cannot survive a winter on the hills. In practice, too, the most productive species give the greatest returns when managed intensively – which means being fertilized, weeded and irrigated. But as meat prices rise and agricultural self-reliance begins to seem attractive, even the hill-grazings, once all but abandoned, are now being assiduously improved and are often showing far greater potential than was ever anticipated.

The British landscape contains a spectrum of grassland. At the bottom end of the scale – but covering 7 of our 15 million hectares of grassland – are the rough grazings. In general, the rough grazings are 'cultivated' only by the sheep, deer and occasional cattle that live upon them (but see p.150). In the best of the rough grazings, sheep's fescue, red fescue and bent are dominant. Such species are not particularly nutritious, but they do form a stable sward, and are far better than the sedges, heather, bracken and scrub that is constantly striving to replace them.

Five million hectares of Britain are covered by permanent pasture. The grazing is mostly poor, but in parts – such as the eastern Romney Marsh, and parts of the Monmouthshire 'moors' and in the fattening belt of the Midlands – it is of high quality. The best permanent pastures are rich in ryegrass, with a fair proportion of white clover, which aids fertility; fescue and bents dominate only in the poorer types. Permanent pastures are cultivated: harrowed and scarified to remove dead material and open up the roots, cut for hay and silage, and often fertilized. But (by definition) they are not ploughed.

Finally, there are the specifically sown and highly cultivated 'leys' (or 'leas'), intended to stand for only a few years in an arable rotation, and often followed by a crop of barley. Ryegrass dominates these leys or, indeed, may be the only species. Leys degenerate into permanent pasture (usually of inferior grade) within about ten years. But as we will see (p.104), the ley is much too important for that to be allowed to happen.

## Typical English Grassland

# Technological grass

In Britain in the 1920s and 1930s the price of meat was so low and imported feedstuffs were so cheap that even potentially good grassland was often used merely to give animals exercise. Now the pressure is on to make the worst grasslands productive, and the best fabulously so.

Effort, as always, is on two fronts: first to find species and varieties that will respond to vigorous management; and second, to perfect the management. Growing the grass (which we discuss here) is only half of management: a bumper grass crop is a waste of effort unless you have the stock to eat it.

Grassland, by nature, is mixed. Sometimes, as when Yorkshire fog grass or heather invades the moor, this is to the farmer's disadvantage. Sometimes, as in the traditional permanent swards in which cocksfoot, timothy, and ryegrass coexisted comfortably with wild white clover, the heterogeneity is to his advantage. Sometimes, as in the chalk grasslands, the species mixture is so rich as to be a botanist's paradise – for as we have seen, grassland is traditionally unstable, forever tending to change into something else; and wherever you find such ecological tension, you find diversity.

The earliest grass-seed mixtures that were sold commercially around the beginning of this century reflected that diversity. The weeds, like thistle and dock, were excluded, but the rest largely imitated the composition of the best local pastures, and often contained a dozen or so grasses and several clovers. But the commercial mixtures have become simpler and simpler. Often, now, the lowland leys are exclusively of ryegrass, either the perennial or the less hardy but lush Italian varieties. Even clover is excluded; nitrogen is supplied mainly 'from the bag'. For the hills, scientists at the Welsh Plant Breeding Station, Aberystwyth, are now developing red fescues, one of the best components of the traditional rough grazings. They are less productive than the familiar ryegrass, but hardier. Thus modern leys, and even the permanent grazings, are becoming increasingly monocultural.

This raises problems. Grass diseases – like barley yellow dwarf virus, or cocksfoot streak virus – have never been a major problem on grasslands because if one variety was affected, others would take its place. But disease can decimate monocultures. The danger is still theoretical, because even the most highly bred of present grass varieties are still genetically varied, so some individual plants within a variety will be more disease-resistant than others. But grass disease could eventually limit productivity.

Productivity itself depends on three major factors – other than weather which we cannot influence. These are NPK, lime and water.

Lack of nitrogen is a major limiting factor. Few farmers regularly apply more than 200 units of N to the hectare, yet most grassland experts agree that few fields will yield their maximum on less than 750 units, and favoured fields can take up to 2500. Such extremes require obsessive management, or the result is to produce grass like bamboo, and to poison the waterways. Phosphorus levels must also be kept up: 100-125 units a year should balance 750 of N. A good rule of thumb is to apply half as much potassium (K) as you do nitrogen. But K requires care. Fast-growing swards may take up too much ('luxury' uptake) which is wasteful and can be toxic. Besides, too much K can limit magnesium uptake so that grazing stock suffer magnesium deficiency, manifesting as 'grass staggers'. In general, the more you push nature, the more precarious your existence becomes.

Calcium constantly leaches from the soil, and fertilizers tend to induce acidity: both trends favour invasion by undesirable coarse species, like Yorkshire fog. So most cultivated grassland is limed, and the acidity of leys should be tested at least once in every arable rotation, and corrected where necessary.

Finally, a surprisingly high proportion of British grass is short of water. South of a line from Exeter to Hull, grassland would respond to irrigation for five years in every ten; south of a line from Hampshire to the Wash, irrigation would be useful in eight years out of ten. High fertilizer application without commensurate water is a waste of money.

In Britain, nature strives constantly to push grassland towards forest. At all parts of the spectrum, farmers strive to reverse that inexorable trend.

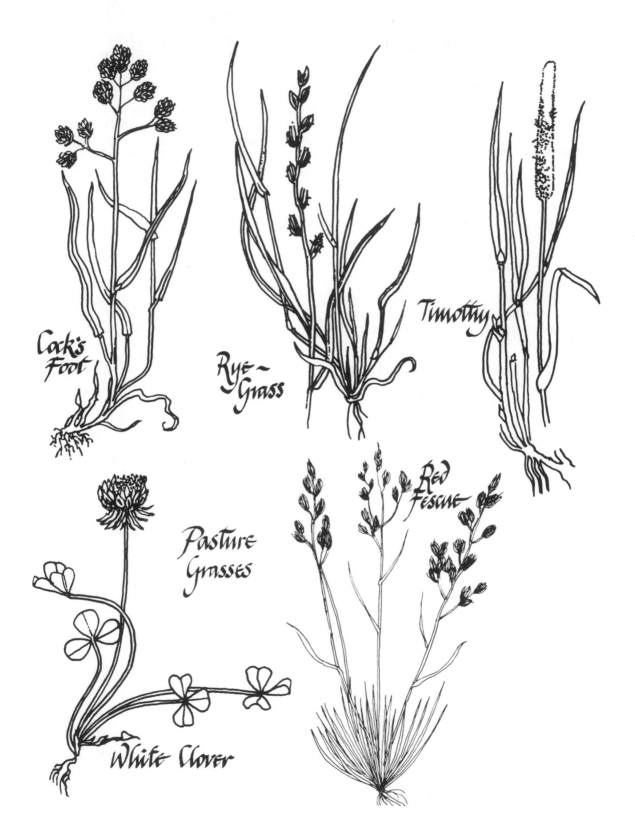

Cock's Foot

Rye-Grass

Timothy

Pasture Grasses

Red Fescue

White Clover

# Grass conservation

All methods of conserving grass are some-what wasteful. In part (as when over-dry hay breaks up) the loss is mechanical; in part it occurs because the grass continues to respire after it is cut, and thus burns away precious sugars. The effect of all three basic methods of conservation – drying, haymaking and ensiling – is primarily to stifle the grass's own metabolism, and only secondarily to prevent invasion by decomposing bacteria and fungi.

Best, beyond doubt, is grass drying – a technique dating back to the 1920s but only now catching on, and still largely experimental. The hardware varies a great deal, but the basic principle is to dry the grass rapidly with hot air as soon as possible after it is cut: it can then be pressed into convenient cubes to be fed to cattle,

used as a filler in pig feeds, or as a source of xanthophyll (yellow pigment) for poultry. Loss of dry matter by this technique is only around 5 per cent. But capital outlay for machinery is high.

Haymaking is by far the commonest method of conserving grass, and the least efficient. When hay is made traditionally dry matter losses may be up to 35 per cent. The slowly dried plant cells become brittle and break easily: hay requires extremely delicate handling as it reaches the final stage, when it will contain no more than 30 per cent moisture.

A compromise between the above two methods is barn drying. The grass is allowed to dry to about 45 per cent moisture in the field, and is then baled while still structurally strong. The bales, which must be correctly and uniformly packed, are then stacked in the barn, where fans – powered by diesel or electric motor or via the tractor's power take-off – subject them to desiccating breezes. If the air can first be warmed (the tractor waste heat can produce a 4°C rise) so much the better. Losses with barn-dried hay are only around 15–20 per cent.

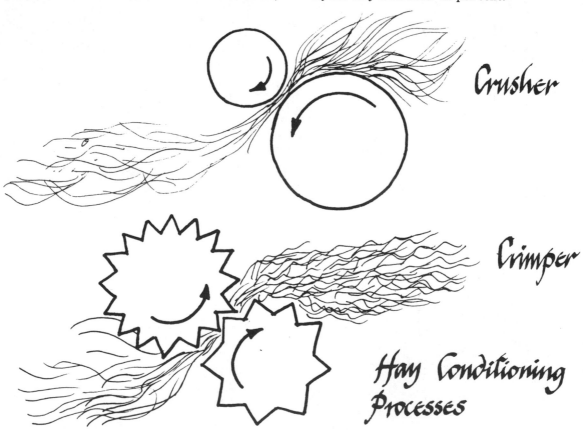

Crusher

Crimper

Hay Conditioning Processes

Ensiling, to produce silage, is a form of pickling. The grass is tightly packed in towers or clamps, and undergoes rapid anaerobic 'fermentation'. Some sugars in the grass are broken down by bacteria to form lactic acid; this acid prevents the grass metabolizing, and suppresses organisms that might cause further decomposition.

Silage making is efficient – dry matter losses are around 15–25 per cent – and, in principle, straightforward. But it is easy to go wrong and produce not good silage but bad compost. You can add molasses to speed the production of acid; but if the finished silage is too acid then the stock will reject it. Patent additives, such as ICI's 'Sylade', are designed to speed acid formation without giving an over-acid end product. It is essential not to let air in (which would produce good compost); grass for silage is compressed, perhaps by running the tractor back and forth over it, and the chore of covering each day's cut with polythene before knocking off is well worth the effort. Silage effluent, formed when the grass contains too much water, is fearful stuff: poisonous and smelly, with no known use. If the dry matter is only 10–15 per cent at ensiling, each tonne will produce 370–460 litres of effluent; but run-off is zero if the grass begins at 25 per cent dry matter. It therefore pays to double-chop and wilt for up to 24 hours before ensiling. Good silage is excellent feed: poor silage is useless.

The final quality of hay, dried grass, or silage depends on the quality of the herbage you begin with. Silage and dried grass offer yet another advantage over hay, in that you can begin with grass that is more lush. You can apply more nitrogen and so increase total yield. In all three cases you should use grass with a digestibility – 'D value' – of 63, which means it contains 63 per cent digestible organic matter in the dry matter. You do not need to calculate this, for the National Institute of Agricultural Botany publishes a leaflet telling you the dates at which each variety is at its best. So it pays to grow swards containing only a single species or a few synchronous species, so that all peak at the same time; you can spread the work load by sowing one field with an early-peaking variety (like Perennial Ryegrass S24) and another with, say S51 Timothy which peaks later. For all species, though, the first and principal cut will be made in the last ten days of May or the first two weeks of June.

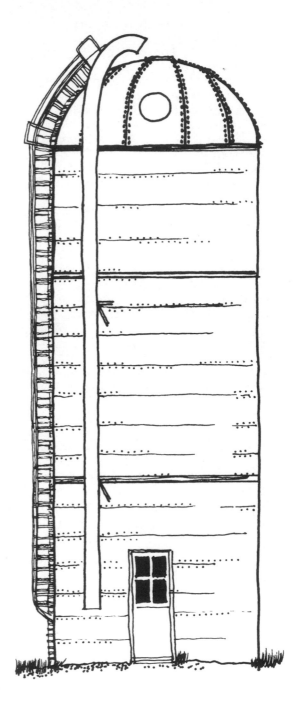

Silo
Air-tight metal tower
for making Silage

## Further reading

**General:** *Ask the Fellows Who Cut the Hay* by George Ewart Evans. Faber.

*Fertilizing for Maximum Yield* by G. W. Cooke, Crosby Lockwood.

*Farming Organically,* booklet published by The Soil Association (see below).

*The Horse in the Furrow* by George Ewart Evans. Faber.

*The Oxford Book of Food Plants* by G. B. Masefield, M. Wallis, S. G. Harrison and B. E. Nicholson. OUP.

*Self-Sufficient Small Holding,* booklet published by The Soil Association (see below).

*The Worm Forgives the Plough* by John Stewart Collis. Charles Knight.

**Weekly:** *Farmers Weekly* (which also issues special numbers on particular topics).

**Viticulture:** *Growing Your Own Wine* by Ben Turner. Garden Farming Series, Pelham Books.

*Vineyards in England* by Edward Hyams.

*Growing Vines* by Nick Poulter.

**Vegetables and fruit:** *Fresh Food from Small Gardens* by Brian Furner. Stuart & Watkins with The Soil Association.

*Grow Your Own Fruit and Vegetables* by Lawrence D. Hills. Faber.

*The New Vegetable Grower's Handbook* by Arthur J. Simons. Penguin.

*The Penguin Book of Basic Gardening* by Alan Gemmell. Penguin.

*Soft Fruit Growing* by E. G. Gilbert. Penguin.

**Soil Association Booklets:** *Garden Compost, Make Your Plants Work For You, The Value of Weeds.*

## Information

Agricultural Development Advisory Service (ADAS), Ministry of Agriculture, Fisheries and Food.

Good Gardeners' Association, Arkley Manor, Arkley, Barnet, Herts.

Henry Doubleday Research Association, 20 Convent Lane, Bocking, Braintree, Essex.

Organic Farmers and Growers, Longridge, Creeting Road, Stowmarket, Suffolk.

The Soil Association, Walnut Tree Manor, Haughley, Stowmarket, Suffolk.

(Viticulture) English Vineyards Association, c/o Mrs. J. G. Barrett, The Vineyards, Cricks Green, Felsted, Essex.

Pilton Manor Vineyard, Pilton, Shepton Mallett, Somerset.

(NFT) Interlates Ltd., 99 The Drive, Rickmansworth, Herts WD3 4DY.

**Nurseries, seedsmen:** Thompson and Morgan, London Road, Ipswich, Suffolk.

Sutton & Sons Ltd., Reading, Berks.

**Vines:** Jackmans, Woking, Surrey.

S. E. Lyle, Park Road Nurseries, Formby, Lancs.

M. Jefferson-Brown, Whitbourne, Worcester.

Pilton Manor Vineyard.

**NFT equipment:** Soil-Less Cultivation Systems Ltd., MM House, Sebastopol Road, Aldershot, Hants GU11 1U9.

# LIVESTOCK

# Who needs animals?

Western agriculture is geared to livestock production. Besides the vast areas of grassland devoted to cattle and sheep, the Western countries feed more grain to their animals than is consumed by the whole of the Third World – people, livestock and all. Britain has 15 million hectares of grass and feeds as much grain to livestock as it grows.

In the 1950s, when intensive livestock production really took off – broiler chicken and pig, battery hen, barley beef – the investment seemed justified on nutritional grounds. It was thought that the great need was for protein, and protein was equated with meat, milk and eggs. Indeed, the world food problem was seen as being largely a protein problem. The view was wrong.

It was understandable, though, given the comparatively rudimentary knowledge of nutritional requirements twenty years ago. The symptoms of hunger and malnutrition that were observed in the poor countries were mainly symptoms of protein deficiency. However, they were not caused by lack of protein in the diet, but by too little food of any kind. The body requires energy, and it requires protein to grow and repair tissue. Of the two requirements, that for energy is more urgent. If the energy content of the diet is too low, then protein will be used by the body to provide energy – the protein is metabolized inefficiently, but without an adequate supply of energy tissue cannot be built anyway. So the consumer may obtain sufficient energy, but

Chinese Rice Dishes

Italian Pasta

Meat is used sparingly in many national dishes

Mexican Chili

Indian Curry

Bread

Pastry

remain short of protein, and symptoms of protein deficiency may appear. If the protein content of the diet is increased some relief may be obtained, but only when the energy need is satisfied.

We know now that human beings can obtain all the protein they need from cereals, potatoes and legumes. Most traditional diets provide all the necessary nutrients provided they are eaten in quantities sufficient to prevent people from feeling hungry (diets based on protein-deficient cassava may be the exception). To give to animals food that is perfectly suitable for humans seems not only muddle-headed but also, in a crowded world, sinful. While agriculturalists continue to argue about whether national self-sufficiency in food is even possible in Britain, vegetarians point out that on an all-vegetable diet these islands could support two to five times their present human population.

Although we do eat more meat than we need, animal products fill several vital roles in human nutrition, and although we do produce livestock in a profligate way so that they actually compete with us for food, they can also be produced without waste and, indeed, they should be a great asset to farms, gardens, and to the landscape.

We do not need to obtain the bulk of our protein from meat, but the high quality of animal protein is useful to raise the food value of cheaper vegetable protein. Meat is used to its greatest nutritional advantage when it is used sparingly, as it is in all the world's great peasant cuisines, and not, as in the modern West, as the *raison d'être* of each main meal. Animal products – particularly the offals – are also the only 'natural' source of vitamin $B_{12}$, and they are a useful source of structural fats. Finally, of course, meat is flavoursome. Its presence in only tiny amounts makes less-glamorous sources of protein more acceptable.

Nor need livestock compete with us, as they do now. Cattle and sheep (in common with goats, antelope, deer and camels) possess a vast extension to their stomach, called the rumen. Bacteria living in the rumen are able to digest cellulose. Cellulose, as one of the chief ingredients of plant cell walls, is the commonest organic polymer in nature. It is, like starch, compounded of glucose molecules and hence is the greatest single source of food energy. It is also indigestible, except to ruminants (animals with rumens), and to horses, elephants, rhinoceroses

and rabbits, which do not have rumens but which do possess analogous bacteria-containing extensions to their gut. So, because of their rumens, cattle and sheep are able to live on grass. Vast areas of Britain are fit only for growing grass, and grass is also a useful 'break' on many an arable farm. The ruminants' gut bacteria can also convert into protein non-protein sources of nitrogen, such as urea or even pre-treated chicken manure or human sewage.

Chickens and pigs, like humans, are omnivores. They cannot thrive on food that theoretically could not sustain a man. However, they have what we would consider low aesthetic standards, and they can feed on what we reject – in other words, on swill. The British are estimated to waste some 25 per cent of all their food after it leaves the farm, the greatest losses occurring in the kitchen (vegetable peelings, the heads and tails of fish, and so forth) and as plate scrapings. This is an immense potential feed source that was exploited during the war, when every town street had a 'pig bin' into which waste food was placed. Both pigs and chickens are accomplished scavengers. So, the proper habitat for both pigs and poultry is on the farm, scratching up the tail corn, cleaning the land of root crops missed in harvesting, in orchards, in the garden and smallholding and – why not? – on urban allotments. The present practice is to raise them in 'factories' on commercial, cereal-based, custom-designed feeds. We simply write off the scrap food that they should be eating, and their willingness to eat it.

We cannot draw an inflexible distinction between competitive and non-competitive ways of feeding livestock. Grass-fed sheep generally need a supplement in winter, when they are pregnant and there is no fresh grass. Modern, high-yielding dairy cows cannot eat enough grass to realize their full milking potential and so they need additional 'concentrate', and as swill and scraps are very variable, in quality and availability, some supplement with cereal and other concentrate is necessary. There is a great difference, however, between using cereal simply to complement animals in their ecological role, and using it to obviate that role. 'Rational' agriculture, making the best use of land to produce the best food possible, would include many animals, but there should not be so many as there are now, and those there are should, in general, be knitted tightly into an intricate fabric of mixed husbandry.

# Is farming cruel?

We have suggested (p.110) that intensive livestock units – 'factory farms' – are now largely inappropriate, because they use enormous resources to produce food we do not need. But should they not also be condemned on humanitarian grounds?

The question is important and far from simple. Certainly, modern husbandry often *seems* cruel. Broiler chickens, raced to slaughter at eight weeks, are commonly kept 10–20,000 at a time in 'deep-litter' houses, where, despite the soothing perpetual twilight, they develop vices such as feather-pecking, which may lead to cannibalism. To curb this, they are often 'debeaked', which means removing a third of the upper and lower bill. Laying birds are usually kept in batteries of cages, 2–25 to a cage, often three to four tiers high, in which they may have only just enough room to sit down. They stay there for a year, while producing around 260 eggs. To prevent feather-pecking they are debeaked, and sometimes fitted with 'spectacles', pinned through their beaks, to occlude forward vision.

The sow commonly spends four months of her five-month pregnancy in an iron sow-stall in which she can only stand or lie, but not turn round. She then graduates to the farrowing stall, where an iron bar prevents her from lying on her piglets, and perhaps, in the Scandinavian-style 'iron maidens', she may be tied to the floor by a short rope. Altogether, with two pregnancies a year, she may spend ten months in every twelve virtually unable to move. The piglets, at eight weeks, then commonly pass to the weaner pool, where they are penned in groups of up to thirty. They are sometimes kept in the dark to quieten them, but still they may bite each other's tails, and if these are docked to prevent biting they may transfer their aggression to each other's ears.

Veal calves, taken from their dams within the first three days of their lives (as is the lot of most calves), are then confined in crates in which, towards the end of their three months' life, they may not even be able to lie down. Craving roughage, they chew their own hair. Beef cattle fed on roughage-deficient barley also chew hair, which often penetrates their gut walls, allowing bacteria to penetrate and often ulcerating their livers. Dairy cows, sometimes kept with scant individual attention in herds of 200–300 (too

A Battery House

large for them to form a stable social hierarchy), also may suffer extreme confinement through most of their staggeringly productive lives.

Here are just a few points in what must be an extremely complex debate. To begin with, simply to identify with the animals – 'anthropomorphism' – and assume that what would make us unhappy must also distress them, is unrealistic. Darkness, for example, need not have the same connotations of fear and mystery for animals that it holds for man. We must, if we really want to improve the animals' lot, show which components of each environment cause them distress. Before that we must be able to measure stress objectively – and this is extremely difficult to do. For example, the output of some hormones fluctuates wildly when animals or humans are under stress; but they also do so when the animal is living a 'normal' life.

On the other hand, to write off anthropomorphism as mere sentimentality, or as being hopelessly unscientific, is to throw away an important source of insight. Animals have similar nervous and endocrine systems to our own; the inference that they 'feel' and 'suffer' is reasonable, even if it is unprovable. After all, we cannot prove that our fellow humans suffer as we do.

The farmers' argument that animals would not grow or reproduce unless they were content merits extreme caution. In humans obesity can be a sign of distress, and our selective breeding may simply have produced animals in whom unhappiness is disguised. Yet the attempt to create livestock systems that imitate wild conditions is fraught with difficulty. Modern livestock differs from its wild progenitors, in psychology as well as form, and many so-called 'natural' husbandry systems are simply picturesque, and may involve extreme suffering – as when hill-sheep freeze to death or are ravaged by blowfly, or the free-range steer has its liver eaten away by flukes.

In short, before we can state definitely that particular husbandry systems are cruel we need detailed knowledge of each creature's psychological requirements, and objective measurements of stress, both of which are largely lacking. In the meantime we should not be afraid to apply humanity and common sense; and by those criteria much modern husbandry, but also some traditional husbandry, is well beyond the pale.

Flat-deck rearing cages for piglets

# Grazing

In general, as we have seen, grass benefits from being cut or grazed; moribund leaves are removed, new growth encouraged, and weeds cut short. In addition, young grass is the most nutritious – highest in energy and protein and lowest in fibre – and some marginal species are edible only when young. But plant growth depends on photosynthesis, in turn dependent on leaf area. If grass is kept too short, by over-grazing or close cutting, the leaf area is reduced sufficiently to inhibit growth rate, and very close grazing may even remove the growing tissues close to the ground. The art is to keep grass not too long and not too short. The optimum length is still a matter for controversy, and in practice depends on geographical area, and on species used; but the principle is universal.

There are two major difficulties. The first is to balance output against stocking rate. Output can vary greatly from year to year: you may be understocked one year, with your beautiful grass going to waste, but find yourself next year with surplus animals, forced either to slaughter them prematurely, or buy in expensive feed. In addition, grass grows in 'flushes' – a good burst in late spring, and another from August to September – and it tends to decline nutritionally as the year wears on. But stock need continuous high-quality grazing, and growing stock, particularly beeves, want more nourishment, not less, as the summer unfolds.

The second problem is disease. Cattle and sheep have always been riddled with internal parasites, such as fluke, tapeworms and a host of roundworms. Traditional systems took this into account: beasts were expected to grow slowly, and the 'store' animal, whose growth had virtually ceased, was the stock-in-trade of the livestock farmer. This drain on productivity is no longer acceptable. But the more intensively you stock, the more likely you are to transmit parasites.

Grazing systems are immensely varied, and often immensely complex, but they all reflect these two basic requirements: to utilize young growth, and to minimize parasite transmission.

Thus by 'rotating' stock – judiciously confining the animals, and periodically moving them – farmers contrive to ensure that they graze the same pasture only at intervals of 21–28 days: enough to allow regrowth, but not enough for the growth to coarsen. There are two main rotation systems: paddock grazing, in which the confining fences are semi-permanent; and strip grazing, in which a temporary (probably electric) fence is edged forward day by day. Paddocks are more expensive to set up, but require less management.

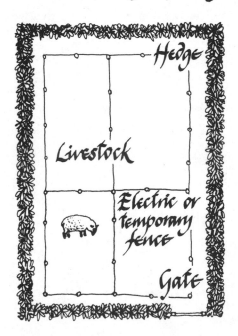

## Paddock Grazing

Hedge

Livestock

Electric or temporary fence

Gate

The animals are confined within the paddock until they have grazed all the grass. Then the paddock is moved and the process repeated. Paddock grazing ensures that all the pasture is eaten and then given time to recover.

ICI have been experimenting with intensive 'set-stocking', in which dairy cattle are allowed to graze the same area from late April until late September, thus obviating the need for fencing and rotation. This seems to flout the basic principles, but by close attention to soil fertility and cattle health they have achieved results comparable with paddock-grazing. Finally, some farmers adopt 'zero-grazing': keeping the beasts confined and bringing them fresh-cut grass every day. The advantages are obvious, but so is the disadvantage: the high labour requirement. In general, zero-grazing is justified where confinement in the field is difficult, or, in the case of dairy cattle, where the parlour is remote from the fields.

In the old days farmers divided permanent grassland into 'pasture', which was used only for grazing, and 'meadows', grown exclusively for hay (although stock was often allowed to graze the aftermath). Modern systems are generally more flexible, but a modern variant is the 'two-sward' system, in which the farmer uses one area for paddock grazing, and another exclusively for conservation. Among other advantages, this method allows the farmer to use different grass mixtures, or monocultures, for the two different purposes. In practice, he often uses permanent pasture for paddock grazing, and an ungrazed ley (part of an arable break) for conservation.

The advantages of mixed stocking have long been recognized. Sheep need shorter grass than cattle, and the two work efficiently together. As stocking rates increased, however, it became clear that conditions which favoured one species tended to disfavour the other, so the two were separated. But parasites can be a major problem with modern high stocking rates, and as cattle and sheep have few parasites in common, it often pays to graze the two alternately, even if actual mixing proves too complex. Calves, which require tender grass and are particularly vulnerable to parasites, constitute a third class of livestock. They may be given first go at each fresh paddock or strip, and cows allowed to 'sweep up' after them.

Because grass and livestock enterprises are so intimately linked, they must be allowed to develop together. Start with a small grass area and a few beasts, and expand only when you have mastered their management. Let either run ahead of the other, and you will be left with massive feed bills and overworked grazing, or with rank sward, expensively produced and useless.

# Strip Grazing

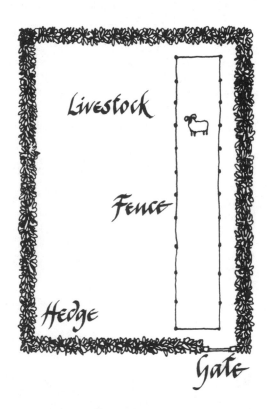

The field is divided into narrow strips, enclosed by electric or other temporary fencing and the animals are confined to each strip until all the pasture is eaten. The fencing is then moved to enclose the adjacent strip. The system is similar to paddock grazing, but often requires less frequent moving of the fencing.

115

# Slurry

Farmyard manure (known sometimes as 'FYM') is an eminently compostable mixture of dung, urine and straw, and is ideal for the fields. It confers fertility and once it has rotted it is pathogen-free. But farmers of intensive livestock cannot always afford, or even obtain, straw for bedding or labour for daily mucking-out. So they keep their stock on solid floors or slats that can be cleaned mechanically by scrapers, and hosed. The effluent thus provided is known as slurry: a minestrone of dung, urine, water and other washings, with some cereal husks, ranging in consistency from thick soup to near solid. With its high but variable quota of nitrogen, phosphorus, potassium and other minerals, slurry is potentially valuable. It is easily stored in tanks, pits or lagoons until the fields are ready to receive it, and spread via pipe systems, tankers, rain guns or sprinklers. It is also potentially highly dangerous, however, and demands very careful management.

The first problem is quantity. Depending on whether they have a dryish or wettish diet, fattening pigs generate 4.5–11 litres of slurry each per day; Friesian cattle, between 11 litres a day for a steer being fattened on silage and barley, and up to 36 litres for a cow on silage and concentrates; while a thousand light- to medium-laying hens would produce about 900 litres a week – albeit of good-quality stuff, with a dry matter of 25 per cent.

The second problem is chemistry. Decomposition may be aerobic or anaerobic (see Garden compost, p.80), the former being quicker and less malodorous, and therefore generally preferable, but slurry lacks the mechanical ingredient, straw, that allows air into the heap. Air must be introduced mechanically – by rotors or paddles that push the slurry round in a ditch, by surface agitators, by filters of plastic or slag in a silo – or in lagoons, where oxygen is generated by algae (which, at least in theory, might be used subsequently to feed pigs). But all these methods are expensive, and none produces perfect results.

Because of its structure, slurry is most amenable to anaerobic decomposition. But this generates so little heat that the slurry must be forced to a temperature of around 95°C, or decomposition is impossibly slow. One possibility would be

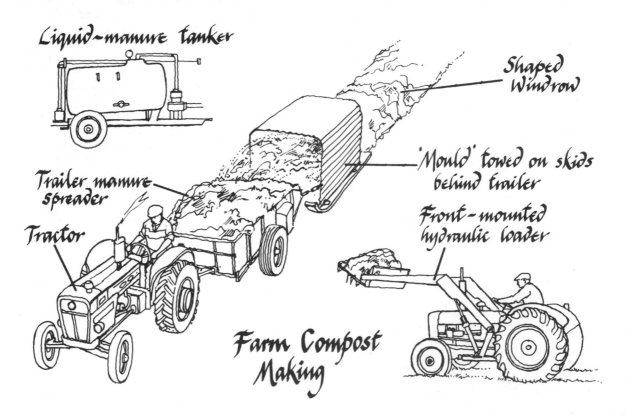

Liquid-manure tanker

Shaped Windrow

Trailer manure spreader

Tractor

'Mould' towed on skids behind trailer

Front-mounted hydraulic loader

Farm Compost Making

to use the gases produced anaerobically, notably methane and hydrogen sulphide, as fuel, which could then be used to warm the rest. All in all, however, anaerobic treatment seems best suited to warm countries.

The third problem is disease. Bacteria and worms in FYM would generally be destroyed by heat as it rotted aerobically in the midden, but *Salmonella typhimurium* (which causes diarrhoea in calves and humans), flukes and the eggs of tapeworms can survive for seven weeks in slurry in winter. Ideally, therefore, slurry should be stored for a month before spreading, and stock should not be put on treated fields for another month after that.

The fourth problem is to use slurry profitably and safely. To pour it into rivers or public sewers is wasteful and generally illegal, but it will finish up in the waterways if you put it indiscriminately on to a field that cannot accommodate it. Fields that are already saturated, or nearly so, may be unable to absorb it. Hard-baked ground may simply reject it. The colloidal materials in slurry may seal the soil surface and thus cause run-off even when the ground seems receptive, and fissures in the subsoil (especially chalk) may carry it straight into the underground watercourses – again, both dangerous and illegal. 'Little and often', therefore, is the general rule in spreading slurry. Most field types can take 56,000 litres a year per hectare (perhaps diluted to 112,000 litres), but on fields with good holding capacity, and with adequate liming, this can sometimes be increased to 170,000 litres per hectare – provided you are organized to manage the resulting enormous production of herbage.

This leaves three more problems. Although such plants as beet, potatoes and especially maize can soak up vast amounts of slurry, the chief recipient is likely to be grass. But grass does not like the high potassium content of slurry, which limits its use, and if you apply slurry in February or March the organic nitrogen it contains will be released only slowly, so you will need to add nitrogen from the bag to provide stock with an early bite. Secondly, cattle do not like to graze contaminated pasture, and though they can avoid cow-pats, they cannot avoid a widely sprayed sward; their grazing may be reduced for a few days if they are turned out too soon. Finally, slurry can be toxic – particularly if too much pig slurry is applied, which may contain the copper that pigs are fed to boost their growth.

All in all, slurry can save money and labour, but it raises biological problems that may never be totally resolved. The midden is still the best.

### Farm compost making

FYM can be applied directly to the fields, provided it is available at the right time of year. Often it is, for the cattle that have been wintered in yards are turned out to graze at about the time that the arable fields are fertilized. On some land, especially on heavy clay soils, the animals may need to remain under cover a little longer. Heavy soil dries more slowly after the winter rain and snow, and must be protected for longer from trampling hooves. Elsewhere on the farm, however, other fields may be ready for sowing. The yards are mucked out as soon as the animals have left: FYM accumulates as soiled and trampled straw is covered with a layer of fresh straw again and again. So if the arable crops cannot wait, but the pasture must, the farmer may have to store his FYM until the following autumn.

The principles underlying the composting of farm wastes are identical to those involved in making garden compost (see p.80), but because of the quantities to be handled the operation is mechanized and bins are not used. Farm compost is made in windrows – long heaps, square in cross-section, left in the open.

The manure is moved from the yards by tractor and manure fork, and fed to a trailer manure-spreader towed by a second tractor. The spreader flails the manure upwards and to the rear.

To shape the heap, a 'mould' can be improvised in the form of a three-sided box, having no ends or floor, made from corrugated iron and mounted on wooden skids. The flails aerate the manure and the mould catches it. As the mould fills, the whole rig is moved forward, leaving behind a neat and ventilated pile.

FYM has a good balance of carbon to nitrogen, but the addition of lime will reduce its natural acidity; the lime is added to the manure in the spreader, a shovelful at a time (there is nothing precise about making compost!). A small amount of green matter also helps, so if the nearby ditch is full of weeds, some of these can be cut down and thrown into the spreader, to be mixed with the manure and lime as everything is flailed out together.

Farm compost heaps are turned, like garden heaps, but using a tractor and manure fork.

# Breeds of cattle

Cattle demonstrate, in an exaggerated form, the two great problems facing the livestock breeder. First, what are you breeding for? Secondly, how on earth do you go about it?

The first problem seems difficult at first, then simple, then it becomes difficult again. Cattle were bred for three things: meat, milk and work (with leather and dung as by-products). To some extent, these are incompatible. The good beef animal, for example, is oblong in profile, with the meat moved from the shoulder, where it tends to accumulate in wild cattle, as you can see clearly with the bison and yak, to the rump, where it grows more succulently. The milker, on the other hand, does not need muscle, except to hold her bones together. She (the males seem irrelevant) needs only the metabolic quirk of turning grass into milk and the anatomical ability – a well-set, non-pendulous, non-fatty, evenly-titted udder – to contain it. The work animal must, above all, be strong and docile. Docility is achieved largely by castration.

So, by an eminently rational division of labour, we need only produce three types of cattle: Beef Shorthorn, chunky Hereford and Aberdeen Angus, able to fatten on highly variable pasture, to epitomize the beef types; the gracile Dairy Shorthorn, Jersey and Guernsey, and the doe-like Ayrshire, typifying the dairy animals; and the massive and lanky Chianina of Italy (2 metres high at the shoulder) and Charolais of France, to show how powerful cattle can be.

It sounds simple, but this is where the trouble starts. Dairy cows will not milk without producing calves. The female calves form the next generation of milking cows, but who needs skinny bull calves? Until quite recently, dairy bull calves were virtually thrown on the scrap heap. Meanwhile, the beautiful Aberdeen and Hereford are all very well, but who can afford to keep a beef cow, just to produce one calf a year? The answer is only those with cheap land, and not many of them. In practice, then, for the most part we cannot afford the extreme types. That is why the principal breed now – present in 70 per cent of all British purebreds or crosses – is the Friesian (called Holstein in North America), which can yield up to 13,000 litres a year (and commonly averages 4,500 litres in commercial herds) and also produces calves that are worth fattening for beef. The Hereford x Friesian – unmistakable with its black or black-and-white body and white face – is the most popular beef calf. The nation's beef herd is now a by-product of its dairy herd.

There have been two other trends working at the same time. Our extreme beef types, bred to fatten on poor pastures, are just too small to make full use of the modern, richer pastures. Suddenly the massive work animals – most of them imported, but including the indigenous (and handsome) South Devon – are getting a new lease of life, not to replace the tractor, but to bulk out our diminutive beef breeds, and to cross with dairy animals (including Jerseys) to produce worthwhile calves. Secondly, although the Common Market may have diminished

*Chianina*

Ayrshire

Charolais

Aberdeen Angus

Guernsey

dairy prospects slightly it has increased the value of the culled cow. So the Friesian, seemingly the perfect dual-purpose beast, may yield to fleshier, bigger animals (perhaps with a touch of Simmental or South Devon) that yield a little less but are worth more dead.

That brings us to the second problem. How do you produce the beasts you want? This is still not solved fully. It is made more difficult by the fact that cattle breed slowly and, in the dairy herd, most of the females born have to be kept as replacements, so that selection, which is a key component of breeding, is not easy.

Nor is it simple to decide which animals really are desirable. 'Scientific' cattle breeding is generally recognized as having begun in the eighteenth century, when improved forages made it possible to keep them through the winter, but the beasts were appraised mainly by eye. To some extent this is fair enough: you can see the general shape of a good beef animal. But aesthetics have often taken over from common sense. Decades were wasted on the curved head-gear of the Longhorn, now defunct. Potentially good Herefords were rejected because they lacked the white face and forelock. Even today, Friesian breeders are reluctant to accept red-and-white Friesians (an entirely trivial colour variant), while beautifully rounded Aberdeens, judged visually as Smithfield champions, have turned out to be too fat for the butcher. Yet other types, such as the Dexter and Belted Galloway, have been bred almost specifically to be looked at.

Things have improved. In particular, artificial insemination gives all herds access to the best bulls, and they can be judged to be 'best' by assessing the performance of a few test progeny before the sperm is offered on the market. Hormones can be used now to induce high-quality cows to produce twins, although this technique is still unreliable. One promising piece of high technology is to remove conceptuses from good-quality beasts and implant them into the wombs of scrub animals, whose task is merely to endure the pregnancy. The high-class animal, thus aborted, can then be made pregnant again.

The most significant change, however, is probably the change of attitude. The Shorthorn Society proposed recently to update their breed radically by out-crossing with a range of other types, including Simmental. The criterion of success was not, as in the past, to produce a beautifully typical Shorthorn, but to produce a measurably high-performance beast. As one official of the Society commented, 'we don't care if the final animal looks like a giraffe'. The agricultural shows, too, where rosettes used to be pinned arbitrarily on beasts that could hardly waddle round the show ring, are fast losing their pernicious influence.

Cattle breeding, then, is moving ahead. For logistic reasons it will be hundreds of years before we see the clearly defined genetic lines and hybrids that are now characteristic of pigs and chickens, and perhaps that day will never come. In the meantime, we must continue to juggle the breeds we have inherited.

*Beef Shorthorn*

Hereford

Friesian

Jersey

Dairy Shorthorn

# The dairy farm

Dairy farming is the most ubiquitous enterprise in Britain (see p.14) and also the most tense. There are three main ingredients for success: feeding, health, and getting the cows pregnant at the right time. Above all, the dairy cow responds to individual care and attention. It is this vital ingredient that the modern, highly mechanized enterprises, sometimes with 70 or more animals to every herdsman, often lack so conspicuously.

Whether the cow calves in spring or autumn – autumn calvers give more milk, but are more expensive to feed – she will be pregnant for 9 months out of 12, lactating for 10 months, and for more than half the year she will be both pregnant and lactating. If she produces 4,500 litres in a lactation, a good average, she may yield up to 36 litres a day at her peak. She must be well fed.

For convenience, farmers consider the cow's diet in two compartments: what she needs to keep body and soul together (maintenance), and what she needs for production. She will get most of her energy from grass, fresh or conserved, but a modern animal at peak output simply cannot eat enough grass to meet her enormous energy needs. Her rumen is not big enough. So in addition to 'bulk' feeds she must be given 'concentrates', to top up her energy and protein without over-stuffing her.

In general, very good pasture can provide enough energy for maintenance, plus a yield of 18 litres. An average winter feed – 9kg of good hay plus 14kg of kale would be about right for a Friesian-sized cow – would provide enough for maintenance plus 4.5 litres. A cow yielding more than those bulk feeds can support needs about 350 grams of concentrate for every additional litre, made up, for example, of beans, oats and cattle cake. If the cow is yielding very heavily (say 27 litres a day, while being fed on hay and kale) then you might have to put her on a special diet: for example cut down the amount of hay and give a stronger concentrate, perhaps containing linseed.

So many ingredients may contribute to the concentrate, and fodder quality can vary so much, that it is hardly worth listing diets in detail. In general, a cow needs 6g of protein and 6.5g of starch equivalent per kilogram liveweight for maintenance, and 50g of protein and 250g of starch equivalent for every litre of milk. So a cow giving 27 litres a day needs about 5 times as much protein and $3\frac{1}{2}$ times as much energy as a dry cow. The bulk feed, which is cheapest, should supply as much nutrient as possible: it pays to make really nutritious hay or silage. Concentrates should be mixed cheaply from whatever is available, with the minimum imported ingredients.

Do not over-feed. A cow's yield potential is determined by her genes. If you feed the potential 22-litre cow only enough for 18 litres, she will at first milk 'off her back' – that is, she will grow thin – but in the end she will lose yield. However, you will not turn a 22-litre cow into a 27-litre cow simply by giving her an extra 1.5kg of concentrates. You will merely make her expensively and unproductively fat.

## Diseases

Dairy cows' diseases are of three types: infections, parasite infestations, and metabolic diseases.

With the exception of Johne's disease and the occasional epidemic of foot-and-mouth, the spectacular infections of dairy cattle are on the way out, although tuberculosis does still linger in the West Country, and brucellosis is not yet eradicated completely. The really invidious infection is mastitis. It is present in almost every herd and it reduces the yield from infected cows by an estimated 10 per cent. Yet the incidence of mastitis can be halved by simple hygiene. Wash the udders before milking, using disposable paper towels rather than ancient rags, and use a once-yearly, post-lactational antibiotic as a prophylactic. It is ludicrous to sink your capital in cows and their paraphernalia and then throw away a tenth of their produce for want of disinfectant.

At the other end of the scale, and increasingly common, are the 'metabolic' diseases, caused by trying to get too much out of the cow. Acetonaemia is among the most common, caused by feeding diets that are deficient in energy, so that the cow is forced to feed off her

# The Chemistry of a Cow

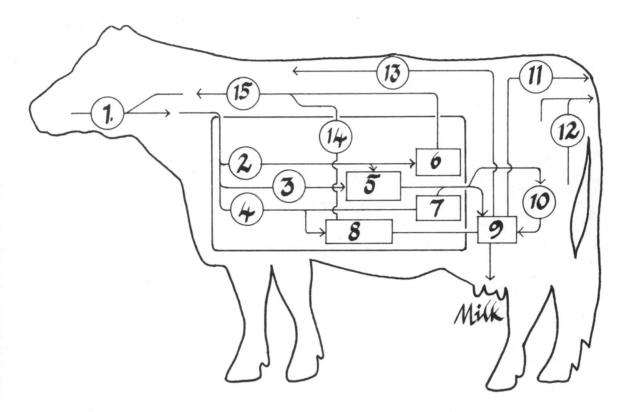

1 Food

2 Protein

3 Non-protein Nitrogen

4 Carbohydrates

5 Microbe Protein

6 Ammonia Gas

7 Starch

8 Volatile Fatty Acids

9 Liver

10 Amino Acid, Glucose, Fat

11 Urea-Urine N.

12 Undigested Protein &
   Carbohydrates excreted

13 Body Tissue & Fat Stores

14 Methane Gas

15 Gas Belched Out

own body fat. Fat breakdown products – ketones – accumulate in the blood and poison her. The treatment is to step up her energy intake, perhaps by resorting to molasses. Many farmers try instead to increase her protein intake, which makes the condition worse (see p.110 for an explanation of the 'protein fallacy', which applies to cows as much as to humans).

**Pregnancy**
The need to keep cows pregnant is obvious: miss one oestrus and you must wait three weeks for the next, which means three weeks' milk lost.

The good herdsman watches hard for signs of 'bulling' (sexual behaviour, including mounting of other cows) and some farmers run a 'teaser' bull with the cows – sometimes vasectomized – because he will be better than any human at identifying the cows in heat.

What of house cows? Maximizing the yield is less of a problem than disposing of the surplus. The chief dilemma is whether to go for the custom-built house cow, like the tiny Dexter, or a cull (probably a Jersey) from a commercial herd. We would plump for the latter. If you lack experience, at least the old cow will not!

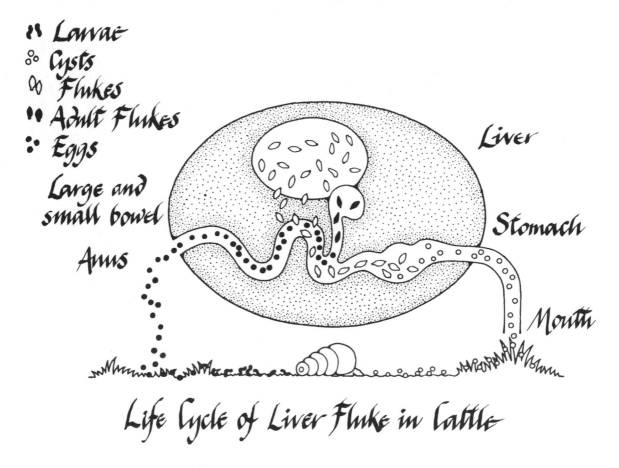

Life Cycle of Liver Fluke in Cattle

Liver fluke is most common in low-lying, wet land where there are muddy drinking places that favour the small snail without which the leaf-shaped fluke – in fact it is a worm – cannot survive. The fluke eggs leave the infected animal in its droppings. Where conditions are moist, the eggs hatch and the tiny larvae seek the snails *(Limnea truncatula),* penetrate their bodies, and eventually develop into a swarm of tadpole-like creatures. These emerge from the snails and attach themselves to damp grass, each 'tadpole' (cercaria) covering itself with a protective shield; each is about the size of a pinhead. When eaten by livestock, the protective covering is dissolved in the stomach, and the young flukes bore through the liver to the bile ducts, where they grow to maturity. Victims suffer from severe constipation, listlessness and anaemia, and they may die.

**Mastitis**

Mastitis is an inflammation of the udder that reduces milk secretion. It rarely causes the death of the animal, but it may occur in an acute or a chronic form. The inflammation is caused by infection by streptococci, staphylococci or other organisms. It can be treated successfully with modern drugs, but scrupulous attention to hygiene while milking and the segregation of affected animals keep the disease under control and prevent it spreading. However, for each cow with diagnosed acute mastitis there may be twenty with undiagnosed, chronic mastitis that is reducing milk yield. The presence of mastitis, and the extent of the infection, can be determined by counting the number of bacteria per millilitre of milk from samples taken over several months.

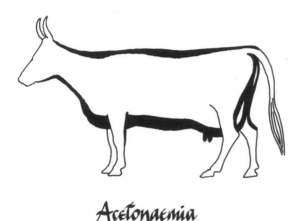

**Acetonaemia**

Acetonaemia, or ketosis, is most likely to affect dairy cows shortly after they have calved. The disease is similar in some ways to diabetes mellitus in humans. The acidity of the blood increases (acidosis), there is a fall in the sugar content of the blood to subnormal levels, and the metabolization of fats becomes abnormal. In effect, the animal is 'burning' body fat to provide it with the energy it needs, and breakdown products of its body fats (ketones) are causing poisoning. The disease is most likely after calving, because it is then that the cow's metabolism is under the greatest strain. The remedy – or better, the prevention – is to feed a diet containing more energy foods.

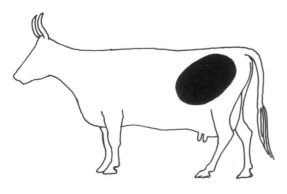

**Brucellosis**

Brucellosis, also called Bang's disease and contagious abortion, is caused by bacterial infection. It causes pregnant animals to abort and causes sterility. It can be transmitted to humans, in whom it used to be difficult to diagnose, causing fevers and other symptoms similar to those associated with more common complaints. In man the disease is called undulent fever. In many countries, including Britain, the disease is being eradicated. Herds are tested and if disease-free, they are so accredited. If the disease is found, a combination of improved hygiene, segregation of affected animals and vaccination is used until the herd can be accredited. After that, the import of non-accredited animals to the farm is forbidden.

# The house cow

The day you buy a milch animal is the day you take a leap into peasanthood. Vegetables you can abandon, chickens can get by on their own, but the ewe, the nanny or the cow need half an hour a day, every day. They need seasonal impregnation, fresh grazing, veterinary attention, and affection.

Goats and ewes seem less daunting than cows because they are smaller. However, cows' milk is more universally acceptable, cows, in general, are easier to fence and less destructive than goats, they can be served by artificial insemination (AI) by the bull of your choice, and they produce a saleable calf. Most home dairymen recommend starting with goats, to get the feel of things, but if you have grazing begin immediately with the cow.

What kind of cow? Generally speaking you have two choices. Either you can go for a specialist house-cow breed, able to live on the kind of rough and varied diet the extended gardener is liable to provide, or you can buy a cull from a commercial herd.

The specialist house cows include the Welsh Black (small and hardy, and bred originally for the hills), the Normande (an unspectacular, all-round, red-and-white peasant-style beast from France that is now being favoured increasingly), and the one that could be the ideal house cow, the Dexter.

We say 'ideal' because at first sight the Dexter has everything. It stands only one metre high. It eats almost anything, and only half as much as, say, a Friesian. It gives up to 20 litres of milk a day at its peak, though a more reasonable average would be 11–16 litres for a mature cow, and for a heifer about 4.5 litres less. Two cows are usually better than one: they like company, and if you get one to calve in autumn and one in spring, you will have milk all the year round; you can keep two Dexters for the cost of one conventional commercial cow. The calf is worth having if suitably sired, say by an Angus. It gives small joints, but of high quality.

Unfortunately, Dexters have suffered even more than most beasts from capricious breeding. They were bred largely as park animals, with heavy emphasis on colour and curvaceous horns (which in house cows should be polled) and without great attention to temperament. Many

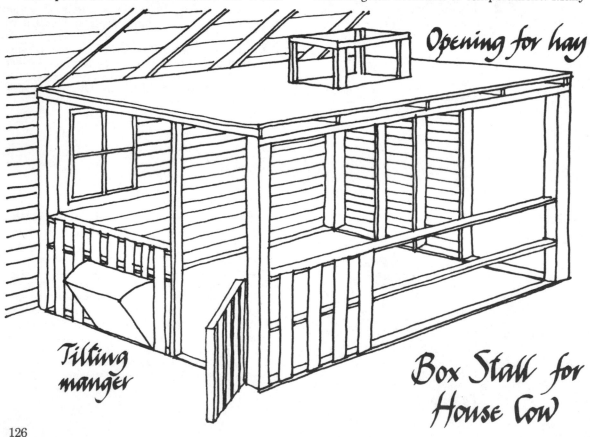

Opening for hay

Tilting manger

Box Stall for House Cow

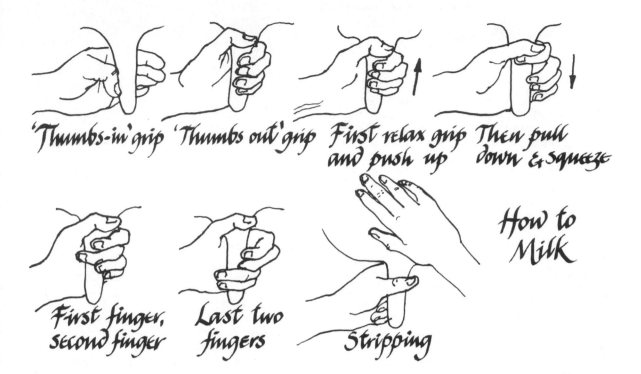

'Thumbs-in' grip   'Thumbs out' grip   First relax grip and push up   Then pull down & squeeze

First finger, second finger   Last two fingers   Stripping

How to Milk

owners have suffered from their temper, and they can show goat-like ingenuity in breaking out. Worst of all though is the possession, by many animals, of a dwarfing gene. This produces a charmingly small beast if inherited from only one parent (heterozygous) but an unviable, stunted monster – 'bulldog' – if inherited from both (homozygous).

Dexters need to be taken seriously. If you decide to invest in them it is well worth becoming involved in the Dexter Breed Society, and perhaps helping, by breeding from good bulls, to improve the type and so help this animal realize its smallholding potential.

Otherwise you should go for a commercial cull, remembering that cows are not culled simply because they are disease ridden or clapped out, but largerly as a matter of routine. Plenty of serviceable, experienced four-year olds go to the knackers that could give you eight or nine good milking years. The Jersey is the obvious choice. It is small, attractive, able at least to make do on inferior pasture, and it gives medium yields of outstanding milk. The advantage of obtaining from a cull, besides the cow's own experience and her tested temperament, is that by buying locally you can attune your annual calf production to the local market. If Charolais x Jerseys are fashionable, then you,

too, can sire with a Charolais. An Aberdeen x Dexter could cause too many raised eyebrows!

We cannot give full details of husbandry here, but some generalizations are in order. First, although the commercial 4,500-litre pedigree Friesian man may strive for a cow an acre (5 cows on 2 hectares), you should allow at least half a hectare, and preferably more, for your tiny Dexter (1–1½ acres); you are unlikely to maintain the grazing quality of the full-time professional. Secondly, ignore the suggestion that cows can be left out, day and night, summer and winter. An out-wintered beast can reduce small acreages to a quagmire, and to leave most breeds out in many parts of the country is simply cruel. Ignore, too, the suggestion that commercial milk may be full of antibiotics (it is not) but that the house cow owner can eschew such drugs. House cows get mastitis as much as do commercial herds. Summer mastitis in particular is serious and demands antibiotics, and antibiotic pessaries should be put in the teat, while the cow is dried off, as mastitis prophylaxis.

Finally, remember that even 16 litres a day is a lot of milk and you will probably not be allowed (officially) to sell it. You must relish making butter and cheese or have plenty of young livestock to utilize the surplus.

# Raising the calf

There are two reasons for raising calves: to provide heifer replacements for the dairy herd, and to produce young beeves. There are also two ways of raising them, each with scores of variations: one natural, where one or several beef calves suckle from their dam or foster mother; the other artificial, in which either replacement heifers or young beeves are fed from a bucket or machine from an early age.

Opinions differ as to whether beef and dairy replacements really have the same early requirements. The general feeling is that beeves should keep up a fairly spanking growth-rate from the beginning, but that the feeding of dairy replacements can afford to err towards parsimony. But calves, above all, are delicate. The overriding essential is to keep them alive and healthy. One death among a batch of ten calves will cost you far more than a small loss of growth-rate among all of them. Softly-softly is the motto with calves. Do simple things, and do them well.

Rule one is to allow all calves to be suckled by their mothers for the first two days of life, in order to obtain the first essential pre-milk – the colostrum. The colostrum contains antibodies, which give protection against many of the infections that the cow has met herself, and that her calf is liable to meet. The calf can absorb these antibodies only in its first 24–36 hours of life. You can feed colostrum from a bucket, but it is nothing like so satisfactory, first because calves have to learn to feed from a bucket, and they are unlikely to drink enough, and secondly because the colostrum is effective only if it passes to the particular compartment of the stomach called the abomasum. It will go to the abomasum if the calf suckles, but if it is forced to drink from a bucket the colostrum is liable to pass to the immature rumen, where its antibodies are wasted and where it is likely simply to cause inflammation (rumenitis).

What happens next depends on circumstances. In the specialist 'suckler' herds, the calves just stay with their dams until they are weaned; but cows with their own calves are of little use as commercial dairy animals, so this ultra-simple system is impractical unless you can justify keeping a cow for no purpose other than to produce one calf a year, and you will be able to justify this only if you are farming on marginal land. You can try to economize by fostering additional calves on to suckler cows, but you will need subtle, patient husbandmen and obliging animals – although many farmers do it, and succeed. If, as is likely, you have bought in the additional calves, you will have to find another way to raise them if the attempt fails.

Most calves are raised artificially. The variety of feeding regimes is legion, but here is a conventional twice-a-day routine that illustrates the principles. After the first two to four days of colostrum, feed whole milk; by the end of the week 3.5 litres should have been given. Increase the amount of milk and milk substitute that you feed by half a litre a week, until you are feeding 6.5 litres at 7 weeks. At this point, the milk ration levels out.

In the second week start offering hay, fresh water, and concentrates – as much as the calf will take. Wean the calf when it is consuming one kilogram of concentrate a day and not at any specific age, because calves of the same age vary greatly in vigour. After weaning, increase the amount of concentrate, giving the calf as much as it wants to eat, up to a maximum of 2.5kg, while continuing, of course, to give it hay and water.

### Where do the best calves come from?
The best place to get calves is from your own farm. You know their breeding, and you know that the antibodies they receive through the colostrum will be directed against whatever pathogens the calves actually do have to face – on your farm. You have control over their first few, vital days. You can see that they get the colostrum.

You can also dress the calves' navels. Some veterinary surgeons say this is unnecessary, but it takes less than 30 seconds, and closes off one of the chief routes by which pathogens enter the body. Why take chances? Soak a piece of string in disinfectant and tie it round the cord about 2cm from the body, squeezing out the jelly from the rest of the cord between your finger and thumb. Then rub, paint, or spray on iodine, or a similar antiseptic.

If you must buy in – as most beef farmers must – then inspect the calves very carefully. Begin at the rear end. Watch for scouring (diarrhoea). This may not be significant, but on

# Raising the Calf

1. Calf suckles from its mother for 2 days.

2. From 2 days feed whole milk rising to 3.5 litres after 7 days.

3. During 2nd week offer hay, water and concentrates.

4. Increase milk feed by ½ litre per week up to 6.5 litres at 2 weeks.

5. Wean calf when it is consuming 1 kg concentrate per day.

6. After weaning, increase concentrate up to 2.5 kg plus hay and water.

the other hand it could mean an infection with bacteria such as *Escherichia coli* or even salmonella, which is hard to eliminate and often fatal. Watch for the calf with no hair on its bottom. It may be a scourer that has been cleaned up. Reject calves that have wet, sticky, smelly, or painful navels. Give the calf a punch in the belly. All calves will jump when you do this (hardly surprising!), but those with sore navels will protest as well. Finally, watch the calf breathe. It should not pant, cough, or stand with its elbows out, and at full inspiration you should see its ribs. After scouring and 'naval ill', pneumonia is the third great calf problem.

If it is at all possible buy all your calves from the same source, and if one should die, never replace it or you will bring in new pathogens.

Always work on an 'all-in, all-out' basis, and between consignments scrub out the housing with a mild disinfectant such as sodium hydroxide. The key words here are 'scrub' and 'mild'. Do not simply splash on some coruscating antiseptic.

### Housing
Use your common sense. Warm housing is not necessary, but it is vital to avoid draughts and to reduce the humidity. Do not wash the place down too often, leaving wet, steaming passage-ways. Install good lighting – fluorescent bars are best, and cheapest to run – so that you can inspect your charges thoroughly and often.

It's all part of the first general principle: don't let them die.

# Raising beef

Successful beef production depends on giving the right kind of feed to the right kind of animal according to principles that run roughly as follows.

The growth of cattle is uneven. First the animals' bones develop (which is why they look so lanky when they are young); then they put on muscle (which becomes the butcher's meat); and then they lay down fat (giving the rounded contours that the butcher calls 'finish' and which help to make the meat more succulent). The aim is to produce a good-sized, meaty, but finished beast, using the minimum amount of feed.

This is where the complexities start. Animals grow only when their nutrient intake exceeds their maintenance requirement – that is, the amount of food they need just to stay alive. When they are fattening they need a particularly high excess of calories. In general, the more rapidly the animal grows the more economical it will be, for even if the beast were to stop growing, it would still feed for maintenance though it would not be increasing in value.

There are five conditional clauses, however, which together largely explain the rational basis of today's breeds and management systems (although there is also an irrational basis, based on the visual appeal of particular kinds of beast, and odd traditions of management). First, big breeds should, in theory, be more thrifty than small ones, since they are better able to conserve body heat, and therefore need less maintenance per unit of body weight. On the other hand – second point – a ruminant's feed intake is determined by the size of its rumen. It can eat only to capacity. If the fodder is too low-grade, then even the full rumen may not supply the animal with enough nutrient for rapid growth, let alone for fattening. In general, the small, barrel-bodied breeds (the Aberdeen Angus is the supreme example) seem better able to flourish on low-grade forage than big breeds, and they will fatten on land where the Charolais, for example, would remain incorrigibly rangy. However – third point – if you raise small breeds on very high-grade feed they will start fattening before they have achieved a worthwhile body size – in the case of the Angus, producing what one farmer contemptuously termed 'black mice'. It is a waste of time feeding an animal after it has grown fat. So, although rapid growth is

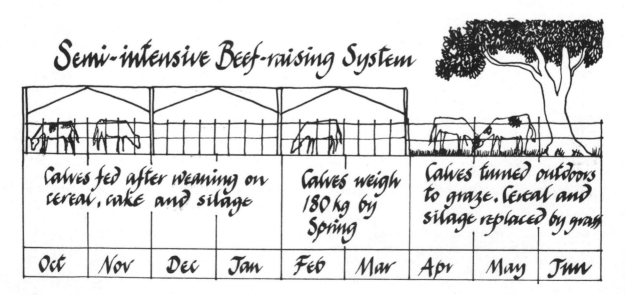

Semi-intensive Beef-raising System

| Oct | Nov | Dec | Jan | Feb | Mar | Apr | May | Jun |
|---|---|---|---|---|---|---|---|---|
| Calves fed after weaning on cereal, cake and silage | | | | Calves weigh 180 kg by Spring | | Calves turned outdoors to graze. Cereal and silage replaced by grass | | |

desirable, over-energetic feeding can, paradoxically, produce an uneconomically small carcass – uneconomic, that is, compared with the initial cost of the calf.

Then again – point four – breeding overlies mere thermodynamics. Hence we find that the light-heavyweight, long-boned Friesian produces fast-growing, useful beef calves; the Ayrshire, which superficially seems only a little more delicate, produces inferior beef calves.

Finally – point five – all livestock farming depends on what feed is available. Though rapid growth is desirable, it is rarely worth trying to produce extra-rapid growth by feeding expensive concentrate. Feed supply is, of course, largely seasonal, and so too is the supply of beef calves, most of which are now derived from the dairy herd.

Thus we see that there is a whole range of breeds and crosses slotted into a range of feeding systems. The most intensive is the 'all-concentrate system', developed in the 1960s, in which Friesian bull calves from the dairy herd are fed more or less exclusively on a barley-based diet, and killed at 10–12 months of age, when they weigh 350–400kg. But 'barley beef' may well have run its course, partly because barley is no longer cheap, but also because calves are now too expensive to be killed when they are only three-quarters grown.

Semi-intensive systems are much more common now: indeed, they are the norm. These are based on grass feeding, to produce a finished beast in 18 months. The calf from a Friesian cow and Hereford bull is most popular, partly because it is the ideal size and weight for the rich, but not over-rich feed, and partly because its black body and white face make it easy to recognize (so the farmer knows what he is buying). However, Friesians crossed with Charolais, or a red breed, or even Ayrshire crosses, or Jersey x Charolais, all fit into the semi-intensive system.

The calf born in autumn, preferably before the end of October, spends its first winter indoors, being fed after weaning on cereal, cake, silage and swedes (if they are available) to achieve a weight of 180kg by the following spring. Then it is turned out to graze, on short, leafy grass that has not been grazed by cattle during the previous 12 months. The turning out should be gradual. Offer the calves a full feed each day before they are turned out, and increase the time they spend on the grass gradually, until the nights are warm enough for the steers to remain out permanently.

By early September you should be thinking about bringing the beasts in at night. By October they are indoors again, penned if possible in groups of 10 to 12 and matched for sex, size and condition. This second winter they are fed on grass silage and barley, the barley adjusted to maintain a daily liveweight gain of 1 kilogram. Their weight, at slaughter in the spring, is between 430 and 545kg, depending on their breed.

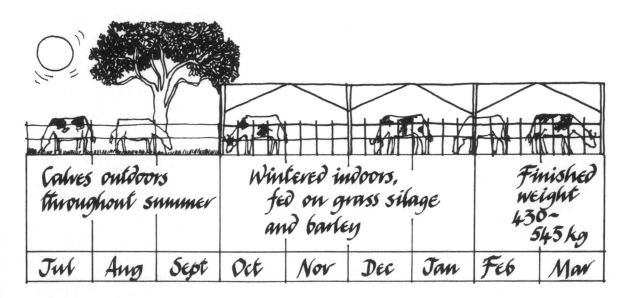

| Calves outdoors throughout summer | | | Wintered indoors, fed on grass silage and barley | | | | Finished weight 430–545 kg | |
|---|---|---|---|---|---|---|---|---|
| Jul | Aug | Sept | Oct | Nov | Dec | Jan | Feb | Mar |

# Goats

Some people keep goats as an apprenticeship to cows. Others just like them – for their keen personality, their ability to forage in wasteland or on kitchen scraps, and their modest yield if you milk them twice a day, all of which corresponds roughly with the requirements of a family. The 'goaty' smell and taste of their milk is said to be associated largely with poor hygiene and diet, or mastitis, and is therefore avoidable (you will taint cow's milk, too, if you feed her badly). Their kids, produced once yearly or once every two years, are as good as lean young lamb if they are killed at 10–12 weeks.

### What is a good goat?
The first problem is to get a good goat. You could go for an unregistered, euphemistically termed 'British' goat of indeterminate breed, which may yield well and should not cost too much, so that early amateurish mistakes seem less disastrous. Or you could go for a recognized breed. This seems to be the best course, since the initial cost of the beast will not be great compared with the cost of its necessary housing, equipment, and feed, and there is nothing so wasteful as husbandry squandered on an animal

that is unable to yield above a litre, when you should be getting four litres or more. On the other hand, milkiness is a highly individual thing. Breed does not guarantee yield, and no one will sell you a beast whose thriftiness is proven.

Anyway, the Saanen, or British Saanen, Toggenburg, or British Toggenburg, British Alpine, Anglo-Nubian and Golden Guernsey all have reputations as good milkers. The sweet-tempered Saanen, originally from Switzerland, are white, and probably they are the goats you see most frequently. The brown and white Toggenburgs are best suited, as goats go, to a high-grass diet, and so they are useful in permanent, fenced pasture. The British Alpine is a great forager, allegedly a devourer of nettles, and is rough and tough. The Anglo-Nubian is tall, floppy-eared, temperamental and multi-coloured, and it gives high-quality milk, though not a large amount in relation to its size. Golden Guernseys are small, pretty, versatile and thrifty. One or other of these breeds will suit most needs.

### Feeding
Feed them whatever you are able to provide. Give them grass, obviously, but not too much, except perhaps with Toggenburgs. Between one-tenth and one-fifth of a hectare of grazing is a

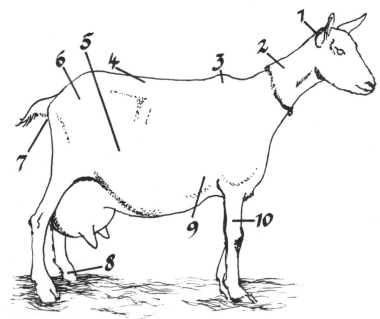

*Good Points in a Goat*
1. *Head; shapely, intelligent*
2. *Neck; long, not coarse*
3. *Shoulders; neat*
4. *Back; long and level*
5. *Ribs; deep, well sprung*
6. *Pelvis; wide*
7. *Escutcheon; wide*
8. *Feet; sound and neat*
9. *Body; deep*
10. *Forelegs; straight*

useful base. Comfrey and all conventional forages are good staples, and they like herbs. Gorse and heather go down well, brewers grains, barley straw, pea haulms and sugar beet pulp – indeed, whatever local food factories have to offer – are all appreciated, as are household scraps. However, the stuff must be nutritious. David Mackenzie, in *Goat Husbandry* (see p.170), suggests that a goat needs 40g a day of starch equivalent and 4g of digestible protein per 10kg body weight for maintenance, and a further 325g of starch equivalent and 50g of digestible protein per day per litre of milk. In practice, the animal might consume about 9kg of grass and 4.5kg of mixed scrub in a day, or 2–4.5kg of heather tips, and you must then work out (from tables) what the food value is and add concentrate of known composition accordingly to match her needs, bearing in mind, as with dairy cows, that an underfed beast cannot yield her full potential, but that overfeeding will not turn a 2-litre a day beast into one that gives 4 litres. A typical feed in winter (from September until kidding in March) might be 2.5kg of good hay a day and a stockfeed turnip for maintenance, with a kilo a day of concentrate for animals milking more than 2.5 litres. The feed combinations are infinite though, and individuals vary greatly in size and yield, so in the end their rations will be balanced by your experience, the advice you receive, guesswork, and the Ministry of Agriculture leaflets that tell you how much of each nutrient there is in the hundred different things that goats eat. No matter what they eat, you should always provide them with a salt lick.

The omnivorousness of the goat is its greatest asset. The adventurousness that inevitably accompanies this is your bane. Hedges they climb, stone walls are for exercise: the only things that will hold them are the electric fence or the tether. The fence is better, but the goat must be trained to it. Get someone to hold the top strand in its mouth while you give it three or four shocks. Then don't ever let that person near the goat again! Tethers usually need moving twice a day, but try slinging the tether, swivelled like a dog lead, not from a single post but from a wire stretched above head height between two posts. This gives the goat a bigger grazing area, with each grazed patch oblong rather than circular, which is a much more economical shape for most fields.

### Housing

Housing is essential, for most nights and for the whole winter. It can be as simple as you like, provided it is warm and strong. A concrete floor is adequate, without straw, if it is insulated with polystyrene, although there is nothing so good as dunged straw for compost. The feed should be presented in racks, for the animals to browse.

Those are the main principles. Consider a goat if you have a fifth of a hectare, or masses of time to forage on their behalf. But do nothing without consulting the British Goat Society (see p.170).

## Goat Stalls

Stall Front

Hayrack from Inside Stall

# Sheep

## Why can't a sheep be more like a pig?

Sheep have so many disadvantages it is difficult to see why anybody bothers to keep them, and it is all too easy to understand their Cinderella status that has persisted throughout this century. While the sow justifies her cost with 20 or so piglets per year, and dairy cows provide most of the country's beef herd merely as a bonus to their milk, the ewe tries to pay for herself with a meagre one or two lambs, and until recently even these had to compete with under-priced imports from New Zealand. Her fleece is a useful perk, if it is kept and sold clean, but it cannot compensate for her fundamental lack of output.

Even to obtain this paltry return involves skilful and subtle management. For example, suppose that your hill flock produces only 80 lambs per 100 ewes (a 'lambing percentage' of

80). You decide to increase the percentage to 100 – one lamb for every ewe. This might seem modest enough, but you are bound to lose some lambs at birth and others by abortion, some ewes inevitably will be barren (the national average is 6 per cent), and rams are notoriously fickle studs. So you will average one lamb per ewe only if some ewes produce twins. Then the problems start. On poor pasture a ewe may have trouble feeding two lambs, and if she does she may lose too much condition to face the following winter. So, if you are to avoid losing the mother, you must try to foster the second of each pair of twins on to ewes that have lost their lambs, or raise the lambs by hand. Both operations are tricky. The lowland farmer, aiming for two lambs per ewe – 200 per cent – has the same problem with the third of each set of triplets. There *are* ways around such problems. You can use particularly milky ewes, you can improve the quality of hill grazing, and you can raise all the lambs artificially in a more or less automated unit (at present there is much research on artificial milks for lambs). All you are doing, however, is raising the problem of

maintaining a steady output to a new conceptual level.

The second great drawback to sheep is disease and parasite infestation. Foot-rot and round-worms can spread so rapidly that there is a saying that 'a sheep's worst enemy is another sheep'. This complicates efforts to intensify. Liver fluke, which recently was the target of a grandiose eradication campaign, is none the less likely to remain in the wetlands for ever. In the hills, sheep are prone to attack from the green-bottle fly, *Lucilia*, whose larvae, emerging from eggs laid around the tail and back, can eat the sheep alive – literally. Fly 'strike' is a major reason why annual sheep dipping is compulsory, and now that the persistent and toxic dieldrin has been banned from sheep dips, dipping has once again become technically critical. The new dips, based on organophosphorus compounds (see p.32) are effective only if the dip bath concentration is maintained carefully and if the sheep are immersed for at least 30 seconds (which seems an awfully long time when you come to do it). Even despite rigorous dipping, many hill flocks are being struck now almost as badly as they were in the pre-dieldrin days.

## Swings and roundabouts

You may be tempted to ask, why bother? Well, sheep have some advantages too. First, and above all, they are versatile. There are almost 40 breeds of sheep in Britain, a number that reflects partly the versatility of the sheep but partly too the primitive state of sheep breeding, that has allowed so many local whims to be indulged (all the breeds are descended from a common wild ancestor, after all).

They are divisible into three main categories, that are almost as different from one another as if they were distinct species. The hill and moorland breeds, such as the Blackface, Cheviot and Welsh Mountain, are closer to the wild state than any other conventional livestock. Their breeding has been concerned mainly with survival, and their biology – a late, limited breeding season, and loss of appetite in winter – reflects this primitive adaptation to a hard life.

The big, longwool types, like Border Leicester and Romney Marsh, are often crossed with smaller types to produce fast-growing lambs.

The shortwool types, including the down breeds like Southdown and Dorset Horn, are traditionally associated with the fairly low-grade, but steady, pasture of the grass downlands.

Of course, they are *not* separate species, and indeed the sheep industry is based on interplay among the three. Lambs born on the hill are brought to the lowlands for fattening. More subtly, small, hill-bred ewes are brought to the lowlands to cross with a large ram, like a Border Leicester, to produce big-bodied, fast-growing lambs.

The second advantage of sheep is that they are excellent grass managers, a valuable asset now that cheap cereal surpluses seem to have passed into history. Their grazing keeps the scrub from the hills, and it is often said that the heavily subsidized hill farmers have been employed largely as park keepers. The astonishingly rich flora of the downs – not to mention the characteristic landscape – is doomed wherever sheep and rabbits have disappeared, unless the invading scrub is kept back by human hands. Sheep show many advantages on both temporary leys and permanent pastures. The feed requirement of ewe-plus-lamb follows closely the growth curve of the grass. Sheep are light on their feet and so are less inclined to poach. This means that they can be left out longer than cattle, and therefore need less concentrate and conserved feed, and their close, assiduous grazing (they nibble) complements that of cattle, which tear at mouthfuls of long grass. Mixed cattle and sheep grazing used to be common, and now more and more farmers are looking at it again. When grass is slack, sheep are readily folded on kale, turnips, or other catch crops, and they can improve winter corn if they are given an early bite at it in the spring.

Their third advantage is that they are cheaper to buy, house and feed than cattle – although, as we shall see (p.138), the higher-cost, higher-output sheep enterprise is likely to prove ever more viable.

Finally, almost as a postscript, milch sheep, such as the Friesland, make excellent 'house cows'.

Sheep have a bright future.

Border Leicester

Romney

Dorset Down

Shropshire

# Origin of Breeds of Sheep

1 Scotch Black face
2 Border Leicester
3 Cheviot
4 Herdwick
5 Rough Fell
6 Swaledale
7 Wensleydale
8 Louk
9 Derbyshire Gritstone
10 Leicester
11 Lincoln Longwool
12 Shropshire
13 Kerry Hill
14 Clun Forest
15 Radnor Forest
16 Ryland
17 Oxford
18 Welsh Mountain
19 Suffolk
20 Exmoor Horn
21 Wiltshire
22 Dorset Horn
23 Horned Hampshire
24 Kent
25 Dartmoor
26 Devon Longwool
27 Dorset Down
28 South down
29 Devon Closewool
30 South Devon

# How to make money from sheep

Because the traditional and natural role of sheep is to sweep up – on marginal grazing, stubble or catch crops – and because returns have rarely justified heavy investment, sheep husbandry has remained the least industrialized and hence the least systematized of all the major livestock enterprises.

So sheep still offer endless scope for opportunism, and for juggling with the many variables that affect output. In theory, you can settle for a low-input, low-output enterprise (the usual kind of sheep enterprise) or you can step up the housing, breeding, husbandry, and veterinary care and hope to recoup the cost with higher returns.

In practice, rising fixed costs, notably of land, are forcing the farmers' hands. The typically depressed flock, with toothless ewes living on the subsidy and barely surviving the winter, and with a lambing percentage of around 60, is doomed, while the new markets for lamb offered by the Common Market are beginning to justify the costs of the high-powered outfit. So let's look at the factors that maximize output.

Welsh Mountain Ewe

×

Suffolk Ram

Lamb achieves 'E' value of 7·1

**E**

The key to any successful livestock enterprise is 'biological efficiency' – what scientists at the Grassland Research Institute, Hurley, Berkshire, call 'E'. E means output over input expressed as a percentage. Output means the weight of lamb produced; input (in this strictly biological context) means the weight of feed consumed by those lambs, and by their dam.

The target is to increase output in relation to input. The difficulty is that the ewe produces so few offspring (compared with a pig or a rabbit) that her own feed cost is a major component of the input. This gives us two choices. Either we increase the number of lambs produced per ewe – which explains the modern interest in breeds like the Finnish Landrace, that may produce five lambs at a time – or we induce ewes to produce big, fast-growing lambs. This is done mainly by crossing small ewes with big rams.

Which is better? Should we concentrate on producing highly prolific ewes, or settle for less prolific animals producing big lambs? Well, the Hurley scientists have worked this out on purely theoretical grounds, assuming grass feeding, and have shown that the small ewe producing big lambs is the better bet. Thus if a small Welsh Mountain ewe (weighing 35kg) is crossed with a big Suffolk ram (weighing 100kg) and produces a single lamb (whose size will be between that of dam and sire), it achieves an overall E value of 7.1 (per cent). A Scotch Halfbred ewe (weighing 75kg) would give an E value of only 5.1 if she produced a single lamb from the same sire, and would only get up to 7.0 if she produced twins. The Welsh Mountain producing twins from the Suffolk reaches an E value of 8.7, while the Scotch Halfbred achieves only 8.1, even by producing triplets. In short, say the Hurley scientists, the man who could guarantee 200 per cent lambing from a Welsh Mountain flock could be rich.

In reality though, as we have seen, you cannot achieve 200 per cent lambing without producing a high proportion of triplets. So perhaps the commercial ewe for the 1980s should be the smallest animal that is capable of producing and rearing decent-sized triplets. She will be a milky beast, probably weighing around 55kg, and roughly the size of the Kerry Hill.

**Stocking density**

Biological efficiency is only part of the story.

Land is now expensive, so we must maximize output per hectare as well as output per ewe. Or rather, we must strike a balance between the two, because if we overcrowd we will depress individual performance.

Stocking density depends on the quality of the land. Strong land can take more punishment, and produce more, than light land can. Having made that generalization, however, we are back to juggling variables.

If you house for a long time in winter you can stock more heavily, since the grass has more time to recover, but you must feed more conserved feed and concentrates. If you stock heavily you must fertilize the ground well; you must also keep the sheep on the move assiduously, by using hurdles or movable fences to contain them in paddocks, moved on regularly, or by some other means. Good farmers have shown that strong land might take 15 or even 17 ewes a hectare, while 10 is probably enough for light land.

Whether you go for the highest density possible, or leave some leeway, depends largely on whether you have some reserve resource you can use in an emergency, such as an orchard, where you can siphon off a surplus of animals. You must maintain E. It costs almost as much to keep ewes averaging 1.3 lambs as it does to keep ewes that average 1.9, yet the difference in output is nearly 50 per cent.

There you have it. The successful lowland sheep farmer of the 1980s will produce up to 30 lambs a hectare, with 15 ewes lambing around 200 per cent. Few flocks today get above half this output; but then there are few flocks today that pay their way.

# The sheep of the future

The husbandry of sheep is changing more quickly and more radically than that of any other class of livestock. It is as though sheep had been held back in the eighteenth century by depressed markets and low inputs, and then, suddenly, they had been released, to hurtle into the twentieth century.

Their unrealized potential is enormous. The Finnish Landrace is only one of several breeds (the Chios of Greece is another) with the potential for astonishing prolificacy. The feral Soay sheep of the Hebrides, linear descendant of

*Soay Sheep*

Britain's first domesticated sheep, dating from Neolithic times, produces the largest lamb in relation to the size of the ewe of all sheep. Perhaps this talent could be exploited, so justifying the faith shown by many enthusiasts in ancient breeds as sources of potentially useful genes. The Friesland sheep is now being imported for its milkiness, which is a great asset not only to milch sheep enthusiasts (it can yield up to 4 litres a day) but is essential if, as seems desirable, lambs born in litters are to be reared by their dams.

Sheep gestate for only five months, and yet have only one pregnancy a year; and most breeds refuse to come into season except for a few weeks in autumn, which leads to a spring birth. Yet there are a few kinds – notably the Dorset Horn – that can be coaxed into heat more readily. This ability is being exploited already by autumn-lambing enthusiasts, but, more radically, it raises the possibility of producing more than one litter a year.

Accordingly, we find the Animal Breeding Research Organization at Edinburgh producing the ABRO Dam Line, a marriage of Finn (prolificacy), East Friesland (milkiness), Dorset Horn (out of season breeding and good conformation), and Border Leicester (good shape and high growth potential). This line is to be crossed with hill breeds to produce small, cross-bred ewes that will produce fast-growing, meaty lambs for fattening on the lowlands. Perhaps the sluggishness of the past will prove to be an asset, as breeders can now apply to a vast range of genes breeding techniques and performance tests not formerly available.

### 'Broiler' lambs

As we have seen, scientists at Hurley suggest that it is better to get a few large lambs from small ewes than to get a lot of lambs from a large ewe. Scientists at the Rowett Research Institute in Aberdeen put the equation the other way round. They point out that the more prolific the ewe, the less of a disadvantage is her bulk. Mainly for future reference, they are seeking to discover just how many lambs a ewe can produce and rear. They use Finn x Dorset ewes, which are both prolific and easy to bring into heat. They coax them into heat by keeping them indoors and gradually reducing the artificial day-length, thus simulating the shortening days of autumn that provide the natural stimulus to oestrus. They contrive to synchronize the ewes' oestrus by fitting them with pessaries containing the hormone progesterone. These are inserted two weeks before tupping (copulation). The Rowett scientists have shown that if they are fed properly, ewes can give birth at seven-month intervals, with the outstanding beasts raising four lambs each per year.

Such extreme output – which justifies the tag of 'broiler lamb' – may be impossible to achieve, and may not be worth while commercially. After all, the high-grade, high-concentrate feed that it requires may not be available in the future, and to take sheep off grass seems to negate their greatest attribute. All the same the research is valuable, because not only does it show that even today's crosses can out-produce the average commercial flock by a cool 300 per cent, but also it is pioneering techniques that more conventional farmers could incorporate usefully.

The trend is definitely towards winter housing, with earth floors and straw bales, which are quite adequate; so why not use artificial light to influence the ewes' breeding cycles? A seven-month lambing interval is hard to achieve and is an awkward period, but why not try for eight-month intervals, giving two litters every three years?

Such short birth intervals demand early weaning – roughly at 28 days, but the lamb's consumption of forage is a better guide to its readiness for weaning than its age. Early weaning is useful in other ways: it makes life easier for the ewe that is producing triplets or quads, for example.

## Improving the grass

At the other end of the scale, scientists at the Hill Research Organization at Edinburgh are showing that hill grazing can be improved greatly, not by replacing all the heather with grass (which is expensive) but merely by replacing *some* of the heather. The point is that sheep will not thrive if more than one-third of their diet is heather. This means that if you increase the amount of grass, the sheep are able to eat more heather.

They have shown, too, that up to a point (the point at which it is over-grazed) herbage is improved by being grazed. Indeed, understocked grass deteriorates, because the uneaten grass dies down to form a mat of dead and indigestible material that inhibits the spring growth of new grass. The cure is to stock more densely. So, the grass and the heather grow more succulently, the scrub and the bracken are kept at bay.

You may feel that in talking about sheep we have talked too much science. This is unavoidable, because much of current practice is anachronistic; it may be romantic (until you try to do it for a living) but much of it is no more than the residue of generations of economic depression. If you begin to farm sheep now – and, as we have said, they could be the animals of the future – you must do so in the spirit of research.

Lamb Quads with a Dorset Ewe

# The pig revolution

A standard agricultural textbook published in the mid 1950s lists 9 of the 13 recognized British pig breeds as being of particular commercial importance. The outstanding pork breeds (that is, the middle-sized animals) were the Middle White and the Berkshire. The former was thought to be descended from a cross of the Large White and the Small Yorkshire; the latter was said to be not too prolific and a bit slow growing, but a neat, blocky shape and a good grazer.

The dual-purpose animals, giving good pork if killed young but growing into big, high-quality baconers, were the Essex and Wessex, the Large Black, the Long White Lop-eared, and the Gloucester Old Spot. The Essex and Wessex, both black with a white saddle, were quaintly and irrelevantly distinguished by the colour of their back feet (black in Wessex, white in Essex) and both were hardy and prolific. The Large Black was an old breed, 'reasonably prolific', docile and good for outdoors, while the Lop, too, was a hardy outdoor grazing beast. The Gloucester Old Spot – black spots on a white background – was known as the 'orchard pig',

142

after its liking for windfalls. It did not grow too fat.

The big, specialized baconers included the Welsh (which was like the Large Black, only white), the Tamworth, which, with its chestnut pelt, most closely resembled the first domestic pigs of Neolithic man, and the Large White, alias Yorkshire. The Swedish Landrace was just creeping into this textbook. Its length and leanness made it an outstanding baconer. Many Large White breeders objected to this interloper: they believed that their own pigs were just as good.

The text is only two decades old, but it reads like ancient history. Of those nine natives, only the Large White now contributes significantly to the modern high-technology pig industry. The Landrace has remained, not to compete with the Large White, but to complement it. Crosses of the two have hybrid vigour, and may show greater mothering ability, fertility and fecundity, and rear more piglets to weaning, than either pure breed. These two have been joined by the Hampshire, originally from that English county but now hailing from America, to produce triple crosses of still greater vigour. Finally, the big Pietrain, from Belgium, has been on the edge of the British pig scene throughout the 1970s, but its meat quality remains suspect – it tends to be pale and watery. Hybridization is now the rage, although the advantage of the first-generation cross poses the pig farmer with a dilemma. Hybrids can produce an extra $1\frac{1}{2}$ piglets per sow per year, but their progeny are not hybrids, they are second generation. Should the farmer buy in fresh breeding sows for each new cycle from specialist breeders, or raise his own replacements from their progeny and sacrifice the hybrid vigour?

Three major trends have been superimposed on this minutely quantified genetic development. At the over-all commercial level, a move to 'vertical integration' has tended to link the whole operation, from the production of breeding stock to processing and marketing, under a single management. This has made it increasingly difficult for the small man, or mixed farmer, running a few breeding sows as a sideline, to latch on to this production line.

Secondly, the pigs' environment has become more and more controlled. The animals are often kept entirely indoors in air-conditioned houses, and the old-fashioned variables of fodder beet and grass have been exchanged for a diet based on computer-controlled compounds of the cheapest available cereals and protein supplements.

Thirdly, producers are manipulating the fundamental biology of the pig more and more, in order to produce more progeny per year.

The logic runs as follows: a breeding sow gets through about a tonne of feed a year, and there is not much room for economy, but you can get more for your money by increasing her output of live offspring. There are three ways to approach this. You can get the sow to produce bigger litters, you can induce her to give birth more often, or you can reduce or eliminate the 17–30 per cent mortality experienced among piglets in the first 8 weeks and especially in the first 3 days.

Producing bigger litters is mainly a matter of breeding.

You can get more litters by early weaning. A sow gestates for $3\frac{1}{2}$–4 months. Traditionally she was allowed to suckle for 8 weeks. Two weeks later she went back to the boar, giving a $6\frac{1}{2}$-month cycle, or two litters in 13 months.

The reduction of weaning to 5 or 6 weeks, allowing two litters per year, is now fairly common, but the technocrats are envisaging separation at birth. They say that greater biological efficiency could be achieved by raising the piglets on artificial milk, since this would avoid the biologically wasteful conversion of feed to milk by the sow. What is more, the smaller pigs of the litter (the runts), which are the ones that suffer the mortality at present, would survive because they would be spared competition. The sow would be spared the physiological burden of lactation, which is a greater strain than pregnancy, and theoretically she could produce three litters a year.

At present, most sows produce only 15 piglets a year, which can barely give a profit. Twenty a year – two litters of 10 – is still considered a good target. Tomorrow's sows could, if the technical problems are solved, produce 30–32 piglets a year, and the total feed consumption, per kilogram liveweight of 8-week-old piglets, would be only half what it is at present.

The pig industry is moving, and fast. If you think it is too industrialized already, or too callous, or too profligate in its use of energy and capital, it could be that you ain't seen nothing yet!

# The pig subculture

Does the technological pig, which we have just examined briefly, really represent the future? Or is it already an anachronism? After all, the pig has three great agricultural assets: it is a scavenger, a cultivator and, because it suffers from diseases and parasites quite different from those of other livestock, it can follow them on to land and be followed by them. All of these assets are squandered in the factory, and perhaps in the years to come we will not be able to be so extravagant.

The pig can utilize swill, made from both household and farmyard wastes and by-products. It will eat plate-scrapings, whey from the home cheese-making, apple windfalls and sugar beet pulp.

As a forager, grazer and copious excretor, the pig is Nature's outstanding cultivator. Iron Age farmers may well have used the rooting pig as much as they used the plough. An area ploughed by pigs is called a 'pannage', and John Seymour, in *The Fat of the Land,* relates how he induced pigs to do his digging, weeding and fertilizing merely by planting Jerusalem artichokes and letting the pigs loose to eat the tops and then the roots. (Don't expect too much, though: pigs will not get rid of *all* the weeds.)

Pigs do not suffer from the same parasites as sheep, cattle or poultry. This means that in theory they can be used to graze and fossick land which, after re-sowing, would be fit for sheep or calves.

Tomorrow's farm may not after all be the factory, which though it is profitable is also very precarious economically. It may be the highly technical, tightly integrated, mixed farm or smallholding. In this setting, the 'natural' – or at least biologically recognizable – pig could play a crucial role.

This does not imply that we necessarily revert to any of the traditional breeds, even though they did evolve in the setting of a mixed farm. Our forebears were too concerned with the colour and the shape of the ear. Tomorrow's custom-bred smallholding pig could be as different from, say, the Gloucester Old Spot as is the modern suburban cabbage from its expansive progenitors.

## Feeding

Let's get back to first principles, from which all systems, from the backyard pen to the factory, are extrapolated.

In practice, the fundamental pig feed is cereal. The in-pig sow should receive 2.3–2.7kg a day, containing roughly half barley meal and half wheatings, and the whole raised to a 10 per cent protein level with fishmeal, meat meal, soya or one of the modern microproteins, such as BP's

*The Pig as a Cultivator*
*Land ploughed by pigs is called a 'pannage'*

Toprina or ICI's Protena. Older textbooks recommend 14–15 per cent protein for the pregnant sow, but this is no longer considered necessary. An in-pig sow can also take up to two-thirds of her ration as green forage. A nursing sow can take up to half.

When she is lactating, the sow's feed requirements increase. The fast-growing sucking pigs take more out of her, and metabolically the conversion of feed to milk is less efficient than pushing it through a placenta. Typically, you might allow the sow one kilogram a day of cereal-based feed for her own maintenance, plus half a kilo a day for each sucking pig, but never less than 2.7kg a day, or more than 6.5kg.

Some young pigs start showing interest in feed at two to three weeks. They should be encouraged to go on to solids as soon as possible. After weaning, they receive the same kind of cereal-based diet as the sow: about 2kg a day up to roughly 45kg liveweight, increasing to 2.25–2.75kg until they reach 70kg, and 2.75–3kg at 80–90kg. Of course, we are talking here of equivalents. If you feed potatoes, whey, catch-crops, swill or the hundred other things that pig flesh is heir to, then you must get out your pocket calculator and adjust accordingly. All you need to remember is that pigs are not ruminants. Their diet needs to be reasonably concentrated.

**Housing**

Pigs like to be outdoors. Raising them indoors, on concrete, as is now general, can create nutritional and behavioural problems. However, they do not like cold, and even though they may endure it, their growth wiii be retarded because they will waste energy keeping warm. Young pigs in particular need a temperature of around 30°C. The introduction of infra-red lamps for young weaners in the 1950s reduced mortality greatly.

The house can be as simple as you like. Walls can be made from straw sandwiched between wire netting, the roof can be of corrugated iron insulated with straw, and you can give them masses of straw to sleep on. Whatever it is, you must provide shelter, and it must be warm, dry and cosy. The best kind of house is some kind of mobile or removable structure. Keep the animals moving, and if they return to the same piece of land only every three or four years half your disease problems are solved, and the fertility of your land can be greatly enhanced.

A word of warning, however. The present economic climate does not favour the smallholding or mixed-farm pig. In the early 1970s, pig enterprises were folding at the rate of a hundred a week as the integrated production lines gathered momentum. For the time being, smallholders should stick to raising a few weaners for family and friends, or possibly for the gourmet market. The tide may turn. The technological pig may not be the ultimate end of pig farming. After all, it is no more than a product of a technological age.

The Pig as a Scavenger

apple windfalls

sugar beet pulp

whey

household scraps

# Wild genes in old stock

The first domestic animals must have been selected – or have selected themselves – largely on the basis of temperament. Beasts that could not be tamed, even by hand-rearing, had no place on a neolithic farm. This must have been especially true of cattle which, in the wild, are large, dangerous animals, shy of man and with an uncertain temper. The wild ancestor of all domestic cattle, the aurochs (*Bos primigenius*) has been extinct for centuries, but where domesticated cattle have been allowed to revert to a wild existence many of their old traits have reappeared. The first cattle to be tamed were probably the calves brought back to the village after their mothers had been killed. The adults that were caught alive were probably the smaller, weaker, slower members of the herd, and an early result of domestication was a marked reduction in size.

The qualities that the modern farmer desires above all others, prolificacy and a rapid rate of growth, must have been low on the selection list drawn up by the first farmers. They could not have handled voracious, promiscuous beasts even if they had possessed them. So the modern breeder is greatly inhibited. He must strive to develop qualities in animals that were selected originally for quite different characteristics.

We could simply go back to the wild and start new strains of domestic livestock based on beasts that really can grow fast and reproduce, but although wild animals are useful in several specific contexts (see p.150), they can rarely replace the established species that have been bred to respond to husbandry for the last 10,000 years. Dr R. V. Short, director of the Medical Research Council's Unit of Reproductive Biology at Edinburgh, has suggested an exciting compromise. If we cannot simply tame wild beasts, why should we not borrow their most desirable genes and breed them into the beasts we have domesticated already? Instead of just crossing and re-crossing our domestic breeds, why not out-cross them with the pick of their wild counterparts?

We can now overcome the technical difficulties of raising breeding colonies of wild creatures alongside standard domestic breeds, and of circumventing the behavioural differences that normally prevent their copulation. Wild animals can be brought down by anaesthetic gun, and their sperm collected by electro-ejaculation and stored in liquid nitrogen. The progeny of inter-specific hybridization are often infertile. The mule (horse x donkey) is completely so, the catallo (cattle x bison) and yakow (cattle x yak) partially so, but infertility is not inevitable. Some inter-specific hybrids breed perfectly well.

So, for what qualities should we be looking and where are we likely to find them? The first requirement may be to extend the breeding season. Extended breeding seasons are a general characteristic of animals from the tropics, where the seasons are poorly defined, but not of the temperate, seasonal beasts from which our domestic types are descended.

Rapid growth and large adult size are desirable and these characteristics are found commonly among species that live at high altitudes or in high latitudes, where bulk acts as a protection against cold but must be achieved in a short growing season (as in deer calves, see p.149).

The goose is an excellent candidate for out-crossing. It is the only domestic bird that can be reared on grass protein alone, and theoretically it is a much better bet than the chicken. However, the domestic Embden or Toulouse type of goose (see p.162), *Anser anser,* most likely derived from the wild temperate greylag, simply is not good enough. Its breeding is seasonal and it incubates for 33–35 days. In contrast, the high-arctic species *Anser caerulescens* (the Greater Snow Goose) and *Branta ruficollis* (the Red-Breasted Goose) incubate for only 23–24 days, and in its first weeks of life *B. ruficollis* grows twice as fast as the Embden. These birds have a very short breeding season, but the endangered Ne-ne (Hawaiian Goose), *Branta sandvicensis*, can lay eggs in winter. The Ne-ne is also the only wholly terrestrial goose, so it can copulate on land and also (probably) is less inclined to put on fat. So the Ne-ne, too, might contribute to some super-hybrid goose. In all there are about 33 species and sub-species of wild geese, of the genera *Anser* and *Branta*, and all of them produce fertile hybrids when crossed with the domestic goose. Among them they might be able to provide us with the most fecund, rapid-growing,

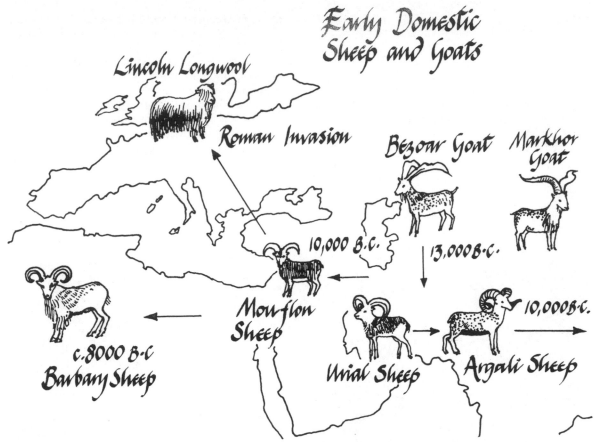

Early Domestic
Sheep and Goats

Lincoln Longwool

Roman Invasion

Bezoar Goat

Markhor Goat

10,000 B.C.

13,000 B.C.

Mouflon Sheep

c.8000 B.C.
Barbary Sheep

Urial Sheep

10,000 B.C.

Argali Sheep

efficient grazing animal the world has ever seen.

A similar argument applies to ducks. The domestic *Anas platyrhynchos* almost certainly is derived from the mallard of the low-temperate zone. It is virtually monogamous, it must copulate in water, it has too much fat below the swimline, too much bone and not enough muscle, it incubates for 28 days, breeds only in spring, and so on... The Muscovy (*Carinia moschata*) is better in some respects but does not produce fertile hybrids with the common domestic duck. However, the 50 or more wild species of *Anas* include many tropical types with a long laying season. The almost wholly terrestrial Laysan Teal (*Anas laysanensis*) should have little fat, and there are many arctic species that incubate for only 22 days and grow rapidly. There is scope here for enormous improvement.

Finally, the domestic sheep (*Ovis aries*) probably is descended from either the European mouflon (*Ovis musimon*) or the Asiatic mouflon (*O. orientalis*). A cross between domestic sheep and the giant Marco Polo sheep of central Asia

(*O. ammon poli*) could produce a beast big enough and rangy enough to compete in the highlands with the deer. After all, *O. ammon poli* stands a metre high at the shoulder and weighs up to 135kg. A back-cross with the mouflon might also help to extend the breeding season: *O. musimon* has been known to breed from January to November.

All of this is fraught with difficulty. For one thing, neither the Marco Polo nor the mouflon have wool. Indeed, why domestic sheep have wool is something of a mystery. Like many animals, wild sheep have two coats, an outer, hairy one and a finer, short one beneath it. Some time after they were domesticated – presumably for their meat – the sheep lost their outer coat and the undercoat grew to replace it, producing the fleece. This cannot have been planned by its neolithic breeders: it was an accidental bonus.

Difficulties there may be, but perhaps they can be overcome. After all, the genetic base of the potato has been rethought from first principles (see p.65). Why not apply the same idea to livestock?

147

# Red deer

Scotland has around 4.5 million hectares of land that are too rough to cultivate, and even the sheep and cattle that graze them are often in pretty poor shape and barely pay their way. Some 2.8 million of those hectares, mostly in the north and west, are occupied by about 200,000 red deer that often seem to thrive where sheep founder. So why not raise them for meat instead?

At first the idea seems irresistible. Many aspects of deer biology do, indeed, seem supremely adapted to the hills and mountains. Because they are alert and well organized socially, with the old experienced hinds (rather than the stags) acting as troop leaders, and because they are strong and fast on their feet, deer can take cover from bad weather which sheep would just endure, dumbly. Deer eat a lot,

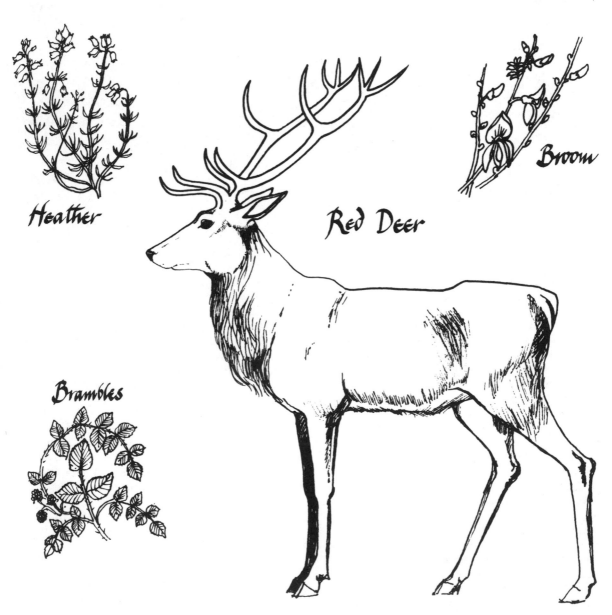

Heather

Red Deer

Broom

Brambles

148

particularly the calves and lactating hinds. They seem to metabolize more quickly than sheep and digest food less efficiently, but they can thrive on a poorer diet than sheep can. They can take a higher proportion of heather and if that should fail they can turn to brambles, broom, birch leaves or even bark. Indeed, their low digestive efficiency is an adaptation to a poor diet, which they push through their guts quickly. Sheep, on the other hand, assiduously hold food in the rumen until they have extracted the last calorie; but this is not cost-effective when the diet is poor.

However, the deer pay for their ability to survive. Like most wild animals, their appetite falls in winter: another adaptation, which prevents a fruitless, energy-consuming search for food that just is not available. Since deer are congenitally lean, they must burn body protein, rather than fat, as a source of winter energy, but protein is much poorer as a source of energy than is fat. Weight for weight, fat provides twice as much energy as protein. So when deer utilize their body protein to provide energy, they lose weight prodigiously: a 30–40 per cent weight reduction in winter is not unusual.

What is more, the calves, which are born in June, must grow rapidly before December or they will not survive the winter (see Wild genes in old stock, p.146). The deer calf doubles its body weight in its first 20 days of life. A calf takes 47 days to do this, a foal takes 60 days, and the human baby, with one of the worst growth records of all species, needs 180 days to double its birth weight. But in order to support this astonishing growth-rate the hind must practically double her energy intake while she is lactating. Suckling cows or sheep – provided they are merely raising offspring, and not pandering to the requirements of the modern dairy farmer (see p.122) – need to raise their energy intake by a mere 30–40 per cent.

When we add all this together, we find that the wild deer has a pretty low output by agricultural standards. Mortality in the first year is 10–25 per cent. The beasts take four years to reach sexual maturity. The hinds, able theoretically to produce a calf a year, in practice produce only two in three years. The mature Highland beasts are only two-thirds the size of the ornamental red deer of the lowland parks. A standard meat output for a Highland deer herd is around 5kg per head per year, only one-third

to one-quarter of the yield achieved in park deer.

Evidently, then, we must do more than merely cash in on the wild beast. We must manage it to raise its biological potential – and scientists at the Rowett Research Institute, Aberdeen, have shown that its potential is astonishing. Calves raised indoors have reached 100kg at one year of age, converting feed as efficiently as a fat lamb, and producing a carcass with 10 per cent more lean meat on it. Indeed, as the Rowett Institute's director, Dr Kenneth Blaxter, commented, we might ask the animal breeders what they have been up to when a wild animal just plucked from the hills can perform as efficiently as their own protégés. Although deer are congenitally frisky and strong, the hand-raised beasts become extremely tame. They are at least as tractable as hill sheep. If deer are raised as conventional farm animals and slaughtered hygienically (and the central abbatoir must replace the rifle if deer are to be a serious meat source) they taste like spring lamb, so marketing should not be difficult.

However, here is the paradox. If you farm deer as if they were suckler cattle, you sacrifice their ability to forage and to survive – the qualities that made them worth considering in the first place. If deer are ever to be worth while, we must find a satisfactory compromise between intensive farming and culling. We must manipulate their ecology. Perhaps, for example, we could pare down superfluous stags, leaving one stag to ten hinds, instead of the present common ratio of one to five. But how many stags can you take out without destroying the deer's social structure? Perhaps, too, we could cull out more of the old hinds. But how many of these can be taken before we rob the herds of the intelligence and experience that enable them to survive? Perhaps we could induce hinds to breed every year with judicious winter feeding, and fatten the superfluous calves intensively, as with hill lambs? In all cases we are liable to clash with the deer-shooting interests that are the source of so much Highland revenue. You cannot manage deer productively without farming them, and that would take the edge off stalking.

In short, red deer show great promise, and agriculturalists are taking them seriously, but the practical and philosophical problems raised by their management are a long way from being solved.

# Unconventional livestock

Mankind has domesticated only a handful of the herbivorous mammals that theoretically are exploitable. The first, apparently, was the reindeer. Then, in chronological order, there followed the goat, sheep, cattle (with water-buffalo and yak), pig, elephant, horse, camel, rabbit and llama. In some cases he has raised the productivity of these animals to amazing heights. At the same time, by intensive concentration on so few species he has annihilated natural landscapes, driven many wild species to the edge of extinction and often over it, and has left a legacy of deserts from the Equator to the Poles.

New, or at least unconventional, species are theoretically useful in four ways. They may be able to exploit environments or food that are totally inaccessible to conventional species, or environments where conventional species may survive but not thrive. They may be able to exploit precarious habitats more efficiently and with greater ecological safety than conventional species, and to squeeze the last few drops from environments that we exploit already.

The absolutely inaccessible environments include desert, waterways, some forest land, and areas harbouring diseases to which only local game is adapted. Camels are exploited already in the desert, of course, but the eland antelope, the addax, and several species of oryx are even better adapted. After all, camels need to drink now and then, but the addax can get by without water. The eland is already ranched experimentally in Africa, and a herd has been maintained at Askaniya-Nova in the southern Ukraine since the turn of the century. Eland are managed as easily as cattle. The Ancient Egyptians evidently flirted with the addax (and with the hyena, gazelle and ibex), but this beast is now almost extinct. All these ungulates have tremendous unexploited potential, and several kangaroo and wallaby species can out-perform sheep and goats in the more arid regions of Australia.

Beasts to exploit the world's waterways – and also to keep them clear of weeds at the same time – include the hippopotamus, each carcass of which is equivalent to 60 sheep, the dugong and manatee ('sea cows'), and the capybara of South America, a rodent that can weigh up to 70kg and produces ten or so youngsters a year. It could have worldwide potential.

In Britain, the nearest we get to exploiting the otherwise totally unexploitable is through the reindeer, a herd of which has been maintained obsessively in the Cairngorms since 1951. Reindeer eat grey lichen, which is useless to other species, although the Scottish ones are also given a daily handful of flaked maize, bran and beet pulp.

The marginal lands, where conventional species may survive but unconventional types out-yield them, include savannah, taiga and tundra, rough hill and moor, and forest. The eland is the supreme beast of the savannah, and in Africa it often appears round and sleek while the local cattle, with ribs like corrugated iron, die on their feet. A notable animal of the taiga is the saiga of the Russian steppe. Usually referred to as an antelope, in fact it is an unclassifiable beast about the size of a roe deer and sporting an odd labyrinthine nose, like an elephant's trunk. Fifty years ago the saiga was almost extinct. Now it is managed, and roams in great herds. It survives natural disasters and yields a steady crop of meat.

On rough hill and moorland, at least in the Scottish Highlands, the red deer could prove a more profitable domestic animal than the sheep (see p.148), and at least one scientist has suggested that the horse could exploit the rough grazing even more efficiently than the deer, as it does in the French Massif Central, and that the llama, supremely adapted to high altitude and a poor diet, could turn out to be the best highland beast of all.

The llama has no wild relatives. It is a completely domesticated animal. The Peruvians, who gave the llama to the world, domesticated two species, both in the same genus, *Auchenia huanacus* and *A. vicunia,* the vicuña. The vicuña, highly prized for its fleece, is now an endangered species. The huanaco, or llama proper, became differentiated into two sub-species, *glama* and *paco*. The *glama* was bred into a beast of burden, like the camel. The *paco* was bred for its wool, alpaca. Will we live to see llama farms in the Welsh and Scottish hills and in the Pennines? It is not impossible.

The elk or moose may be the best animals for forested land, as the Russians at least are beginning to appreciate.

In environments that are intrinsically vulnerable, with drought and erosion a constant menace – and these include much of the deceptively lush rainforests with their wafer-thin topsoils – the natural fauna, adapted to the natural flora, might provide the only conceivable source of meat. Attempts to adapt the habitat to conventional cattle or goats would merely create desert. However, an intimate knowledge of each beast's ecology is vital if the maximum sustainable yield is to be cropped, and, in general, only those individuals that are not vital to the continuance of the species must be culled. The nine most abundant ungulates on the Serengeti National Park in Africa, with its balanced mixture of browsers (such as the elephant and giraffe), grazers (such as buffalo and kob), and rooting beasts (such as warthog and bushpig) yield almost 13,000 tonnes liveweight per year, on a 10 per cent cull, which is believed to be far more than could be obtained by putting the area down to domestic cattle. Even so, the over-all yield, equivalent to about 10.3kg per hectare, is only about 1 per cent of what is achievable on intensively managed British grassland.

Finally, there are new or unconventional species that can be allowed to forage, and so exploit the environment more fully than is possible otherwise. Into this category fall pigeons, guinea fowls and bees, which are provided only with shelter and supplementary feed, and are encouraged to make their living as best they can. The principle is good, but dangerous. The rabbit, after all, was introduced as a food source, to breed in half-managed warrens, but it became a major pest.

The one animal that really has proved its worth as a semi-domestic forager is the guinea pig, which, in parts of Peru and Ecuador, was for centuries the sole source of animal protein. It ran (and runs, for it is still used in this way) around the kitchen picking up scraps, and was put into the pot as required.

Theoretically attractive though it may be, the business of cultivating unconventional species is much more difficult than it seems. Should the animals merely be hunted and culled? If so, problems of hygiene appear, and the size and distribution of the population must be monitored constantly to prevent over-hunting. Should they be ranched, to give greater control? If so, at what point does the new species become less desirable than conventional stock which, after all, has been bred specifically to respond to husbandry? The dilemmas will be with us always, but they are worth facing, and the husbandry of unconventional species is being looked at seriously all over the world.

Elk or Moose

# Hens

Chickens span the whole spectrum of farming practice. At the big-money end of the scale their production is more highly mechanized, their environment more closely controlled, and their genes more tightly defined, than any other class of livestock.

The reasons behind the factory approach are not difficult to find. First, chickens are potentially highly productive and there is a firm traditional market for their eggs and meat, so it is worth investing money in them. Secondly, they are small, so the cost of controlling their environment is far less per head than it would be, say, with pigs. Thirdly, their high prolificacy, short generation time, and range of well-defined breeds enables rapid genetic progress. Indeed, the commercial chicken may now have 'progressed' along factory lines almost as far as is possible. Some birds are laying almost 300 eggs a year; broilers are ready for the table (in so far as such beasts can ever be considered fit for the table) in 6–8 weeks; and breeders and husbandmen are now measuring improvements in fractions of 1 per cent. As we have seen (p.142), that other factory beast, the pig, is still an industrial novice compared to the chicken.

There is a fourth, more subtle reason. Traditionally, the non-ruminant livestock (hens and pigs) were marginal enterprises on most farms. They were fed 'wastes' and surpluses. The picture of the traditional farmyard that still survives in some children's books (but probably nowhere else) shows hens scratching around. These birds ate grain spilled on the way to and from the barns and scraps thrown to them by the farmer's wife. The number of birds (and pigs) varied according to the amount of food available, so that in years when there was more grain than could be sold, the non-ruminant population increased in size; in lean years the meat was eaten. In a sense, these animals were biological storehouses. Between the 1950s and the early 1970s, the world as a whole had very large surpluses of grains. They were plentiful and they were cheap. It is not surprising, then, that the non-ruminant populations increased in those countries wealthy enough to buy in the feed for them. Indeed, they grew to such an extent that entirely new systems of management had to be devised to cope with their numbers. This required heavy investment of capital, and so there was a need to improve the efficiency of the enterprises by trying to match the biology of the operation to the technology. Now that the grain surpluses have gone, feed prices are rising and we should expect to eat less poultry and pigmeat, and fewer eggs, in years to come.

In practice, commercial chickenries are of two main types: the battery, in which hybrid laying hens are kept in tiers of wire cages, usually three or four but sometimes up to a dozen to a cage; and the deep litter system, generally used for broilers, in which young chickens are kept on wood shavings, or something similar, on the floor of a large house, usually darkened to prevent the 'vices' such as feather-pecking that otherwise would break out. At first, when they are only a few days old, the broilers are confined in one corner, to prevent them from running around too much and wasting energy, and to help keep them warm. As they grow their confines are widened progressively, until the finished birds fill the entire floor almost exactly. Then they are shuffled out to be killed, scalded, mechanically de-feathered, gutted, wrapped in polythene and frozen.

The monotony of their diet, their speed of growth and immaturity at death, the reduction or absence of the traditional 24-hour hanging time between de-feathering and gutting, conspire to ensure that the carcass has virtually no flavour. It is not easy, perhaps impossible, to distinguish a backyard egg from a battery egg (if you think you can, be sure you are not distinguishing between a fresh egg and a comparatively stale one), but the contrast between the frozen broiler and the backyard chooky is astonishing.

The factory end of the chicken market is largely sewn up. Vertical integration, too, is the order of the day, with each step in the operation (hatching, rearing, packing, distribution) being undertaken by a different specialist, all working for the same corporation. There is little to be learned about husbandry from studying it, except, perhaps, what too many battery farmers learned too late: that ventilation without draughts is the key to successful livestock housing, and the more closely you pack in the beasts, the more assiduously must you circulate the air. The modern battery house (or intensive piggery) is built not so much around the cages as around the ventilation system.

## The free-range hen

We can learn more from looking at the systems employed lower down the scale, on general farms. A word of warning first. You will make a profit from the more traditional methods of raising birds only if you can find a premium market for free-range eggs, or, perhaps, for organically fed table birds (see p.42), but you may be able to justify a small to middle-sized enterprise through the fringe benefits it brings: the improvement to soil fertility that chickens contribute and their economical use of odds and ends, including dairy by-products.

The simplest and healthiest venture at the smallholding scale involves portable huts. These are simply moved from field to field and the birds – not more than 125 to the hectare – allowed to graze with other stock. It is difficult to discover exactly what they eat under such circumstances, but they must have had a wide choice of herbs in traditional meadows. They still find the creepy-crawlies stirred up by hooves and gathered round cow pats. Sometimes fields are allocated specifically for fowls, in which case 250–370 birds per hectare is permissible.

An alternative system – the familiar Morant method, as employed for rabbits, with variations for sheep and farrowing pigs – is simply to keep 25 or so birds in a run, which is covered at one end and provided with perches and nesting boxes for laying birds, the whole run measuring about 6 x 1.5 metres. This is moved forward its own length each day.

## The backyard chicken

So we come to the backyard chicken, which is possibly the simplest of all livestock enterprises. Laying birds need plenty of air. They are best if they are kept hardy, and the more air they have the less likelihood there is of disease. They need light. Their breeding cycles are controlled by day length and they tend to stop laying during the short days of winter. Ideally, as in the general farm systems, they should be given an open run, which allows them both air and light. If you lack the space for this, then the chicken house must be wire fronted for two thirds of its length. If you allow the birds a run, a simple wooden hut, opened first thing in the morning, is good enough. If you are confident that the run itself is very secure – hen-proof, fox-proof, wild mink-

proof – and if the henhouse has a hen-sized door as well as the human-sized door you use for cleaning out, then the hens can be allowed to go in and out as they wish. They will go into the house at dusk, and sometimes in wet, cold weather, and will come out at dawn.

A hut 2.5 x 1.5 metres and 1.5 metres high does for 6–8 birds if they have no proper run. If they use it only for sleeping, then a hut 2 metres long could accommodate 10 birds easily.

The birds must have somewhere warm, but airy, to roost at night, so a closed-in sleeping area is essential in a wire-fronted cage. In practice, the roosting birds often huddle together, but allow 20cm of perch per bird. Young birds, freshly introduced, and any birds that you rescue from intensive units where perching is not permitted, may not find the perch. You may have to lift them on, but they soon learn, if not from you then from their older colleagues. The perches must all be at the same height. Roosting birds cannot abide being looked down on, and if the perches are at different levels all the birds will try to roost on the highest.

Outdoor Nest Boxes

Finally, hens like somewhere cosy and dark to lay their eggs. Fix nesting boxes to any convenient side of the house. Each compartment should be about 30cm deep, 30cm high and 25cm wide. The birds should be able to reach it from the inside of the house and it should be covered with a lid that can be raised to remove the eggs from outside. Provide one nesting compartment for every two to three birds.

It is always better to put litter on the floor, even when the birds spend their days out of doors. The litter absorbs the dung they produce during the night, makes cleaning much easier, and provides you with first-class compost. Virtually anything rottable will serve as litter. Straw is very easy to work with, sawdust or dry, dead leaves are perfectly adequate, and dried lawn cuttings are excellent.

Feeding is catholic. You must provide a constant supply of fresh, clean water, preferably dispensed from some kind of drip feeder, although any heavy metal bowl will do, provided they cannot turn it over. A little garlic – about one clove to ten litres of water – acts as a mild insecticide and helps keep the water clean. The birds must have grit, to lodge in their gizzards to help them break up corn, and they must have plenty of calcium, to help them form their eggshells. You can give them their own eggshells (if you dry them in the oven they will be easier to crush, and the heat will prevent the recycling of infections) supplemented with crushed oyster shells which you can buy from the local feed merchant.

After that, almost anything goes. You can feed proprietary feeding pellets ad lib, but then you may find yourself wondering why you bother to keep hens at all if you feed them in the manner of battery hens, and at great expense. You can make up special diets, based roughly on 120 grammes of grain per bird per day, supplemented with some household scraps of cooked meat and some greenstuffs, which is the method used by one of the present authors (MA), or you can adopt the system by which the other author (CT) used to keep eight Rhode Island Light Sussex hens. Every kind of plate scraping, including the remains of the dog's dinner and the birds' own eggshells, was put into a large saucepan, together with potato and other vegetable peelings, and any bread or plate scrapings donated by neighbours and friends. Enough water was added to prevent burning, and the whole thing simmered at the end of each day. While still hot the mixture (which often smelled delicious) was mashed with a potato masher. At first, a proprietary mash was added to the mixture, but this was soon abandoned as a waste of money, for what can feed a human can, by and large, feed a chicken – although chickens are more productive. This mash formed the first and main meal of the day. In the afternoons, as near to evening as possible, since late meals are said to be better digested, the beasts were pelted with a fairly arbitrary amount of mixed corn, which they enjoyed scratching for. In addition, the birds were given all the greenstuff available, including all weeds from the garden. They particularly like Fat Hen *(Chenopodium)*, chickweed, groundsel, comfrey and chives, but also cabbage, runner bean leaves and many other plants. They are perfectly able to select the food they like and the rest serves as litter in the run and, later, pre-mixed with dung, it makes excellent compost. Snails and worms from the garden (including the small red worms from the compost heap) are also received warmly.

This system was haphazard. The birds' diet

Green Food Gallows

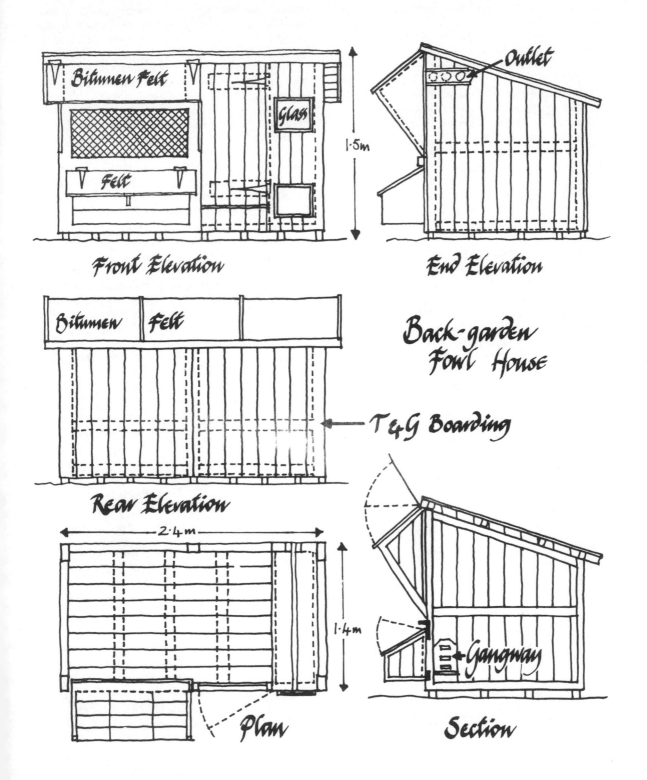

Front Elevation

End Elevation

Bitumen Felt

Glass

Felt

Outlet

Back-garden
Fowl House

Bitumen Felt

T & G Boarding

Rear Elevation

1·5m

2·4 m

1·4 m

Gangway

Plan

Section

undoubtedly varied somewhat from day to day, but they did not go hungry. There was usually spare corn to be found underneath the litter in the run, but daily flocks of starlings ensured that no mash was allowed to hang about and rot. The birds thrived for two years, often laying an egg each per day for two weeks at a stretch, and at the end they curried beautifully. However, although some backyarders keep the same hens for three years or more, it is doubtful whether the second year is really worth while.

Our point in describing this somewhat fatuous system at such length is that backyard chickens really are simple if you stick to first principles, and certainly pay their way since they give you eggs, compost and meat in return for next to nothing.

So how do you start? First, what kind of bird should you buy?

### Backyard breeds

As with house cattle or goats, there are two main stratagems. You may go for solid workaday birds that will lay 130–160 reasonable-sized eggs in their first year, without going broody and without succumbing to disease, and that will fatten into a family-sized meal at the end. If you get a second year's egg crop, so much the better, but longevity is not one of the prime desiderata.

Many different types will meet these rough requirements. Rhode Island Red, Light Sussex, Plymouth Rock, Wyandotte, North Holland Blue, and Cuckoo Maran (which lay beautifully dark tan eggs) may all do sterling service. But be warned. These established breeds, though they may have an impeccable pedigree, are highly variable genetically. The particular flock from which you buy them – the 'strain' – can have more effect on output than the breed. Cross-bred birds, such as Rhode Island Red or Plymouth Rock crossed with Light Sussex or Wyandotte, should bring benefits of hybrid vigour, with the good points of each combining to produce birds better than either parent. Such crossbreeds make excellent workaday birds, but you may get the best results of all by joining the commercial world and buying birds bred for the battery. We have heard bad things of the Warren: that they keel over after eight months' frenetic laying, but we have also heard of them vastly out-producing

White Leghorn (hen)

Light Sussex (hen)

old-fashioned breeds during a year in the backyard, with never a hint of broodiness. Battery birds are designed to produce so heavily that you can even get a second year out of them by buying birds due to be culled from battery houses at the end of their first year. They are very cheap, often take on a new lease of life when given such luxuries as fresh air, green food and perches, and will still out-lay their traditional rivals.

The second stratagem is to become a chicken buff by going for one of the 200 different colour variations among the 60-odd breeds recognized by the Poultry Club of Great Britain, and become known as a guardian of a rare breed. Actually, it is a good deal less than certain that most old breeds are worth preserving, except for their handsome appearance. Occasionally some ancient type comes up with qualities that have come back into fashion (as have the South Devon and Dexter among cattle) but most minor breeds are half forgotten precisely because they lack desirable characteristics. Poultry have suffered even more than cattle from the ravages of the show bench, and beasts bred specifically for their plumage or for wattles of varying deg-

rees of absurdity are not likely to out-perform those whose survival depended upon output.

Buy the initial flock all at once. If you mix livestock from different sources you run a risk of introducing disease. You can buy day-old chicks, which are inexpensive, but there are snags. Half of them may turn out to be cocks, and they are delicate and need the attention either of a broody hen or artificial heat at night, a constant supply of clean, fresh food, and gradual hardening off by steadily increased exposure by day. If they survive, twenty weeks will pass before you see your first egg.

More sensibly, you can buy point-of-lay pullets. These should be about 18 weeks old and they will come from a dealer, or farmer, who has done the hard work already.

If you have opted for one of the traditional breeds, then from time to time hens will go broody. There is no mistaking the symptoms: the broody will simply sit, usually in a nesting box, and if you lift her out she will go back within a few minutes.

You can deal with this problem in one of two ways. The first is to coop her. Shut her up in a coop, which is a prison cell with bars at the front

Rhode Island Red (hen)

Plymouth Rock (cockerel)

## Indoor Nest Boxes

and a bare floor on which she cannot make a nest. Give her access to drinking water and at feeding times let her out. An hour or so after the birds have been fed see whether she has returned to her nesting box. If she has she must go back into the coop. If you take no action, a broody hen will stay broody for three weeks. If you coop her she will stop brooding within a few days.

The second way is to provide the flock with a cock. This does not prevent broodiness, of course, but it does offer the possibility of avoiding the hens wasting their time and your food. If a hen goes broody, just leave her alone. From time to time she will leave her nest to feed – the eggs do not suffer provided she is not away for too long – and you can check the number of eggs in the clutch (or you can simply push her to one side to count, but she will try to peck you). An average hen can sit on a dozen eggs or so, and for two or three days you can add more eggs: place them beside her and she will move them to where she wants them to be. By a curious law of nature, all the eggs that are going to hatch will do so within a few hours of one another.

When the chicks hatch, you must remove them and their mother (move the chicks first and mother will be more willing to follow them). They need private accommodation, with a dry floor to sleep on, fresh air and daylight, fresh water in which they cannot drown, and 'chick crumbs' which you can buy from any corn merchant. This is a measured ration of cereals, crushed because tiny chicks are not supposed to be able to eat whole grains. Feed chicks and mother separately – they will eat one another's food quite happily – and mother will do the rest. Hens are good mothers by and large. Bred from your own hardy flock, chicks can be startlingly tough. One that turned over its water container one evening, simultaneously soaking and trapping itself, was found next morning cold, stiff, with glazed eye and the barest murmur of a heartbeat. It was warmed in its owner's hands, then placed in a small basket, with warm bedding, in the airing cupboard, and within a couple of hours it was hopping about, chirping furiously to be let out.

Birds kept on a small scale, with fresh air, water and food, and not allowed to sit in their own dung, should not be unhealthy. Healthy birds have an unmistakable brightness of eye and deliberation of movement.

You will need to know whether they are in lay, because those that are not are first for the pot. One indication is the comb. In a laying bird it should be red, in a non-layer merely pink. The finger test is more exact. If the distance between the pelvic bones is the width of three fingers, then the bird is laying. If it is the width of two fingers, she is probably laying. If it is the width of only one finger, she is out of lay.

When you have established your small flock of laying hens, utilizing all waste food, tidying and fertilizing the garden (but do not let them loose in the garden or they will do considerable damage), you will wonder how you ever managed without them.

Look for birds for sale in the classified columns of local newspapers if you live in a rural area, or in *Exchange and Mart* or the Yellow Pages for the names of dealers.

### Killing, plucking and drawing

Unless you kill surplus cockerels by the time they are sexually mature, you will have a conflict in the flock. You can fatten them by shutting them away for two weeks before slaughter and feeding them barley-meal and skimmed milk twice a day, but it is not essential.

To kill young birds, hold them under one arm, with their feet uppermost. Place a hand over the head, catch the feet with the other hand, let the body fall so that the neck is bent backwards, and at the same time twist and pull firmly until you feel the neck stretch and the wings flap violently.

Older birds may be too tough for this treatment. Hold the body in one hand close to the ground so that the neck touches a hard, solid surface. Place a bar or a piece of wood – preferably round – across the back of the neck, put one foot on each end of the bar and pull the body until the neck stretches and the wings flap.

It is best to pluck the bird immediately, but if you delay plucking then pour boiling water over the carcass before you start – it will stop the feathers from flying everywhere and will make them come out more easily.

Hang the bird by its feet for 24 hours or so, then cut off the head where the neck joins the body, cut off the lower legs and feet, use a sharp knife to widen the anus sufficiently for you to insert your hand, catch hold of the viscera and pull them out all in one.

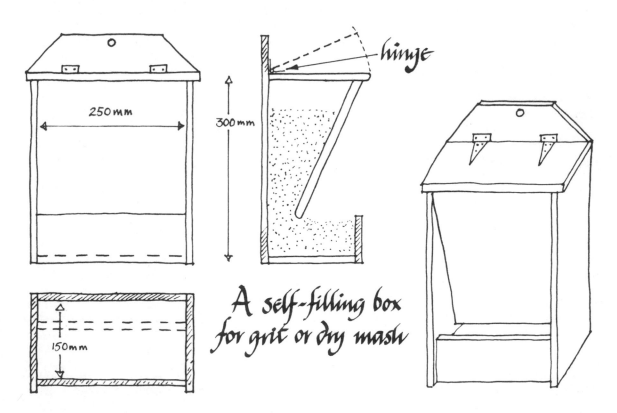

A self-filling box for grit or dry mash

# Ducks, geese and turkeys

All three of these are suitable for rearing on a small scale, although most commercial production is more intensive. The ducks and turkeys that are marketed deep-frozen have all been bred and raised in systems that are adaptations of the broiler methods used for fowls.

Being birds, they also lay eggs. Ducks are kept for eggs as well as meat. Goose eggs, which are large, are also edible. Turkey eggs may also be edible, but turkeys are produced for meat only, and breeding them is not easy for the novice. They are a fairly recent introduction to northern Europe from much warmer climates, and they need careful attention, especially when young.

## Ducks

**Breeds:** Which breed you choose depends first on whether your main interest is in meat or eggs. Duck eggs are larger than hens' eggs, have a stronger flavour, and do not keep so well. They can be used in just the same way as hens' eggs, however.

The most popular duck for its meat – indeed, the most popular duck – is the Aylesbury. This is the large white bird with orange legs that you will see in every children's book about farmyards and the countryside. It grows at a phenomenal rate. Fully mature, an Aylesbury will weigh in at about 4.5kg for a drake and about 4kg for a duck, but they can reach about half this weight in the first eight to ten weeks of their lives. This is a valuable asset because they are 'gross feeders' (they have big appetites). Aylesburys have the further advantage of rather small skeletons. Ducks tend to be large-boned, so that the splendid bird that reaches the table provides far less meat than, say, a chicken of the same size. It is true of all ducks, but less true of Aylesburys than of other breeds. The deep-frozen ducks they sell in the supermarkets are invariably Aylesburys. Aylesburys are not particularly good layers. Well cared for and fed, you can expect about 100 eggs a year from each duck.

The egg-layer is the Campbell. There are three strains – the white, the dark and the khaki, and the khaki is probably the most popular. The colouring is darker on the upper side of the body, the bill is green or (in the duck) greenish-blue, the legs are orange. A Khaki Campbell can produce up to 300 eggs a year. They are rather small birds, the adults weighing about 2.5kg (drakes) or 2kg (ducks).

The Pekin, first introduced into this country from China in 1872, is a kind of compromise. It is white and rather like the Aylesbury to look at, though its posture is more erect. It grows to a larger size than the Aylesbury, but takes longer to do so and actually provides less meat because of its larger bones, so that size for size a Pekin will weigh about half a kilogram less than an Aylesbury. Some people say the meat is inferior to that of the Aylesbury, but it is the standard table duck in America, where the original Chinese version was improved by selective breeding. It will lay about 130 eggs a year.

For flavour of meat the Rouen is said to be the best of all. A French breed, the Rouen is a handsome bird, black and white with a greenish-yellow bill and dark red legs in the drake, and brown with smart wing-bars, orange legs and a bright yellow bill in the duck. A Rouen grows to the same size as an Aylesbury but, alas, it takes far longer to do so: nearly six months to reach table size. The Rouen is a poor layer – less than 100 eggs a year.

The Indian Runner will lay up to 180 eggs a year, which made it the best layer of all until the appearance of the Campbell. It is a comic bird in appearance, having no shoulders. The duck is fawn in colour, the drake much darker with some bronze and green, but there are also white and fawn-and-white varieties. The Indian Runner is probably the hardiest of all ducks. Give it some water to splash about in and it will thrive almost anywhere. It is not particularly athletic and so is not difficult to confine.

By cross-breeding two varieties of Khaki Campbells, the Welsh Harlequin was produced. It gains weight slowly (about 16 weeks to reach a weight of about 2.5kg) but it lays like a Campbell – about 300 eggs a year. When the Welsh Harlequin was crossed with the Aylesbury the product was called the Whalesbury, which is now a popular dual-

**Khaki Campbell (drake)**

**Aylesbury**

**Embden (gander)**

purpose bird, growing to 2.5–3kg in 16 weeks and producing well over 200 eggs a year.

The Muscovy (at various times also called the Peruvian and Barbary) has never been really popular. It is a large bird, white with red flashes on the face, it wanders far and wide often staying away from home for days on end, and although it can become very tame with humans, with other livestock its evil temper is notorious.

**Rearing:** Ducks are poor mothers. Duck eggs are generally hatched in incubators, or under broody hens. Ducklings must be kept warm; a hen (or an incubator) will achieve this, and the hen has no urge to take her brood into the water almost as soon as they can totter along behind her, as a duck will do. You can crowd ducklings together far more closely than is possible with any other kind of poultry. At about four weeks of age the ducklings can be allowed to swim. At about ten weeks they will moult and are especially vulnerable at this age. That is when the meat birds are separated from the egg-layers. The meat birds are killed, the layers given extra food. The first eggs will be laid when the ducks are four to five months old.

Ducklings are timid. Especially while they are very small, try to keep visitors away from them, and always warn them of your own approach by making some kind of noise while you are still some distance from them.

When driving ducks of any age, remember that they expect to be attacked from above. Don't use your feet or a stick to coax them along at ground level, but your arms, at shoulder height.

**Housing:** While they are very young ducklings require warmth, but the accommodation need not be elaborate. A packing case, closed on all sides and with an entrance cut in it, will be perfectly adequate – remember, though, that one side or the top must be removable for cleaning. Give them straw for litter. When they have feathers one box large enough for all of them, with straw on the base and a piece of sacking over the open end, will provide adequate shelter against really bad weather.

Adult ducks like space, but if you are keeping them in the garden you will need to clip their wings to prevent them from flying over the wall. Clip one wing only, during the first ten days of the bird's life. Stretch out the wing, use a very sharp knife, and remove the outer 6–7mm. It may frighten the duckling but it will cause no pain. If the bird is older you will need to remove rather more wing: about 6cm.

Ducks are water birds. They enjoy a pond or stream, but they will not die without one, although the large adult birds such as Aylesburys may have trouble mating except on the water. They must have clean water to drink at all times, of course, and if they jump into their drinking water and look happy – well they are ducks, after all. If you do have a pond or stream, keep it clean, watch for pollutants that could contaminate the water and the natural food the ducks will find for themselves, and try not to make it too favourable a habitat for predators. Keep the vegetation a little away from the edge so that should the enemy approach it must cross some open ground before it can reach its prey.

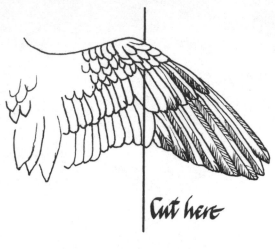

*Cut here*

### Wing Clipping
### Trimming the wings
### of 10-day-old birds

**Feeding:** Ducks are big eaters but, like all water birds, if they eat too much they will produce a lot of fat. If they have a reasonable amount of space they will eat grass, some other herbs, worms, snails, slugs and insects. These are their natural foods. Augment this either with a proprietary feed that you can buy from any corn merchant, or, when they are young, with barley meal made into a kind of porridge and served warm, with oatmeal, boiled rice and, if they are not able to hunt for their own meat, a little butcher's meat. When they are being fattened give them barley meal and offal. All meat must be cooked to sterilize it. Feed twice a day, morning and evening, and experiment with the rations until you find that all the food is eaten within about an hour of feeding, but if you give them more, some is left.

**Health:** Ducks are not prone to disease once they are past the crucial first few weeks. If during those weeks several die suddenly, inform the Ministry of Agriculture. It is not very likely, but possible, that they might have contracted a virus disease that is notifiable.

Because they tend to resist infection ducks

can be reared on the same land year after year, but do not raise any other poultry on the same land as there is a risk of infecting other species.

**Laying:** Unlike hens, ducks do not stop laying in winter. Most eggs are laid at night or early in the morning, but ducks will not use nesting boxes and the eggs are laid wherever the bird happens to be at the time.

#### Geese

Geese have been kept from time immemorial as feathered watchdogs. They are noisy and aggressive, and will chase away dogs and small boys. As they eat grass they are often kept in orchards, where they provide an effective deterrent to scrumpers.

Once past their vulnerable first few weeks of life, they are very hardy and long-lived. Geese of 19 years old have been known to continue to lay eggs. A good layer will provide about 100 eggs a year. The eggs can be eaten, but fertilized eggs are valuable, as newly hatched goslings can cost £1 each or more.

The taste for goose meat has declined over the years as turkey has become more popular. Goose has more fat than turkey, and the fat was once valued in itself. Many people believe that goose is better eating than turkey; I agree with them, but that's only opinion.

**Breeds:** The most popular goose is probably the Embden, which is also the largest. A gander can weigh 14kg or more and a goose 9kg. The Embden is pure white, with orange bill, legs and feet.

The Toulouse is darker in colour, with a dark grey head and some grey in the plumage. It is a smaller bird than the Embden, growing to about 12kg for a gander and 9kg for a goose.

The Brecon Buff looks like a Toulouse, except that its bill, legs and feet are pink rather than orange, and it is smaller (7kg or 9kg) and quieter.

The Chinese is smaller still – not much bigger than a large duck – but it grows more quickly than most geese. It is generally brown in colour or white: there are two strains. The birds reach table weight (5.4kg or for the goose about 4.5kg) in eig'ıt weeks. The Chinese is a good layer, producing up to 60 eggs a year.

The Roman is another small breed (7kg or 6kg), not a particularly heavy layer, but said to be a good mother.

**Rearing:** Like all young birds goslings need warmth and protection, but they are hardier than, say, ducklings. For the first ten days, or longer if the weather is very cold, keep them in a box with a light bulb burning day and night. A 100-watt bulb will keep up to a dozen birds warm, a 250-watt bulb will look after 50 birds. The box need not be large – one metre square is large enough for half a dozen goslings; cover the floor with hay, and arrange the light bulb so that it hangs about 40cm above the birds' heads. One thing goslings must have is water, and plenty of it. They run a grave risk of dehydration, but they are great splashers, and before long they are almost bound to splash enough cold water on to the hot bulb to burst it – so have some spare bulbs handy.

Eggs are usually hatched in an incubator or under a broody hen (unless you have a Roman goose). A large hen can sit on four goose eggs or, at the very most, six.

After ten days or so, depending on the weather, the light bulbs can be turned off, and after three to four weeks, again depending on the weather, the goslings can be turned out of doors permanently. However, this should not be a sudden change. By the end of their first week they can be allowed out for periods that are increased gradually, so that by the time they move into the open permanently they have been spending all day out of doors for a week or more. You will have to carry them in and out of their box to begin with, but by the time they are ready to go out for good you should have no trouble with them. They prefer to live in the open.

**Feeding:** Goslings can be fed on boiled rice and ground grains, the kind that corn merchants sell as 'baby chick food'. They need some green food: dandelion leaves are particularly good, but you should chop them up while the birds are very small.

Once the young geese are living out of doors they will find their own food, mainly grass. The grass must be short, however. They cannot eat the kind of long grass that cows like. So where the grass is long allow other animals to graze it first, or else mow it and feed the cuttings to rabbits or dry them and use them as bedding.

Provided they have enough grass geese need nothing else, but they will grow slowly. If you want to accelerate their rate of growth, feed them grain in troughs.

**Health:** Like ducks, geese are hardy creatures, provided they are protected during the first weeks and that there is always shelter for them – from intense sunshine as well as from cold winds. If you should find a goose (or a duck for that matter) lying on its side, apparently unable to move, place it in a warm box for 24 hours and probably all will be well. It had cramp.

## Turkeys

Turkeys are bred only for their meat, and the original strains have been cross-bred so intensively that nowadays they are all hybrids – and a bewildering number of hybrids there are. The one you choose will depend on how much meat you want. The larger breeds will grow to nearly 14kg (for stags) in six months. At the other extreme there are some small varieties that will grow to about 4kg, but in half the time. time.

**Rearing:** Unless you have some experience of turkeys, don't try to hatch eggs. Buy the birds young, as poults. They are not entirely adapted to our climate, they are inclined to be delicate, and they need TLC (tender loving care). If you

cardboard

250 watt lamp

water

feed

Housing for Young Ducklings

*Movable housing for geese. Building can be moved by carrying handles. At 2m × 1½m the house will take 5 birds*

want them for Christmas, buy them in July or August – which is when they will be available anyway – and expect to pay up to £2 each for them. Keep them indoors and feed them on a proprietary food, mainly because that will be the diet to which they are accustomed. Make sure they have plenty of water to drink, try to serve their food in containers they can reach but not walk about in, and examine them regularly to make sure they are actually eating. Just below the bird's throat is its crop. If the crop is bulging all is well. If not, it has not eaten. Use a pipette (a medicine dropper with a rubber bulb on the end will do) to force some water through the beak and into the crop. That should start the bird feeding. Tapping the side of the food container will attract interest, as will using a pencil (especially a shiny one) or even your finger to move the grain about. Really, one begins to wonder how evolution managed to produce a creature that must be coaxed just to stay alive, but there it is.

**Feeding:** When you buy the poults they will be about six weeks old. At this age you can begin to 'dilute' the proprietary feed with stale bread or wastes from a bakery or confectioner's shop, mixed with the crumbs (the proprietary food) and served moistened. Then, about two to three weeks later, cut back on the crumbs and give them whole grain, soaked overnight in water. By the time they are 20 weeks old, whole grain can comprise two-thirds of their diet.

They like green food, and herbs, especially legumes such as clover and lucerne, will provide about 15 per cent of their diet if they are allowed to graze.

Turkeys convert about one-third of the food they eat to body weight.

**Housing:** You can keep a few turkeys in quite a small space, in a 'pole barn'. This is a kind of lean-to, with wooden walls on three sides and the fourth side either covered with wire netting, or having wire netting with a door opening into a pen, or simply left open entirely with a pen outside. Do not overcrowd them. An adult bird will need about 4.5 square metres of floor space. If you cover the floor with rubble or clinker this will help drainage and so improve hygiene. Give them a perch or perches to roost on, but with all poultry the perches must be at the same height or the birds will only use the top one. It's the way feathered democracy works.

**Health:** When they are a few weeks old the young birds will begin to grow those peculiar red 'caruncles' that turkeys wear on their throats. Once the red is clearly present, the birds are fairly hardy. The delicate period is past.

Turkeys are prone to one nasty disease, called black head because in extreme cases their heads turn black. It is caused by a parasite. The first symptoms are general apathy, loss of appetite, weakness and drowsiness. Often, droppings turn bright yellow, after which death comes suddenly.

The best cure is prevention, and this means treating the birds with an anti-blackhead drug throughout their lives. When you buy them as poults it will have been added to their food as a routine measure. Continue to feed it – its presence will be mentioned on the label. As you dilute the proprietary feed, remember that you may also be diluting the dose of the drug and this could be dangerous. You can buy the drug in a soluble form and add it to the birds' drinking water.

Lean-to shelter for turkeys.
This 2·5m × 1·2m house
holds 6 birds of 17 weeks

### General hints

All poultry must be given grits throughout their lives, unless they spend most of their time ranging free in which case they will find their own. Grits are small, sharp stones which serve the birds as teeth, grinding up the food in the crop. Lack of grits can lead to malnutrition no matter how much food you provide, or how much they eat.

For most of the time geese will feed themselves. Ducks that are allowed to roam free will also find much of their own food, but turkeys must be fed. Any food that you provide, to birds of all species, can be augmented by kitchen scraps of most kinds. Green foods (the outer leaves of cabbages, for example) are excellent, as are meat scraps. To prevent passing parasites up and down food chains, waste food should always be cooked.

Egg-laying birds need a supply of calcium. Their own egg-shells dried (place them in a dish in the oven while you are cooking) and crushed, will do well.

A little garlic, say one clove to about 20 litres of water, will help keep the drinking water clean and it does seem to have a generally beneficial effect on health. It will not taint eggs or meat.

### Killing

Ducks are killed in the same way as hens (see p.159). Geese and turkeys, although much bigger, are still killed most quickly and painlessly by dislocating the neck. Hold the bird by one foot and the other wing, upside down. Lower it to a flat, hard surface. The bird will bend its head back, so that its 'chin' is on the ground. Have a companion place a stout wooden or metal bar across the neck, place your feet one on each end, and pull the bird upwards. The neck will break. Pull a little more to stretch it about a further 5cm, then stop or you will pull the head right off – which happens to everyone one time or another. The bird will struggle violently, but it is quite dead: the struggling is a reaction to the severing of the spinal column.

If you are not sure you can do this, then hold the bird upside down and give it a sharp blow with a blunt instrument on the back of the head. This will stun it. Then use a sharp knife to sever the jugular vein, in the throat just below the 'chin'.

Killing anything is unpleasant. Don't hesitate. Make up your mind to do it, then do it as quickly as you can. Your hesitation merely prolongs the suffering.

### Before and after

Starve poultry for 24 hours before you kill them. If possible, pluck them as soon as they are dead. This is more important in the case of geese and turkeys than with the smaller birds, but they really are much easier to pluck while they are still warm. Plucking is a messy, untidy business. Wear old clothes and work out of doors or in a shed or garage, not in the house. If you want to keep goose down for stuffing pillows, make the plucking a twofold operation. Remove the feathers first, then the underlying down separately. Finally singe off the bits you fail to remove. You can use a candle or a taper, or a blowlamp, which is quicker.

Truss the birds straight away, but unless you feel bound by Common Market regulations, they need not be cleaned until you are ready to cook them. Cleaning and trussing are as for fowls (see p.159).

# Pheasants and peafowl

Many farmers who have small areas of woodland derive a small but useful additional income from the sale of shooting rights. The game is most commonly pheasant, and the pheasants are raised – sometimes intensively – for the purpose.

There are about fifty species of pheasant, all members of the family *Phasianidae* (which also includes the quails and partridges) and, apart from the quails and partridges, all Old World. Legend has it that pheasants were introduced to Europe from Asia Minor by the Argonauts, and to Britain by the Romans.

They are colourful, decorative birds, and so, predictably, they have been bred as much for their looks as for their food value. The even more splendid peafowl (several species of the genus *Pavo*) are also pheasants, and, like their cousins, they were once kept mainly for food. Their gastronomic popularity waned when a new wave of immigrants – the New World turkeys – arrived to out-produce them.

Pheasants have never supplied food for more than a minority of any population, and they never will, for they are poorly adapted to any kind of intensive mass-production. So their potential contribution to world food balances is virtually none. All the same, they are one of those members of the animal kingdom that can thrive to produce food from marginal environments without detracting from other uses, such as forestry.

All the pheasants are combative birds, and if they are kept crowded together they will indulge in such 'vices' as vent-pecking, egg-eating and varying degrees of cannibalism. Cocks often fight one another, and the more aggressive of them should be consigned to the pot in the interests of peace. The hens nest on the ground; the nests are usually filthy, which means the eggs are also filthy, and this can cause health problems among the chicks.

Common Pheasant

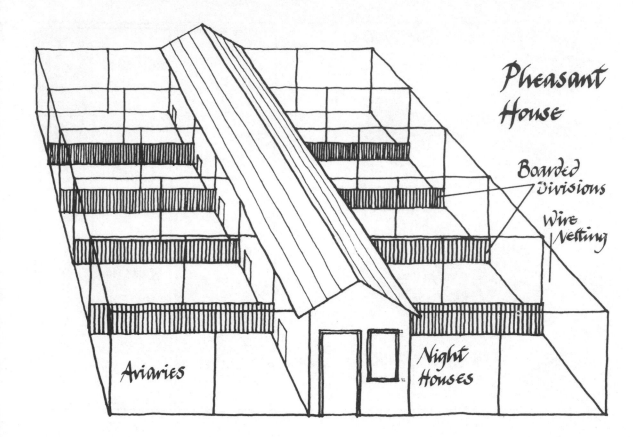

**Pheasant House**

Boarded Divisions

Wire Netting

Aviaries

Night Houses

## Housing

Commercially, most game pheasants are kept for breeding in large outdoor pens, containing 50–150 birds, with one cock to every 6–8 hens, and an allowance of about 10 square metres of space for each bird. If the pens are not covered over with wire mesh, the wings of the birds must be clipped: pheasants are strong fliers.

Game pheasants are hardy and well able to withstand the British climate, but they do not like wind and damp so it is a good idea to provide a night house, with perches to allow the birds to roost. The front can be covered with wire mesh if the house is placed with its back to the prevailing wind, and the floor should be of concrete, stone or wood. If the house is completely closed, make sure that it is well ventilated.

The pen should be well drained, fox- and cat-proof, and provided with an open container for fresh water.

## Breeding

The mating season is short, lasting only about 12 weeks, starting in February. During it the cocks are even more aggressive than usual. On no account try to introduce a new cock into an established flock: it will be killed by the others. You may need to clip the claws of the cocks to prevent them from injuring the hens, and if the pen includes some shrubs or other shelter, it will be easier for the hens to find a little seclusion.

The eggs tend to be laid all over the place, but if you make small, shallow depressions in the ground to provide very rudimentary 'nest boxes', the birds may use them. Don't try to keep the nests tidy or the hens will avoid them altogether.

You can leave the hens to hatch and rear their own chicks, or you can use an incubator in which case the eggs should be collected once or twice a day – most are laid late in the day – and washed in detergent and then dipped in a sanitizing liquid before being put into the incubator.

## Rearing

If the eggs have been hatched in an incubator, the chicks will have to be reared in a brooder, where they will remain for 6–8 weeks. Allow the

167

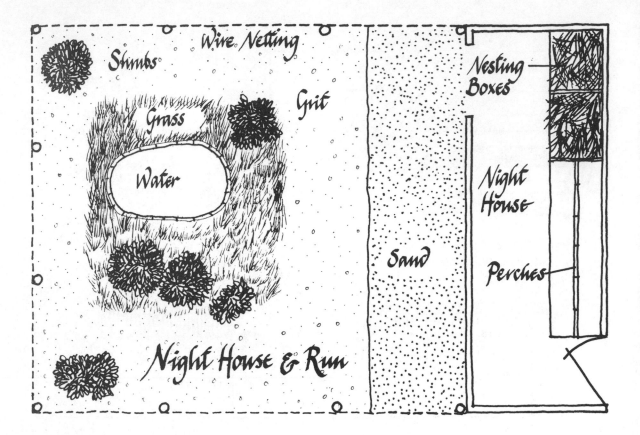

**Night House & Run**

Labels in the figure: Shrubs, Wire Netting, Grass, Grit, Water, Night House, Nesting Boxes, Perches, Sand, Night House & Run

chicks access to the open air, preferably on grass, in which case the grass should be kept short and the mowings removed. Provide some gentle heating in the brooder until the chicks are fully feathered, avoid draughts as far as possible, and keep conditions clean.

### Feeding
Pheasants are grain eaters. You can make up your own mixture for them, consisting mainly of wheat but with some whole or broken maize, or you can use proprietary turkey feeds. (You can buy pheasant feeds, but turkey feeds are probably better, not least because they contain cocci-diostats, to prevent one of the most common diseases of both pheasants and turkeys. Pheasant feeds are not always so treated.)

Feed ad lib., especially during breeding. This may produce rather fat hens, but there is a real danger that any alternative rationing system may lead to starvation. Place the feed in troughs or some other container, under shelter to keep it dry, and clear away spilled food to prevent the birds – and especially the chicks and poults – from eating contaminated feed.

Young chicks can be started on proprietary pheasant starter crumbs or turkey starter crumbs, with a balance of about 25 per cent crude protein, 2.6 per cent oil, and 4 per cent fibre, giving a total metabolizable energy content of around 2375 MJ per kilogram.

### Diseases
The most common disease of pheasants is avian tuberculosis, and it can be minimized by not keeping laying birds for more than one season. The disease is transmitted through the eggs.

Salmonellosis can also be serious, and *Salmonella typhimurium* can be transmitted through the eggs, to cause high rates of mortality among chicks in their first two weeks of life. Other enteric infections may also occur. The best prevention is to maintain a high standard of hygiene, and this will also reduce the incidence of another disease of chicks, brooder pneumonia (aspergillosis).

Coccidiosis is very common, but can be kept under control by feeding coccidiostats, and fowl pest can be prevented by vaccination. The vaccine is administered in the drinking water.

168

## Release

If the pheasants are to be released for subsequent shooting (the alternative being to keep them in captivity until maturity), the release should be phased to allow some acclimatization to the new environment.

When the poults are 5–7 weeks old, clip the main flight feathers on one wing – they will grow again in a few weeks. Move them into a pen sited among dense cover, but with some open ground nearby as well. The pen should have a small but fox-proof hole at ground level through which the birds can re-enter the pen. As soon as they are able to do so, they will begin to fly out of the pen, but for a time they will return to feed or at night. The hole is necessary because they lack the intelligence to fly in. If you plan to feed the adult pheasants, put one or two (depending on the number of poults) feeders into the pen so that the birds come to recognize them as sources of food.

Pheasants hatched from eggs laid in the spring will be ready to be harvested the following autumn and winter (the shooting season runs from 1 October to 31 January).

## Peafowls

Peafowls eat grain and grass and if they are allowed their freedom they will find most of their own food. They are polygamous, one cock having usually about five hens. They nest on the ground and roost in trees. Each hen normally lays 4–8 eggs, which take 27–30 days to hatch. The hen is a good mother and the chicks are easy to rear, but do not grow very quickly. They assume their full plumage only in their third year.

The most common variety is the Indian Peafowl *(Pavo cristatus)* which also has a common albino form. The slightly less common Green Peafowl *(Pavo muticus muticus)* comes from further east than the Indian, with sub-species associated with Java *(muticus muticus),* Indo-China *(m. imperator)* and Burma *(m. spicifer).*

These species are all hardy and need no protection from the British climate, although the Green Peafowls appreciate an unheated closed shelter in which they can be protected against night frosts in winter.

Peafowls live happily in parks, but can also be raised in pens (allow them plenty of space for their tails). If you are breeding them in captivity, treat them as you would any other pheasants.

Common Peafowl

## Further reading

**The vegetarian argument:** *Food for a Future* by Jon Wynne-Tyson. Davis-Poynter.

**General:** *The Survival Handbook* by Michael Allaby, Marika Hanbury-Tenison, John Seymour and Hugh Sharman. Macmillan, Pan.

**Historical:** *Farm Stock of Old* by Sir Walter Gilbey. Spur Publications.

**Small-scale dairying:** *The Backyard Dairy Book* by Len Street and Andrew Singer. Whole Earth Tools.

**Goats:** *Goat Husbandry* by David Mackenzie. Faber.

**Sheep:** *British Sheep Breeds, Their Wool and Its Uses.* British Wool Marketing Board, Education Dept., Oak Mills, Station Road, Clayton, Bradford, W. Yorks.

**Poultry:** *The Backyard Poultry Book* by Andrew Singer. Prism Press.

*Keeping Ducks, Geese and Turkeys* by John Walters and Michael Parker. Garden Farming Series, Pelham Books.

*Poultry Culture for Profit* by Rev. T. W. Sturges. Spur Publications.

*Bantams for Everyone* by H. Easom Smith. Iliffe.

*Turkeys: Production and Marketing Problems* by W. Dyfri Jones. Crosby Lockwood Staples.

*Pheasants, Including Their Care in the Aviary* by H. A. Gerrits. Blandford Press.

## Information

**Animal health and artificial insemination for cattle and pigs:** Contact the Animal Health Office of the Divisional Office of the Ministry of Agriculture, Fisheries and Food.

**Dexter cattle and artificial insemination for Dexters:** Contact Mrs. B. W. Rutherford, The Dexter Breed Society, Bunksland Farm, West Anstey, N. Devon.

**Goats:** The British Goat Society, Lion House, Rougham, Bury St. Edmunds, Suffolk.

# FOOD FROM A SMALL SPACE

# Rabbits

Rabbits pose the same kind of dilemma as pigs or hens. You can keep them as scavengers and fillers-in, to give a modest output of, say, 20 offspring per doe per year in three litters, or you can use them as factory-style, computer-fed broilers, bred to the last gene and producing 60 or more bunnies per year in six or more litters. We believe that the rabbit belongs in the smallholding or back garden, where it can utilize odds and ends, contribute to the over-all biological efficiency, and provide a steady supply of meat. As a broiler it is merely one more competitor for food we could be eating ourselves.

### Breeds
First, choose your animals. Old English, Giant Flemish, or Belgian Hare were the traditional smallholding beasts, sometimes crossed with the small black-and-white Dutch to give a compact carcass. The New Zealand White and the Californian, sometimes crossed to give hybrid vigour, have now been added to the list. You should not go wrong with the traditional types, but we have heard stories of highly bred New Zealanders, doubtless reared commercially on pellets and reluctant to change their diet, that refused to breed in backyard hutches.

### Housing
Any system of housing is good enough, so long as it provides dry, draught-proof sleeping quarters (rabbits hate the damp more than the cold), a quiet, isolated place for the doe to raise her youngsters, separation of buck and doe except when you want them to be together, and plenty of light (which to some extent affects their willingness to breed).

In practice, it is difficult to improve on the traditional hutch. This should be about a metre long, 75cm deep and 45–60cm high. Wire netting covers two-thirds of the front. The remaining one-third is partitioned off and has a solid door, to form a sleeping section. The opening between day and night quarters should be near the back, and only just big enough for the doe to squeeze through.

At backyard levels of production you need four or five does, and one buck, to give you a constant supply of one or two young rabbits throughout the year. This means you will need half a dozen hutches, which you can arrange neatly in a block, two wide and three deep.

A second kind of house, which is cheap and especially useful for raising the young bunnies, is the Morant. This is shaped like a ridge tent. One end is covered with wire netting and open to the ground, and the other end is enclosed and floored to make a sleeping section. On light land you may need to put 50mm netting across the floor of the 'run' end, to prevent burrowing.

Morants are designed to be mobile. You should move them once or twice a day to 'rotate' the animals around the grazing. About ten young rabbits can fit in a Morant that is roughly 3 metres by 125cm.

Straw is the best bedding, and gives good compost.

### Breeding
Backyard does need to be nine months to a year old before breeding. Put the doe into the buck's cage. If you do it the other way round they may fight. Ten minutes should be enough. Then allow the buck to rest for a day before you offer him another doe.

The babies are born, blind and helpless, 30-31 days after mating, and the trick is to leave them strictly alone, particularly for the first week, or the doe will kill them. After 6 weeks you can separate the youngsters, and after a further 8 weeks or so they should weigh about 2–2.5 kilos, which will give you a table weight of 1–1.4kg. If you feed pellets to one of the modern breeds, the animals should reach this weight in 8 or 9 weeks from birth, but we are meant to be talking about backyarding!

The doe can go back to the buck two weeks after you have taken away her youngsters.

### Feeding
You can base your feeding system on pellets, but we think most of the feed should consist of items that cost little or nothing. Rabbits like green of all kinds, especially dandelions, groundsel, chickweed, sow thistles, cabbage leaves, clover,

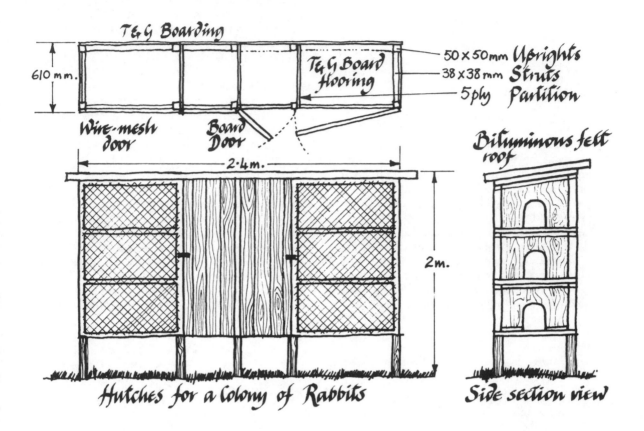

**Hutches for a Colony of Rabbits**      **Side section view**

Labels in figure: T&G Boarding · 610 mm. · T&G Board Flooring · 50×50mm Uprights · 38×38mm Struts · 5ply Partition · Wire-mesh door · Board Door · 2·4m. · Bituminous felt roof · 2m.

lettuce that has run to seed, meadow grass, pea tops, wilted comfrey and chicory. Cabbage and brussels sprouts stalks provide them with a good chew, which they enjoy. They also appreciate bread (preferably baked first), small cooked potatoes, acorns, bran, and hay in winter. The suckling mother will benefit from bread soaked in milk, and crushed oats and wheat are a great standby. With so many of their foods dependent on the season, it is difficult to feed them scientifically. If in doubt, allow them cereal ad lib. They will not usually eat cereal in preference to fresh herbage, so it will become a 'top-up' for when they are hungry.

Finally, although rabbits are extremely good at conserving body water, water should always be available, preferably from a bottle with a feeder attachment that you can buy from any pet shop.

## Killing, paunching, skinning

The quickest and cleanest way to kill a rabbit is with an air gun. Place the muzzle to the back of the head between the ears and pointing at the tip of the nose.

To remove the viscera, make a straight cut down the belly, from the centre of the ribs to between the back legs.

To skin the rabbit, continue the paunching cut down the back legs to the joint. Cut around the joints and work the skin back up the legs to the tail bone, then cut through the tail bone. Hold the rabbit by its back legs and pull the skin forwards as far as the front legs. Cut the skin around the legs and pull it off, then work the rest of the skin over the legs to the neck. Cut the skin around the neck and remove the head. You will be left with a rabbit ready for jointing, and a complete skin, which can be cured.

# Bees

Bee-keeping is one of those simple and rewarding activities that is made inaccessible by its mystique. It employs animals of an alien culture, half wild and potentially highly dangerous, managed by oddly gifted beings, even more oddly attired.

The intricacies really are infinite, and you should not begin without consulting the British Bee Keepers' Association and the Ministry of Agriculture's Bee Advisory Officer (see p.194); you should also team up with local bee-keepers who will be able to tell you, as well as much else, which of the many strains of bees will thrive in your area.

The underlying principles are straightforward. They involve the gentle manipulation of bee biology to induce them to stay in the hive, and to make life easier for them so that they store more food than they need, leaving you with a surplus.

## Basic principles

The bee colony, which on eight combs may number about 25,000 individuals, contains three kinds of bee. There is one queen, the only fertile female and mother of them all, whose sole task it is to lay eggs. There is a variable number of drones, the males, which are killed off in the autumn, whose only function is to impregnate the next generation of virgin queens. And there are the workers, thousands of them, sterile females, the chief of whose many tasks is to gather pollen and nectar to feed the larval bees, and make honey, from nectar, to serve as a general food store.

The basic unit of the honey-bees' nest is the cell, made of wax secreted from between plates

Drone

Queen

Worker

Honey Bees

of the workers' abdomens. The cells are packed tightly together into 'combs'. Thus packed, there is only one shape they can be: hexagonal. Inside the cells eggs are laid, the resultant larvae are raised, and honey is stored. In the wild, the waxen combs are constructed in any suitable hole. Hollow trees are particularly favoured.

### The hive
The modern hive is essentially a tidied-up version of the wild nest, designed to make life easy for the bees so that they have more time for making honey, and to ensure that some parts of the nest are used exclusively for honey storage, to make it easier for the bee-keeper to expropriate his share.

So, instead of asking the bees to build their own wax cells from scratch, the keeper provides them with wax sheets, already stamped out in hexagons, and contained in wooden frames that are hung vertically, close together, like files in a filing cabinet. The distance between these frames is critical: it must allow the bees access, but not allow them so much space that they start making combs between the frames, which would lock them all together in a single solid mass. As it is, the bees will stick everything together with 'bee glue' (*propolis*) and the keeper must prise the frames loose, preferably with a special 'hive tool', although a screwdriver will do. Then he can lift out a frame at will. Before the modern hive was invented, bee-keepers had to break up the entire nest to get at the honey.

Keepers provide the bees with two sets of these frames, one set above the other. The colony proper lives in the lower tier, where honey is stored for the bees' own personal use, and where the queen can lay eggs in whatever cells she chooses. The lower tier is therefore called the 'brood box'.

Sandwiched between the brood box and the upper tier is the 'queen excluder'. This is a sheet of perforated metal or wire mesh, with holes that are just big enough to allow a worker to pass, but that are too small for the queen. This tier is called a 'super', and because only the workers can reach it, its cells will be filled only with honey and will be free from egg, larvae and pupae. In practice, the keeper uses three supers, obtaining his honey by exchanging a full one for an empty one.

The only other components of the hive are the floor and the roof, and a quilt for insulation and an insulated cover. Without such insulation the bees may depart, or at best they will fail to make full use of the super.

### Getting the bees, and keeping them
Having set up your hive, two problems remain. The first is to get the bees into the hive, and the second is to persuade them to stay there.

You get bees in one of two ways. You can buy them from a commercial dealer, in which case they may come already ensconced on frames, one queen and her attendant workers, which you slot into the brood chamber on your own hive. Alternatively, you can gather a swarm, which you may obtain from a local bee-keeper, or by telling the police that you want one, in which case they will tell you when one turns up.

If the swarm has formed on a tree branch you just shake it into a box or bucket, making sure you are prepared for the sudden increase in weight of 4.5kg or so, then leave the container upside down on a sheet of white cloth spread on the ground, with one side propped up slightly so that any stragglers or strays can wander in. In the evening you gather up the whole lot, take it to your own hive, and shake the bees on to a ramp covered with a white sheet that leads to the hive entrance. The bees move upwards naturally, and into the enticing dark crevice. If they move in during the evening they should not depart again.

The main way of keeping the bees, besides making sure they are comfortable, is to seek out and destroy the large acorn-like cells that are built specially to house new virgin queens. These are built when the colony is ready to swarm.

If you need to move the bees, do it in May if possible. This is also the time to start bee-keeping; a July swarm will barely have time to establish itself, let alone to provide you with a surplus.

### Equipment
As well as the hive itself, there are a few items of equipment that you will need.

The first, and in many ways the most important, is a veil to protect your head. When handling bees always cover your entire body, tuck your upper garment into your belt, and tuck trousers into your socks or boots. You will still be stung, but less often.

You need a smoker, to subdue the bees before

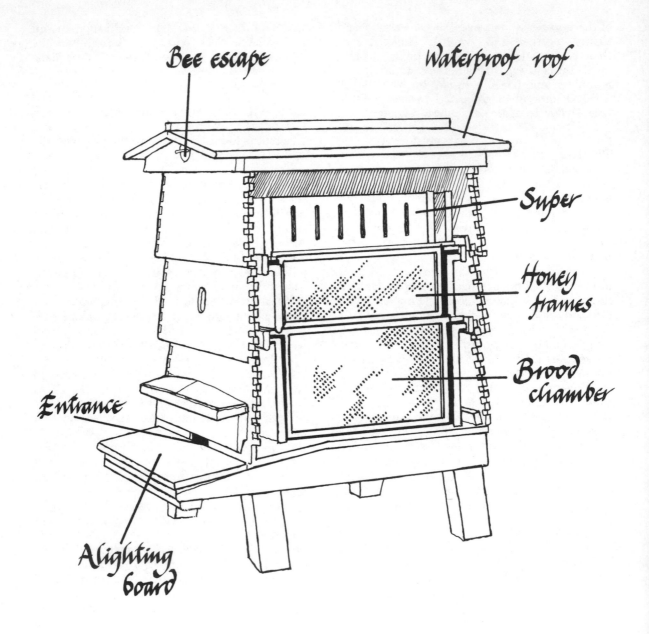

Bee escape

Waterproof roof

Super

Honey frames

Brood chamber

Entrance

Alighting board

A Bee-hive with side removed to show interior arrangement

you open the hive. The smoke makes the bees go down on to the combs.

You need a feeder to supply the bees with sugar syrup in late summer, when the honey flow is finished, and sometimes in spring if the queen is breeding vigorously. Even if you reckon to forego some of your harvest and let the bees overwinter on their own honey, there may be years when this is not enough.

You will need a super clearer, which is a device that fits beneath the super and is left in position overnight before the super is removed. Bees can pass through the clearer in one direction only, so that when you remove the super it is clear of bees.

Unless you eat honey in the comb, you will need a centrifuge to extract it, although you may be able to borrow this item.

That, at least, is the skeleton. Carry out the tasks well and you should have beautifully pollinated beans and fruit, and an average of 14kg of honey per year as a bonus.

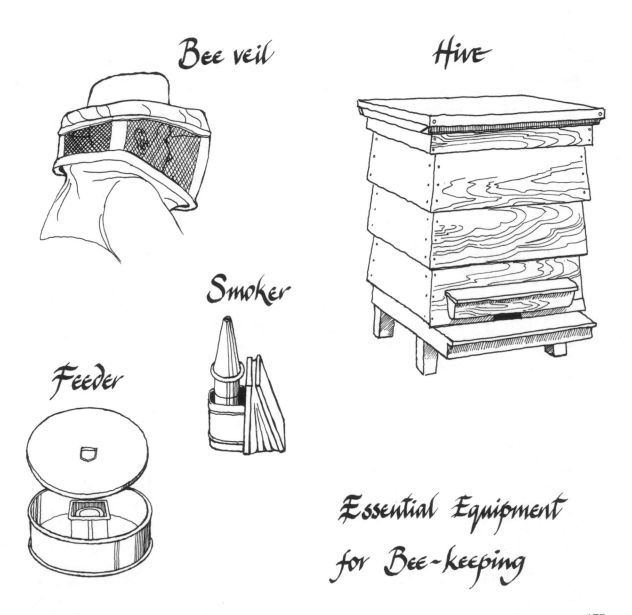

Bee veil

Hive

Smoker

Feeder

Essential Equipment
for Bee-keeping

# Mushrooms

The mythology of mushrooms is endlessly fascinating, with its tales of moonlight and fairy rings and of fruiting heads rising from the onanistic semen of tupping rams. The biology is more useful, however.

Mushrooms belong to the *Basidiomycetes* class of fungi. They consist, fundamentally, of a mass of threads, or 'hyphae', which collectively form the 'mycelium'. The mushroom itself is formed from hyphae compacted together (just as the horn of the rhinoceros is formed from inspissated hair). It is the fruiting body, and bears the 'spores', which are the fungal equivalent of seeds.

The cultivated mushroom is derived from the wild field mushroom, *Psalliota campestris*. Most of the psalliotas are edible, including *P. abruptibulba*, the wood mushroom, and *P. augusta*, which seem to have eluded the acquisition of common names. But beware: some psalliotas, like *P. xanthoderma*, are poisonous, and others, notably *P. abruptibulba*, resemble closely things like *Amanita virosa*, whose common name of Destroying Angel is only too apt.

Fungi are always thought of as plants, yet they lack the outstanding quality of the plant kingdom: the ability to synthesize carbohydrate from gaseous carbon dioxide by photosynthesis. Instead, fungi must live either as parasites, like the potato blight or the cereal rusts, acquiring carbohydrate and protein by digesting the living tissues of their hosts, or as saprophytes, deriving organic matter from dead tissue.

Mushrooms are saprophytes, and therefore must be supplied with dead tissue. In effect this means that mushrooms need compost, and that the art of growing mushrooms is the art of compostmanship.

However, as we saw on p.80, the ecology of the compost heap is almost infinitely intricate, whereas the basic chemistry is simple. We saw,

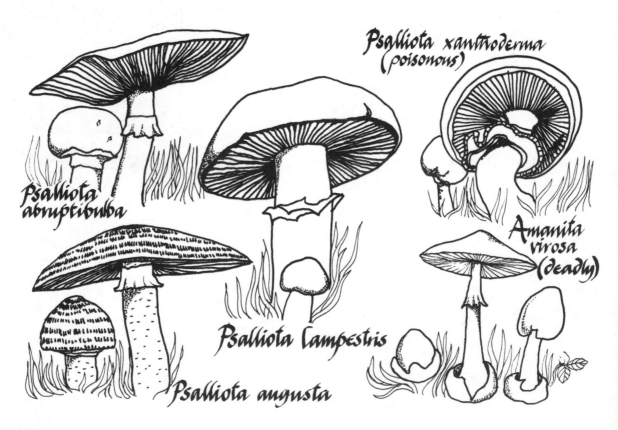

Psalliota xanthoderma (poisonous)

Psalliota abruptibulba

Amanita virosa (deadly)

Psalliota campestris

Psalliota augusta

too, that when we are simply preparing compost to put on the garden, for all practical purposes we can ignore the ecology. It really does not matter which species of aerobic bacteria assault the ingredients of the heap initially, or which particular fungi follow in their wake, so long as the heap itself fininishes up with the right texture. This approach will not do for mushroom compost. Here the heap ecology is vital. We must create conditions that suit *P. campestris* to the exclusion of all else. If we do no more than build a compost heap, and let wild bacteria and fungi fight over it as we do normally, then we will be extremely unlikely to end up with mushrooms – even if we plant mushrooms officiously. Probably they would be ousted by *Aspergillus,* or some other species.

In practice, mushrooms seem to favour compost based on horse manure. Immediately, this sounds like more 'muck 'n mystery', for surely manure is manure is manure. A moment's thought shows that this is not so, however. The eating practice of a horse resembles that of the deer (see p.149). It pushes low-grade fodder through its guts quickly. In addition, it does not ruminate, which implies endless chewing and re-chewing. So its dung tends to be fibrous, giving it a potentially more open structure than that of, say, a cow. This structure lends itself to rapid aerobic decomposition, and it tends to make the manure more nutritious. The much denser cow dung rots more slowly. So far as we know, the only dung that is comparable to the horse's is that of the elephant, which is another hind-gut fermenter.

Horses use food wastefully, and the rich diet given to racehorses is said to yield particularly nutritious turds. One highly successful commercial mushroom grower uses dung from the Newmarket stables, mixed fifty-fifty with straw to give it a good, open structure, and to every tonne he adds two buckets of deep-litter poultry manure, which is very high in nitrogen and therefore useful for balancing all that straw.

The first assailants of an open-structured compost heap are thermophilic bacteria. Fungi, including mushrooms, take over after they have done the initial breaking down. If you put in the mushroom spawn before the bacteria have had their turn, it will simply be killed by the heat.

Those are the underlying principles. The practice is straightforward. First, you make a compost heap out of the dung–straw mixture, to which should be added 13kg of gypsum per tonne, to stabilize the acidity. The heap should heat up within a week and when it has, turn it over at intervals of three to five days, so that it breaks down uniformly. When the compost is dark brown, without lumps, and spongy, it is ready for the mushroom bed.

The beds can be made by piling the finished compost on the floor, up to 45cm deep (a concrete floor is non-messy) or by pressing it firmly into boxes, 15–20cm deep. Mushrooms are not tropical, for all their exoticism, but are plants of the English autumn. So the shelter that houses the boxes or heaps should be cool. The temperature should not be above about 18°C, and 13°C is probably the optimum. The humidity should not be too high, but neither should the compost be allowed to dry, not least because it must not be watered once the mushroom spawn has been sown.

At this stage, the aerobic bacteria should be allowed one more crack at the compost. It should heat up to about 43°C. When your soil thermometer tells you the temperature has dropped again to around 21°C, introduce the spawn. This, as purchased commercially, should consist of disease-free mycelium ensconced in compost. You break off lumps the size of walnuts and press them in to a depth of about 3cm, 15cm apart.

After five days or so the hyphae should have spread through the compost. About three or four days after that, you 'case' the compost: put about 4cm of damp, sterile soil or peat, mixed with chalk or gypsum, on to the surface of the compost and press it down firmly. This is to encourage the mycelium that penetrates this upper layer that is poor in nutrients to throw up fruiting bodies: nature often tries to ensure survival by laying the foundations of the next generation when conditions get rough. Some writers recommend putting 15cm of straw over the casing, which presumably helps to regulate the humidity and temperature, but commercial growers do not usually do this.

Commercial growers raise mushrooms on a staggering scale, yet the mushroom has one biological quirk that – at least at present – puts it beyond automation. The fruiting heads all appear at different times. The indiscriminate mechanical scythe can never replace the picker. As mushrooms are bound to remain expensive, and as labour can never be replaced fully, the skilled small-scale grower should always be in business.

# Food in the house

When the farm crops are sown, the garden or allotment fully stocked, the greenhouse crammed with plants, it is time to start looking at the inside of the house for windowsills and odd corners that will accommodate edible plants. Even if you live half way up a skyscraper, you can grow some food indoors.

The crops to choose, obviously, are those that require the least space, and this generally means those that produce the most flavour per square centimetre, since they cannot compete with outdoor crops in terms of bulk. Herbs are an obvious answer, but they are not the only one. Thompson and Morgan, the Ipswich seed merchants, suggest a range of tropical crops that cannot survive outdoors in our climate, but that might do very well in the centrally heated house. Their list includes yellow and red strawberry guavas, papaya, cherimoya (a pear-shaped fruit that tastes like pineapple, peach and banana all at once), passion fruits, watermelon and granadilla, as well as a miniature citrus that produces small oranges, and a coffee plant that produces beans.

These may sound a trifle too exotic. Perhaps the easiest food crop of all to produce are beansprouts, and they take up virtually no space. Simply fasten a piece of muslin over the open top of a jam jar into which you have placed what looks like a reasonable quantity of beans, pour in enough water to fill the jar, shake well, and pour the water out again through the muslin. Repeat this night and morning until the beans have sprouted and are ready to eat.

There are several beans and grains that can be harvested as beansprouts, including alfalfa, fenugreek, adzuki, mung beans and triticale, the wheat–rye hybrid that is being developed as a farm crop but that so far has been unable to

## Purple Granadilla & Cherimoya

compete in terms of yield with either of the original cereals. Thompson and Morgan also supply a mixture of seeds for sprouting. The original Chinese beansprouts come from mung beans.

Tomatoes can be grown indoors very satisfactorily, provided you keep them well watered, and provided you have space for enough plants to make it worth while. Tomato plants have a distinctive smell, which some people may not like.

Other salad crops, such as cucumber, lettuce and (obviously) mustard-and-cress, can be grown indoors, although cucumbers will require about 1.5 metres of vertical space.

### Indoor herbs
You can increase the space available for indoor herbs by installing troughs along windowsills: if you are building a house, or a new window is being put into an existing wall, the sill can be set down to take the trough. Shelves, each large enough to hold a plant pot, can be put beside the window, one above another, and a container beside a table lamp may do well.

## Mung Beans (Bean Sprouts)

Not all herbs are suitable for indoor cultivation, and of those that are, some are best brought indoors as plants, rather than being grown from seed in the house.

Maintain as constant a temperature as possible, at about 15–16°C, provide the plants with a richer soil than they would find in the garden, and change the soil in pots at least once a year. Make sure the pots are well drained, water not more than once a week or so and do not allow the plants to stand in direct sunlight when their leaves are wet. Pot growing will stunt the growth of the plants, so cropping must be done carefully. Herbs can be grown well and attractively in window boxes.

The herbs most suitable for indoor growing are as follows:

**Basil** *(Ocimum basilicum)* is very sensitive to frost and should be potted and brought indoors in September. Cut the plant back to the first leaves above the base of the stem, use bush basil rather than sweet basil, and plant half a dozen seedlings in a 20cm pot, with a rich soil.

**Borage** *(Borago officinalis),* which is an annual, can be grown indoors from seed or from seedlings.

**Chervil** *(Anthriscus cerefolium),* which looks rather like a lacy, fern-like version of parsley, is said to improve the flavour of other herbs as well as providing flavouring in its own right for soups and sauces. Grow it from seed on the kitchen windowsill, and if you acquire the taste for it, grow plenty, because it is used generously.

**Chives** *(Allium schoenoprasum)* are very hardy once they become established and they do well in window boxes. Plant them as bulbs and cut back the stalks to about 5cm. Give them plenty of root space and a rich soil. Indoor chive plants die almost always for lack of room for adequate root development.

**Dill** *(Anethum graveolens)* takes little from the soil, but when grown in pots or window boxes there is insufficient room for full root development and so the plant does not reach its full potential height (90cm) nor produce seed heads, but it does produce leaves. Dill is an annual and must be grown from seed.

**Fennel** *(Foeniculum vulgare)* is a perennial, but is often cultivated as a biennial. In parts of the country it grows wild. It can be grown from seed, or established plants can be transferred to pots and moved indoors or into a window box. It will grow in poor soil and in a smoky atmosphere.

**Lemon balm** *(Melissa officinalis)* is a perennial, grown from seeds, cuttings, or root divisions. It should be planted in October for indoor growing or in March for a window box. It needs good soil and plenty of moisture, and when it has flowered it should be cut to soil level.

**Marjoram** *(Origanum onites),* Pot Marjoram, is one of three marjorams grown in Britain (the others are Sweet Marjoram and Wild Marjoram, or Oregano) and the only one suitable for growing indoors. Grow it from a cutting, or cut down outdoor plants to about one-third of their size and when they have recovered pot them in soil with plenty of rotted compost and sand and adapt them to indoor conditions gradually.

**Mint** *(Mentha)* is a genus of the family *Labiatae,* many of whose species are used as flavourings. Probably the best for indoor growing is Spearmint *(M. viridis* or *spicata),* which is the one most people use for mint sauce. Its main rivals, Apple Mint and Bowles Mint, grow too large for convenient indoor plants. Grow the plants from cuttings in 10cm pots in order to contain the roots which spread readily and rapidly unless they are controlled. Place the pots on a window sill and turn them from time to time so that the sun falls on them evenly. Provide them with a good, rich soil, keep the roots moist, and keep cutting the plants so they do not grow more than 15cm high. Plant the cuttings in May or June, and cut the plants down in September and provide a dressing of rich compost.

**Parsley** *(Carum petroselinum)* comes in several sub-species and varieties of sub-species. The best for indoor growing are probably 'Triple Curled' and 'Green Gem', which grow to 18–30cm and 13cm respectively. Parsley is a biennial, but is often grown as an annual. Grow it from seed in pots or window boxes, sowing in succession from February to late summer, or bring in plants from the garden in the autumn. Seeds are slow to germinate and when the plants appear they must be thinned. Indoor plants require a richer soil than they would find outdoors.

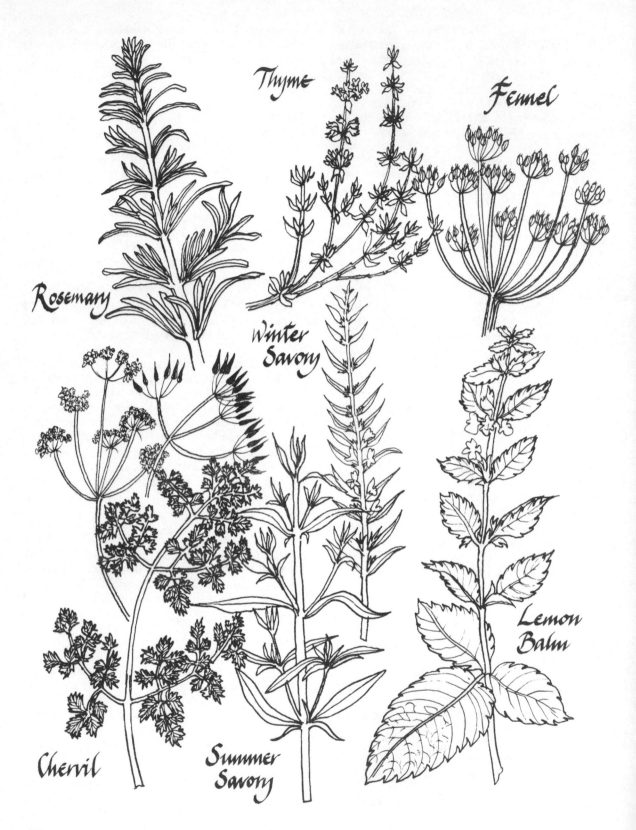

Thyme

Fennel

Rosemary

Winter
Savory

Lemon
Balm

Chervil

Summer
Savory

They prefer partial shade, but not damp conditions. Cut plants to be brought indoors to a height of about 5cm, and allow room in the pots for the substantial root system. If you cut off old, tough leaves, you will stimulate new growth.

**Rosemary** *(Rosmarinus officinalis)* is a perennial bush that can grow to a height of more than 1.5 metres, but only in the south. In cooler climates it may not grow outdoors at all. Grow the plant – either bought from a nursery, or raised from a cutting – in humus and sand. If you are bringing in an outdoor plant, trim it back to about one-third of its normal size, allow it to recover, pot it and then acclimatize it gradually.

**Sage** *(Salvia officinalis)* is a perennial small shrub that grows well and easily in a window box or indoor pot, provided the plants are kept well shaped by cutting back new growth. The plants will need to be renewed from time to time. There are many different sages, but the best for indoor use are Pineapple and Dwarf Garden Sages.

**Savories** (Summer Savory, *Satureia hortensia* and Winter Savory, *S. Montana*) can be planted in boxes or pots in August. Summer Savory is an annual and Winter Savory a perennial. Trim back the winter variety outdoors to a height of about 10cm and when the plants have recovered put them in a sandy soil with plenty of humus, and acclimatize them gradually to indoor conditions, then, like Summer Savory, find them a sunny spot in which to thrive.

**Thymes** (Garden Thyme, *Thymus vulgaris* and Lemon Thyme, *T. citriodorus*) are perennial bushes that can be grown indoors in a fairly rich soil, kept well watered, especially in summer. Their roots tend to spread, so they are best grown in pots, in a mixture of compost and sand.

**Lemon Verbena** *(Lippia citriodora)* is an imported plant, native to South America, that is quite different from the related *Verbena officinalis* (Vervain), associated with ancient Druid rites. Both are perennial bushes, but only Lemon Verbena grows well indoors, from cuttings in a rather poor soil.

**Woodruff** *(Galium odoratum* or *Asperula odorata)* is a native wild plant, a perennial found in beech woods. It can be grown from seed, but germination is often very slow, and it is easier to propagate it from cuttings or by dividing the roots of older plants. It likes a soil containing some leafmould, potash and sand to simulate a woodland soil, and it does not like direct sunlight. It grows well in pots indoors.

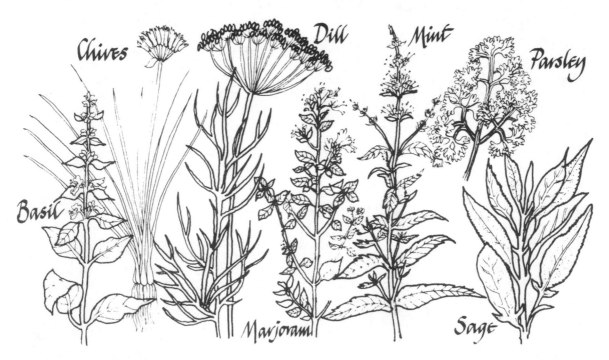

# Leaf protein

Ninety-five per cent of the protein eaten by humans is generated by plants. Most is eaten either directly as seeds (which usually means grain), or after it has passed through an animal. The remaining 5 per cent is synthesized by bacteria, from non-protein nitrogen and carbohydrate, in the guts of ruminants, and reaches us as meat and dairy produce.

Yet over the world as a whole, by far the largest source of protein is the green leaf. This statement still seems ludicrous, so conditioned are we to equating 'protein' with meat or, at best, with beans or cereals. The fact is obvious, however, for the protein that finds its way into the seeds or flesh that we are used to eating is generated in leaves, and most of it is lost in transit. A hectare of maize forage may contain nearly 400kg of protein, whereas the grain itself will contain only 257kg, and the most generous protein producers of all, per hectare, may be cabbage or continually cropped spinach.

Human beings (and pigs) are unable to make much use of leaf protein because it is so dilute. Cabbage, for example, is nearly all water and the small percentage of dry matter is mostly fibre: cellulose and hemicelluloses. Only ruminants, or comparable specialists like the rabbit, horse or hippopotamus, are able both to accommodate such bulk and then, with the help of their gut bacteria, to break down the plant cell walls and release the nutritious cytoplasm inside.

Ever since the eighteenth century, and particularly since N.W. Pirie of the Rothamsted Experimental Station devised a suitable machine in 1948, scientists and governments have toyed with the idea of extracting protein-rich leaf pulp mechanically and using it either to bolster human rations or to feed pigs and poultry. The residue, consisting mostly of fibre but with some pulp still remaining, would be an adequate feed for cattle, especially if it were fortified with a cheap non-protein nitrogen source, such as urea or sterilized chicken manure.

At first sight, the idea seems to solve all our food problems at a stroke. Remove the toxins, and suddenly all foliage, from wayside weeds to the hundreds of tonnes of leaf produced annually in a deciduous forest, appears as a potential food source.

In practice, there are three snags: botanical, mechanical, and gastronomic. Not all leaves are suitable. Many – holly and bracken are obvious examples – are just too tough, fibrous or mucilagenous to make extraction worth while. Secondly, the protein content of leaves is highly variable, and diminishes rapidly as they become moribund, as we saw with grass conservation (see p.106). Leaves that had been shed naturally from a tree would be a poor source, while to harvest them when they were young and fresh would be difficult technically and would certainly harm the tree, or even kill it. Thirdly, wild vegetation often looks lush, but it rarely is. The vegetation of a tropical rain-forest is prolific because it contains so much water, while the plants that Pirie has called 'the unmanured rubbish of the roadsides' are unlikely to be high either in biomass or in protein content.

In fact, we would have to grow plants specifically for protein extraction. This does mean we could cultivate more species than we do now – *Chenopodium* species, including the familiar 'weeds' Good King Henry or Fat Hen, might be particularly suitable – but it also means that for the most part the technique would have to compete with conventional agriculture. Only a few wild plants, including perhaps the otherwise pestilential water hyacinth of tropical waterways, would be suitable.

The mechanical problems are not yet solved fully. Too vigorous an attack on the leaves generates too much heat, and so coagulates the protein and makes it unextractable. Adding water to float out the protein makes the resulting pulp too wet. Various designs of mincer and roller have fallen foul of this paradox.

Finally, leaf pulp is not always accepted readily as an item of diet.

All the same, the problems are being solved. Scientists at the University of Wisconsin have produced a machine that flails the leaves gently and then squeezes out the pulp, and they believe they can produce a useful version for producing leaf protein on a village scale. In one project at Coimbatore, India, leaf pulp from specially grown lucerne (alfalfa) is helping to enrich the diets of children, who take to it well enough if they are not prejudiced against it first. In Britain and in Eastern Europe work is still afoot to get more out of grass, by extracting the pulp to feed to pigs and feeding the residue to cattle.

Dairy & Beef
102

Beef
27

Broilers
92

Pigs
50

Dairy
115

Sheep
23

Wheat
350

Edible Protein
(kgs per hectare)

Peas
280

Cabbage
1100

Potatoes
420

Eggs
80

# Microbial protein

Some technophiles would have us believe that unless we learn to eat protein made by bacteria, fungi, yeasts or algae, then all of us are doomed to starve. Indeed, so they suggest, it is only the peevish predilection of Africans for bananas or of Britons for mutton chops that caused the world's food problems in the first place.

Others regard microbial proteins with hysterical distaste. They will give us cancer, make monsters of our children and, besides, they are a capitalist plot.

As always, the truth lies between the two extremes.

Microbes can be a splendid source of protein. They can, in theory, use any organic molecule as their raw material, which means, quite simply, virtually any molecule that contains carbon and hydrogen. Thus yeasts can be grown on the waxy by-products of oil, and they are so used, by BP, to make 'Toprina'. Various fungi can grow on almost any kind of carbohydrate, from wood pulp to sugar cane waste (bagasse). Tate and Lyle plan to use bagasse in this way in sugar-growing regions. There are fungi and bacteria that can grow happily on methyl alcohol, made easily from natural gas or a similar hydrocarbon. Indeed, ICI use the fungus *Methylophilus methylotrophus* to produce their proprietary 'Pruteen' from such a source.

In general, microbial protein is of high concentration and quality. 'Pruteen', after drying, is 70 per cent protein and its quality compares well with that derived from soya. The biological efficiency of microbes is staggering. Typically, they double their weight in a few hours. Even the fastest-growing farm animal takes weeks or, more likely, months. Microbes can be produced – indeed, for agricultural purposes they must be produced – by continuous culture. Output is absolutely reliable, standardized, and immune from the vagaries of weather. For those who worry about the efficiency with which energy is used in food production, microbial protein production is so efficient that any kind of farming looks like the most extravagant indulgence.

The theoretical dangers of microbial protein seem fairly readily surmountable. They have been exaggerated, largely because of the prejudice that associates 'microbe' with 'disease'. Theoretically there could be problems caused by the high nucleic acid content of yeasts. Nucleic acids are rich in purines, and purines are associated with gout. In tests with laboratory animals the dangers have not manifested themselves. Theoretically, the oil by-products used as substrate for microbes could contain carcinogens, but in practice chemists seem able to remove them and the proportion of carcinogens may be far less than that on, say, the surface of a well-charred steak – and it does not follow necessarily that carcinogens present in the substrate will be taken up by the microbes and end in the ultimate food product. We use yeasts already, and have done for centuries, to make some of our most revered delicacies, from champagne to Roquefort, from draught bitter to double Gloucester, not to mention bread. All of them depend on the gentle attentions of yeasts, bacilli and various fungi.

Can microbial protein be produced on a worthwhile scale? Will it make an impact on world food supplies?

The raw statistics suggest that it might. Europe's pigs and poultry get through 6 million tonnes of fishmeal and soya-bean meal a year. The world's total fishmeal production varies between 3 and 5 million tonnes a year, but already the major fisheries are showing signs of severe strain, and all maritime states are seeking to conserve stocks of commercial fish species within their territorial waters and main fishing grounds. By 1980, the demand for fishmeal is likely to exceed the supply by 2 million tonnes. BP's largest yeast protein plant, in the south of France, will produce 100,000 tonnes a year; ICI's new *Methylophilus* plant, in Cleveland, will push out 50,000–75,000 tonnes a year. The USSR is producing protein from wood waste – probably about 100,000 tonnes a year. The output from a few dozen such plants would match the world's fishmeal supply and could even steal a march on the world's soya production – currently 50 million tonnes, of which 80 per cent comes from America.

Add to these plants those designed to utilize wastes from the food processing industry, and the total annual output begins to look very large

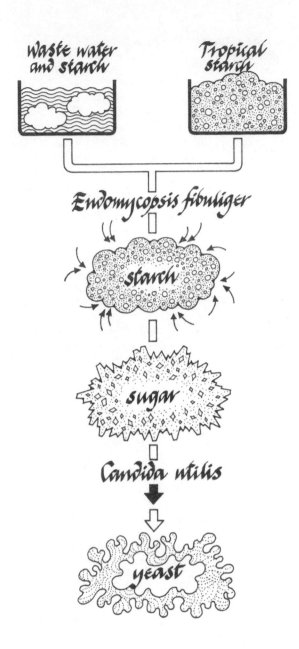

Waste water and starch

Tropical starch

Endomycopsis fibuliger

starch

sugar

Candida utilis

yeast

stuffs suggests that a market for microbial proteins exists.

These are powerful arguments, but microbial protein is far from being a world saver, and it is irresponsible to suggest that it might be.

First, microbial protein is of little use except for feeding livestock. This is not because it is poisonous, but because human beings with a diet containing an adequate amount of staples – potatoes or cereal, but possibly not the protein-deficient cassava eaten in some tropical countries – are unlikely to be short of protein. Only beasts bearing enormous physiological loads – the lactating sow, or the 280-egg-a-year battery hen – need such protein supplements.

Secondly, microbial protein, although it is grown on 'wastes', has a price. Quality control is paramount. This is expensive and requires highly qualified technicians. So the oil-based and gas-based ventures in particular are aiming their products at the top end of the market, at people who are not short of food. Worse, the intensive livestock enterprises that will benefit from microbial protein can be regarded as a major drain on the world's grain resources. By helping to prop up these enterprises, microbial protein might, paradoxically, reduce the total food resources available to the hungry world.

Finally, even those microbial protein schemes that are intended to make use of local by-products, such as Tate and Lyle's project for growing fungi on plantation wastes, should be treated with suspicion. We should ask, perhaps, whether it is in the best interests of the local people to use their best land for plantations at all, growing cash crops to be fed into the markets of the rich countries? Would it be better for them to use that land to create an indigenous agriculture, designed specifically for their own food needs, and to find other ways of developing products for export to earn foreign exchange, products that would be sold for a higher price than primary agricultural produce? Certainly, if they did this they would need no residue-based protein supplements.

Microbial protein is far too good an idea to be abandoned. It will be developed, but it will not feed the world. The world's food problems do not spring from a lack of technology, but from inappropriate agricultural and trading policies. If the new technologies simply detract from the political inequities that are the real root of most of the world's hunger, as they may well do, then they will do more harm than good.

indeed. The pressure to construct plants for using wastes comes from two directions. The first is the need to improve the quality of the effluent discharged from factories into waterways. Pollution legislation is becoming more strict, and British industry may find itself having to meet quality standards designed to improve the purity of the Rhine. Since the effluent must be cleaned, there is an obvious attraction in deriving a marketable product from it. At the same time, the anticipated shortage of animal feed-

# The bioplex

Everything produces wastes. It is, you might say, a fact of life. Wastes are substances for which we have no use, that we think of in terms of disposal, and pollution. What might happen if, instead, we were to think of them as raw materials? What if we were to use our own sewage to produce food?

We might create a 'biological complex', or 'bioplex'. The idea is theoretical, since so far no city has built one, but it is an idea that is being taken seriously, and in the years ahead it is far from impossible that every major city will have one or more units producing large quantities of food.

They will be located at combined sewage-and-refuse treatment works, and their raw materials will be sewage from humans and animals, together with the contents of our dustbins, the wastes from shops (especially food shops), from restaurants and from food processing factories. The amount of food you can produce may depend, in the end, on the amount of refuse you can collect.

The raw materials must be separated. Metals and other inorganic substances will be sent for recycling, leaving behind solid organic wastes and sewage, which is liquid. Both may be contaminated with industrial wastes, so the first step might be to remove the pollutants and sell them back to the industries that discharged them.

Solids and liquids will be separated, to produce a liquid with a heavy load of plant nutrients (see p. 30) and a wet sludge, which would then follow different routes.

The sludge would be fermented anaerobically to produce methane. The material that remained after fermentation could be used partly to extract chemicals for industry, partly as a straightforward manure for growing plants to feed humans or herbivores such as rabbits and goats, and partly to produce single-cell protein (see p. 186). The advantage of processing the material through yeast fungi rather than feeding it more directly to animals lies in the greater ability of these single-celled organisms to break down cellulose.

The liquid would be fed into tanks in which algae would be grown – single-celled green plants that are able to reproduce very rapidly. The algae could be eaten by such herbivorous fish as carp, and the carp harvested for human consumption (the parts of the carp that were not eaten being returned to some other part of the cycle).

The water would also support other minute living creatures and these, together with some of the algae, could be fed to shellfish. The species of shellfish produced would depend on the salinity of the water. If the city were near the coast, for example, oysters and mussels could be raised in sea water.

Most of the shellfish would be eaten by humans, but not all of them. To add variety to the diet, some of the mussels could feed carnivorous fish, such as trout.

As fish take a certain time to grow to their full size, but sewage would be entering all the time, there would be a surplus which could be used for hydroponic cultivation of a range of salads and vegetables (see p. 72).

Single-cell protein, made from the organisms grown on the sludge and possibly, to a lesser extent, on the liquid, could be fed to livestock that require a more protein-rich diet, such as pigs and poultry.

## The Bioplex

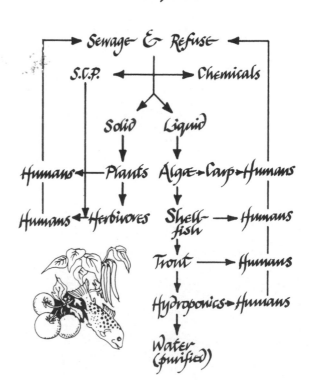

Sewage & Refuse

S.C.P. ← → Chemicals

Solid   Liquid

Humans ← Plants   Algæ → Carp → Humans

Humans → Herbivores   Shell-fish → Humans

Trout → Humans

Hydroponics → Humans

Water (purified)

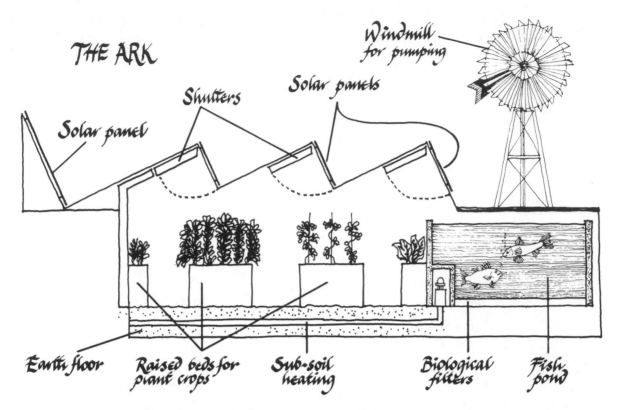

# THE ARK

Solar panel

Shutters

Solar panels

Windmill for pumping

Earth floor

Raised beds for plant crops

Sub-soil heating

Biological filters

Fish pond

The water that leaves the complex could be fed back into the domestic supply, in a purified form.

The system need not be confined to an urban setting, of course. It could work just as well on a farm, where it might be combined with a unit that converted straw into a more acceptable and nutritious feed for livestock. Ruminant animals will eat straw, but its high cellulose content allows less of its nutritional value to be realized than would be possible with pre-treatment. The technique for achieving this was devised many years ago but never developed, partly because there seemed to be no need for it, but partly because it involved the use of concentrated caustic soda, a dangerous and unpleasant chemical to store and handle on a farm. Modern research is likely to offer improvements.

Although no bioplex exists as such, polyculture farms being developed experimentally are based on rather similar principles. They are farms rather than urban complexes, they do not produce single-cell protein or chemical by-products, but they do use the wastes from one enterprise to provide raw material for the next, so that cereals, vegetables, livestock and fish are all produced in a highly integrated way. 'The

Ark', at the New Alchemy Institute, Woods Hole, Massachusetts, is a solar-heated greenhouse-cum-fishpond that uses flat-plate solar collectors to provide heat and a windmill to pump water.

The Ark uses its 60,000-litre pond both to raise fish and to store heat, and the warmed pondwater passes through pipes beneath the earth floor. The vegetables are grown in raised beds, fertilized by wastes from the pond.

In any system as intensive as The Ark or a bioplex, disease, pests and, to a lesser extent, weeds will present acute problems. The standard of hygiene throughout must be very high, the care with which each section is tended must be thorough. If a pest infestation should occur, if disease should strike, the result could be disastrous.

That is the disadvantage. The advantage lies in the very large amounts of food that could be produced in this way, and in the degree of control that people would exert over the technologies involved. The success of the enterprise would depend on care and attention to detail by humans, so that while the system would produce food intensively, it would employ people intensively also.

# The city farm

How much food can we produce in an urban setting? The question is asked frequently, probably because people doubt very seriously whether it is possible for Britain, with its large, densely packed, urban population, to feed itself.

In a sense, there is no answer. It is a bit like asking the length of a piece of string. We can produce as little food as we wish – and, up to a startlingly high ceiling, almost as much as we wish. It all depends on how desperate is our need, and how great our determination.

The best way to have a look at the problems and the potential is to take a fairly typical situation in a big industrial city (in fact, this approximates to an actual area that one of us was asked to examine in Manchester).

Let us suppose that some buildings have been demolished, to leave an area of open ground beside a main road. There is a wide grass verge between the ground and the road, and on the other side the area is bounded by a small road and a row of factory buildings. The area is also residential. Some old terraced houses border two side roads, and some newer three-storey blocks of flats are built between the main road and the first row of terraced houses.

We may take it that in its present form no food is produced here at all, but let us assume that the local residents, the owners of the factory and its workers, and the planning authorities all agree that it would be desirable to maximize food output.

| 1. | Open Space |
|----|------------|
| | Six pigs<br>One hundred hens<br>Greenhouses<br>Allotments<br>Compost bins |
| 2. | Grass Verge |
| | Play area<br>Rabbits<br>(and grass mowings) |
| 3. | 3 Storey Flats |
| | Fruit trees<br>Bees<br>Geese<br>Glass roofs for growing crops |
| 4. | Factories |
| | Glass roofs for growing crops in tubs, barrels and boxes<br>Rooftop gardens |

## Basic principles

The first thing to establish is that the aim is not to make the immediate area self-sufficient in food, which may or may not be possible, but to produce as much food as can be produced with the resources available.

The second point is that the aim is not primarily to provide hobby-occupations for everyone. A major problem with allotments, for example, is that enthusiasm can wane all too easily, and the plots can revert to weed-infested wilderness as the tenants, exhausted by a few weekends of frenetic digging, collapse in front of the TV. So although there can be allotments and gardens for those who are genuinely enthusiastic, all the enterprises must be managed efficiently, and someone must be in charge of each of them.

Having made clear the aims, the next thing is to survey the resources that are available. We have assumed that the area of open ground amounts to one hectare (fairly large, but not unrealistic, and convenient!) and the roadside verge is one-quarter that size. The factory buildings have flat roofs, and so do the blocks of flats. The flats are surrounded by open space covered with grass. Since all local residents are involved, we can count on being given all the household scraps as raw material.

## Getting started

We can take it that the open ground is covered with weeds, and that an analysis of the soil (carried out, at cost price, by the city university, which approves of our efforts) has shown that it is not heavily contaminated with industrial toxic wastes. If it were, we might be forced to buy in topsoil to cover the poisoned ground, and then grow only grass for several years. As it is, however, the need is to clear the weeds and add some fertilizer.

The obvious answer is to buy some pigs. These should be bought as weaners, to be raised as porkers, and for this area a herd of six animals will probably be adequate. Before they arrive we will need to buy some movable fencing to enclose them, and knock up some movable 'arcs' to shelter them (see p.145). Start them at one end of the patch, enclosed in temporary pens, and let them eat and trample and root to their hearts' content, augmenting the food they find for themselves with household scraps made into

a swill (see p.144), supplemented perhaps with scraps from the greengrocer and bakery wastes (but make these into swill, too, or you may pass parasites back and forth along the food chain). While the porkers are guzzling happily, build them some permanent pens at one end of the patch: the end nearest to the houses will be most convenient.

As the pigs clear each patch and are moved forward, rotavate and rake the land they leave behind them, ready for sowing.

Not far from the pig pens, build a henhouse and fence off a run for poultry, large enough to accommodate, say, 100 layers. It would not be wise to opt for an intensive battery or broiler house, because of nuisances caused by smell and the difficulty of disposing of the large amounts of manure that would be produced. The hens, too, can be fed on scraps, but both they and the pigs – once these are into the pens – will also need some bought-in cereal (see p.154).

In the same general area, build some glasshouses. The floors should be well insulated, and a solar heating system will minimize running costs, increase yields, and add little to the capital cost if they are built into the system from the start.

The compost bins should be located nearby. In this way the enterprises that are likely to require most management, or most transporting of heavy or bulky materials, are close together and not far from the houses from which materials will be collected.

Depending on the area under glass, half of the open ground will be left for cultivation and possibly more.

This can accommodate allotments, or community crops, or a mixture of both. If, say, the community as a whole were to devote 0.25 hectares to potatoes, they could expect to harvest 6 tonnes or more – but they may prefer to grow other crops.

All that is needed now is a building in which to store tools and other equipment, and perhaps some of the crops after harvest.

The intensive glasshouses, based on the NFT technique (see p.72) to use space and nutrients most economically, will produce the high-value items such as tomatoes, cucumbers, lettuces and other salads, and they can also be used to germinate seeds for moving outdoors later.

All the wastes from vegetable production can be given to the pigs and poultry, all the manure from the pigs and poultry can go on the land

191

after composting (see p.80).

We cannot waste the grass verge beside the road. It amounts to only a quarter of a hectare, however, and so it is really too small to feed a grazing animal, even a goat – and the amount of milk a goat yields would not go far among so many people. Nor do we wish to plough it all up and grow vegetables so close to the road. In any case, the children need somewhere to play.

The solution may be either to leave it as grass and feed the mowings into the rest of the system, or to feed the grass to rabbits, which can be folded across it like hens. If this is what we plan to do, it might be best first to plough up the Council's slow-growing lawn grass and reseed with a mixture more appropriate for an agricultural ley (see p.104).

A third alternative might be to excavate the verge and make it into fish ponds, but some complex water management would be needed on this particular site, and the yield of, say, carp would not be high enough from so small an area to make it worthwhile.

Now we should look at that grassy area around the blocks of flats. This is too irregular in shape, and probably too windy, for vegetable growing, but if we plant a line of trees around the outside to form a windbreak, then inside we can plant fruit trees – probably apples would be best. The trees can be planted directly into holes cut in the turf, and we should bring in a few geese to graze the (fenced) grass and keep away invading small boys.

As we now have fruit trees that require insect pollination, and as we may decide to grow beans and herbs as well, it would seem sensible to install a couple of beehives. The best place for them will be inside the orchard itself, as far from the houses as is convenient.

We still have the flat roofs of the blocks of flats and the factories. These are high up, away from obstacles that would shade them, but exposed and windy.

If we put them under glass we will shelter them from the wind and make the best use of the sunshine they receive. The limitations of course are that the roofs themselves cannot take more than a certain weight, and everything needed to grow food on them must be brought up from ground level.

We could turf them and graze small animals with the minimum of wind shelter. Or we could cover them with glass, import soil, and grow crops, or cover them with glass and grow crops in tubs, barrels and boxes. This last technique would reduce the loading on the roofs by allowing us not to cover the parts that were not to be sown, and it would make it easier to move the soil containers to the ground when the soil needed changing.

The roof might be used to grow such crops as capsicums, courgettes, aubergines and other exotic, warmth-loving plants, as well as, say, strawberries, which grow well – and very prettily – in tubs with holes in the sides (the plants are placed into the soil through the holes, and the runners trail down the sides). Runner beans might also be grown in this way, planted in tubs and trained along frames that run the length of the building.

These warm, colourful rooftop gardens might be very pleasant places to sit in the evening.

Finally, the Council might be persuaded to allow us to use some of our own sewage, and the factory might allow us some floor space to produce single-cell protein by a fungal fermentation process (see p.186). The resultant protein could be fed to the pigs and poultry, so cutting down on or perhaps eliminating entirely bought-in supplements.

### What have we achieved?
Quite a lot, and the food that we produce is only part of it.

The pig unit will produce about 300kg of meat (live weight) per year. The poultry will produce 10,000–12,000 eggs per year, and something like 100 birds for eating – some for roasting and some as culls for making casseroles. There will be about 120 rabbits for the pot and half a dozen or so geese. Two beehives will produce about 30kg of honey a year. We will grow maybe 6 tonnes of potatoes, and useful quantities of a wide range of other vegetables, salads and fruit as well.

We will have made a true urban farm, and we will have altered the appearance of the entire site. The windswept open space will have gone, to make way for a very complex environment, full of visual interest. In the process we will have involved the community in a long-term project that brings together a wide range of skills – there is no handiman or do-it-yourselfer who will not find employment, with the added bonus that although the produce will not be entirely free, at least it will be very much cheaper, fresher and more varied than shop-bought food.

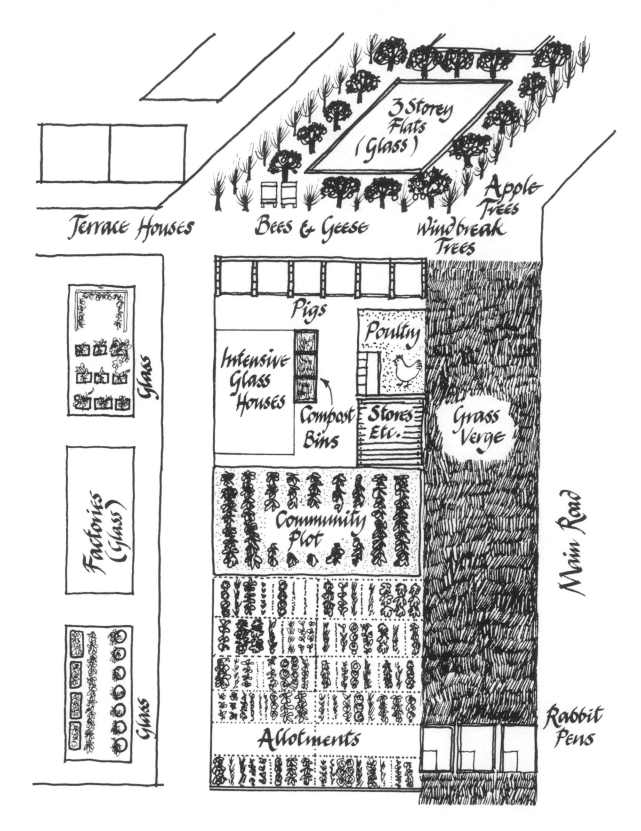

Terrace Houses

Bees & Geese

Apple Trees

3 Storey Flats (Glass)

Windbreak Trees

Glass

Factories (Glass)

Glass

Pigs

Intensive Glass Houses

Poultry

Compost Bins

Stores Etc.

Grass Verge

Community Plot

Allotments

Main Road

Rabbit Pens

## Further reading

**Rabbits:** 'Raising Rabbits' by J. A. Baldwin.

*Practical Self-Sufficiency* (Broad Leys Publishing Company, Widdington, Saffron Walden, Essex) Number 3, March/April 1976.

*Rabbit Keeping* by C. F. Snow. A Foyles Handbook.

*Home Rabbit Keeping* by Marjorie E. P. Netherway. Interest in Living Series. EP Publishing Ltd.

**Bees:** *Diseases of Bees* Bulletin 100. Ministry of Agriculture, Fisheries and Food. HMSO.

*The Joys of Beekeeping* by Richard Taylor. Barrie and Jenkins.

*The Art and Adventure of Beekeeping* by Ormond and Harry Aebi. Unity Press, Santa Cruz.

*A Manual of Beekeeping* by E. B. Wedmore. BBNO (Bee Books New and Old), Warminster, Wilts.

*Guide to Bees and Honey* by Ted Hooper. Blandford Press.

**Indoor food plants:** *Window Box Gardening* by Xenia Field. Blandford Press.

*Herbs: A concise guide in colour.* Hamlyn.

*Herbs: How to grow and use them* by Louise Evans Doole. The Oak Tree Press.

*Herb Gardening* by Claire Loewenfeld. Faber.

**Novel proteins:** *Food From Waste,* edited by G. G. Birch, K. J. Parker and J. T. Worgan. Applied Science Publishers.

*Food Standards Committee Report on Novel Protein Foods.* Ministry of Agriculture, Fisheries and Food. HMSO.

**Bioplex:** 'The Bioplex Concept' by C. F. Forster and J. C. Jones, in *Food from Waste* (see above).

'A modest proposal: science for the people' by John Todd, in *Radical Agriculture,* edited by Richard Merrill. Harper and Row.

## Information

**Bees:** British Bee Keepers Society, 55 Chipstead Lane, Riverhead, Sevenoaks, Kent.

MAFF (Min. of Agric., Fish. and Food) Bee Advisory Officer, Luddington Experimental Horticulture Station, near Stratford-upon-Avon, Warwickshire.

# FISHING & AQUACULTURE

# An island race

It sounds heretical to ask whether the British are a maritime nation, but the question must be asked. Apart from a romantic – and distinctly un-nautical – attachment to sandy beaches and pleasure trips round the bay, much of our history and our present-day behaviour is more typical of a continental nation that looks for trade, alliances and enemies across the narrow Channel into Continental Europe rather than further across the ocean, that takes its army seriously but is indulgent towards its navy, which is not concerned with important matters on land. The 'Cod wars' with Iceland were reminiscent of the imperialist adventures of a land power whose dignity had been affronted. A truly maritime response might have been to recognize the inevitability of the Icelandic limits and to set, and if necessary defend, similar British limits. That, in fact, is what the fishing industry would have welcomed.

Fish does not form a major part of our diet, but it could contribute much more if we took to eating the immense quantities of perfectly edible fish that are made into fishmeal – for pet foods, livestock feed and fertilizer. People who themselves consider entering food production think almost invariably of farming, rarely of fishing, and almost never of aquaculture – fish farming or 'ranching'.

## Inshore v. distant water
Commercial sea fishing can be broken down into main types, in two ways. The first distinction is between inshore and distant-water fishing.

By official definition, inshore fishing is fishing from boats that are 24 metres in length or less. Vessels larger than this are 'distant-water' boats. In fact, 80 per cent of all British fishing boats are less than 24 metres long, and one-third of them are less than half that size. Together they catch most of the fish that we eat. The distinction based on vessel size is somewhat arbitrary, because a 20-metre boat may work a long way out at sea, and stay away for several days and nights, while the larger vessels may make short trips in coastal waters.

The second distinction is between industrial and non-industrial fishing. In the Common Market, 'industrial' fishing is understood to mean fishing by industrial methods: which are probably impossible to define, as we shall see. In Britain, the term 'industrial' means fishing for the fish processing industry – catching fish for fishmeal, rather than for human consumption.

## How do you start?
The fishing industry produces small, tightly-knit communities, societies that exist within the wider community and are only partially in contact with it. However, this does not mean the communities are exclusive. It is possible – even easy – to join them and, in time, to be accepted.

Traditionally, the way to become a fisherman is to find your own way to a port and stand around on the quay. Watch the boats unloading, find out who are the skippers, and then ask them for a berth. Eventually – it may take days, or it may take weeks, depending on circumstances – someone will take you aboard for a trial.

The method still works (although with unemployment running high at present it is more difficult than it was), but these days there is a formal training, at least for the big ships of the distant water fleet. You will have to attend school on shore, pass written examinations, and work as a deck hand before you can become fully qualified. The qualifications will lead to a mate's and then a master's ticket, which allow you some control over the management of a vessel that costs hundreds of thousands of pounds, and that you will never own.

Joining the inshore industry is less formal. A fully equipped fishing boat of about 20 metres will cost far less than the cheapest farm, so with a certain amount of capital you can become an owner.

Until you obtain your own master's ticket (which will require you not only to pass written examinations but to have spent six years at sea), you will need to hire a skipper. You cannot land fish commercially except from a registered fishing boat, and you cannot take a registered boat to sea unless there is a qualified skipper on board. There is nothing to prevent you from owning a boat, though, and sailing as crew, and skippers are not too difficult to find.

At a more modest level, waiting on the quayside, drinking in the right pub and talking to the right fishermen should find you a berth.

Distant-water fishermen work for companies and are paid wages. Living conditions on the big vessels are good. Inshore men are paid no wages, but work for a share of the catch. Every member of a crew – up to about ten on the larger boats – receives a share, and the boat itself gets a share for maintenance and fuel. When you start you will not be paid a full share. To earn that you must prove that you can work as hard, and catch fish as well, as anyone else. When you have proved that you will be accepted into the community.

## Where to go?

The largest fishing ports, in terms of quantities of fish landed, are:

*Hull:* landing mainly cod, haddock, redfish, saithe and halibut, caught mainly in distant waters by big trawlers.

*Grimsby:* another big trawler port, landing cod, haddock, saithe, sand eels, plaice and redfish.

*Aberdeen:* also big trawlers, landing haddock, cod, saithe and whiting.

*North Shields:* landing sprats, herring, cod, haddock, whiting and saithe.

*Fraserburgh:* landing Norway pout, cod, haddock and whiting.

*Fleetwood:* landing cod, herring, saithe, haddock, plaice and skate.

*Ullapool:* landing herring, whiting, dogfish and haddock.

*Lowestoft:* landing plaice, cod and haddock.

*Leith:* landing sprats, haddock, saithe and whiting.

*Buckie:* landing sprats, haddock and cod.

*Brixham:* landing sprats, whiting and mackerel.

*Whitehaven:* landing herring, plaice and cod.

*Newlyn:* landing mackerel, skate, ling and dogfish.

*Scarborough:* landing cod, whiting and haddock.

*Milford Haven:* landing cod, skate and haddock.

*Bridlington:* landing cod, whiting and haddock.

*Whitby:* landing cod, whiting, haddock and lemon sole.

*Hartlepool:* landing cod, haddock, whiting and plaice.

There are of course other types of fish, and shellfish, and fishermen catch whatever is there and whatever they can sell, so the list is not complete. There are other fishing ports, too, although many of the smaller fleets have disappeared. However, these are the principal ports, in descending order of size, and the principal fish, in descending order of the species being caught a year or two ago.

If you want to become a fisherman it is to one of these ports that you should go first, although you may be successful at any of the other minor ports shown on the map.

## Conservation

Times change, and over the years some ports become more important commercially, others less so. In general, the past generation has seen an increase in the quantities of fish landed, but a decline in the number of fishing fleets and ports.

The change has been brought about by the 'modernization' of fishing. Ships have become larger and are fitted with ever more sophisticated equipment. This means, on the one hand, that they are able to catch more fish, but on the other hand it means that they must catch more fish in order to repay their cost. What has happened parallels the changes that have taken place in agriculture, but only loosely, and the effects are very different.

A vicious spiral has been created. For a number of years, official policy – backed by a system of loans, grants and subsidies for the purchase, equipping and operating of fishing vessels of more than a certain size – has encouraged 'greater efficiency'. Efficiency in fishing is measured in terms of the size of the catch compared with the number of man-hours spent at sea obtaining it. So the distant-water fleet, based on large ships, grew, and because of their cost more and more of them were owned by large companies. Their equipment – for navigation and the location of shoals – was developed from wartime devices manufactured by the electronics industry, and it became very effective indeed.

A small, relatively inexpensive boat, owned by the fishermen who sail her, costs little to operate, and loses little if she has to spend a few days tied up against the harbour wall. If the weather is bad, if the fish are not there, it is not the end of the world. A large, expensive boat, on the other hand, cannot lie idle. She has been bought with borrowed money, so a debt has to be serviced. All her fixed overheads, such as insurance and harbour charges, are higher. She must spend as much time at sea as possible. As soon as she sails, she costs even more. Fuel is expensive and her large engines burn a lot of it. Wages must be paid and the crew fed. A distant-water trawler can cost £2,000 a day or more while at sea. So, having sailed, she must catch fish. There is too much at stake for her to be able to afford to return home with empty fish holds. Not only must she catch fish, but she must catch as much as she can, as quickly as she can, of the fish that will fetch the highest price.

The 1960s were the good years, when world catches were increasing and money for investment was fairly plentiful. Profits were ploughed back, and this tightened the spiral.

Then things started to go wrong. Stocks of the most popular species, such as herring, were being overfished. The difference between fishing and farming was becoming apparent. Unlike a farmer, a fisherman does nothing to ensure that his crop is sustained from year to year. He is a hunter, not a husbandman. His new armoury had given him tremendous killing power, while at the same time ensuring that this power was used to the full. The catching capacity was never large enough; ways were being sought constantly to increase it, for by now it was not only the cost of the hunt that had to be borne, but the cost of onshore processing plants that had to be paid for and fed with fish for canning, but more and more for making fishmeal. This was – and is – 'industrial fishing'. The power and cost of the weapons meant catches had to increase. The size of the catches meant processing plants were needed. The processing plants had to work at optimum capacity, so catches had to increase further, which meant new and better weapons.

Nation by nation, sea area by area, species by species, steps were taken to conserve stocks, to limit the power of the hunters. This forced them to search further afield, but then they found themselves competing too severely for the fish that remained. By the mid 1970s, the combined effects of stock conservation measures, rising operating costs and consumer resistance to high prices for fish had reduced the industry to deep economic and psychological depression, while forcing the distant water ships to work closer inshore in their own waters, where they were causing considerable disruption to inshore fleets by glutting markets, damaging and disturbing shoals and – inevitably – overfishing.

Fish stocks can be conserved in several ways. The first method is to regulate the mesh size of the nets used. When you buy a net the size of its mesh will be designed to allow smaller fish to pass through, and you will break the law if you fish with a smaller mesh. The second limitation on fishing method is to ban certain methods, or ships of more than a certain size, from particular waters.

The third step is to impose quotas for particular species, so limiting the quantity that can be landed and sold. This is the most publicized conservation measure, but probably the least satisfactory. The quotas themselves are based not on a scientific assessment of the sustainable catch, but on records of actual catches averaged over a number – usually three – years. This means the quota must be retroactive: it can be adjusted only when catches fall and not always then. Sometimes the permitted quotas have not been landed, which probably means the stock is badly depleted: earlier quotas were set too high. When the quota for one species is filled, ships have little choice but to turn to alternatives, so pressures on other species mount. If it is likely that a quota will be imposed for the new species, the fleets will do all they can to catch still more, so that the starting quota is set very high. Many of the ships that descended on the mackerel off the south-west coast of Britain in 1976 and 1977 moved because the herring quota had been filled and because they believed a quota was to be established for mackerel. At present, mackerel are unprotected.

The final conservation measure is to declare wider territorial limits inside which foreign vessels can fish only with permission. The concept of a 200-mile Exclusive Economic Zone is being used in this way by a number of countries, and within the EEC 200-mile EEZ, Britain and Ireland are demanding limits inside which only their own fishermen may work. This can work in conjunction with limited fishing seasons for some species and with total bans on all fishing in important breeding grounds.

Fishing Ports

Scalloway Lerwick

Stornoway
Uig Ullapool Buckie
Lochboisdale Fraserburgh
Peterhead
Inverness Aberdeen
Mallaig

Oban Leith
Eyemouth
Tarbert Seahouses

Ayr North Shields
Portpatrick Hartlepool
Portavogie Whitehaven Whitby
Ardglass Scarborough
Kilkeel Peel Bridlington
Hull
Fleetwood Grimsby

Gt. Yarmouth
Lowestoft

Milford
Haven

Newlyn Brixham

# How fish is caught

Modern fishing vessels are required by law to carry certain minimal radio equipment so they can maintain contact with a shore station, and have access to the distress frequencies.

They navigate, almost universally, by the Decca navigator system. A radar scanner, mounted on the roof of the wheelhouse, is linked to a display unit. The instrument is first zeroed, by adjusting its dials until all of them read zero, then set to three coordinates that correspond to the position of the harbour. Once the boat leaves port, the display unit shows three sets of numbers which relate to a grid pattern on the charts. By plotting the coordinates on the relevant chart, the boat's position is determined accurately to within a few metres.

The fish are located by sonar, or a variant of it, displayed on an oscilloscope screen, or in ink on a paper drum, or both. The most common echometer scans the water below the boat's keel and can, with certain species at least, detect a single fish. It shows the presence of fish and their density, but not the species, although a fisherman will usually know this from the season and the boat's location. Large fish generally show as a stronger signal than small fish, but fish with swim bladders (such as pilchards) return a stronger signal than fish (such as mackerel) without.

## Lining

The most primitive method used commercially – and it is still used extensively – is lining, using either a long line or a hand line.

A line is just that: a line to which hooks are attached. The long line may be very long, and carry a thousand hooks or more, each hook being fastened to a finer line attached to the main line, so that if there should be a break the chances are that the main line will survive and only some of the finer lines will be lost.

A hand line carries 20–30 hooks, and is usually wound in around a small drum turned by hand. A long line may carry a very heavy load of fish, and so requires a mechanical winch to haul it in,

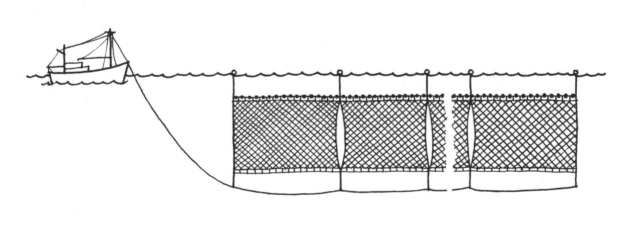

*Drift Netting*

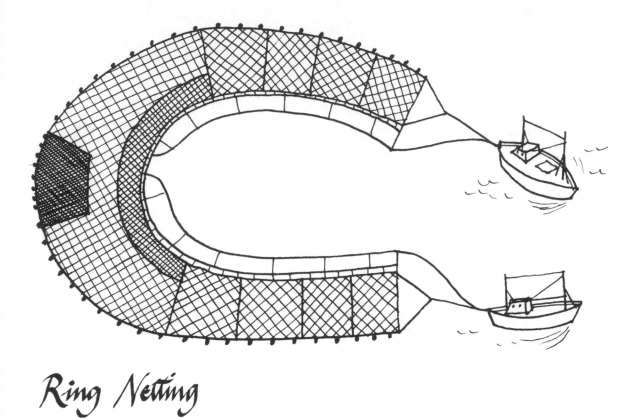

# Ring Netting

but a hand line with up to 30 fish is manageable by a strong man.

### Drifting

Long lines can be used to catch fish that do not swim in shoals, or that are in dispersed shoals; hand lines can be used either for dispersed or dense shoals. A drift net is useful only in fairly dense shoals that swim close to the surface ('pelagic' fish), typically herring, pilchards, sprats and mackerel.

The drift net is a curtain of net that hangs in the water, weighted along the bottom and attached to floats along a headline at the top. The entire net sits beneath the surface and hangs from surface floats, which also mark its position.

The drifter 'shoots' a series of nets as it sails in a straight line, forming a wall that may be 15 metres from top to bottom and well over 3.5km in length. The nets are linked at the top, and a line passes along the bottom of each of them to the drifter. Once the nets are shot, both they and the drifter drift – hence the name – with tide and current.

The catch is made when a shoal swims against the nets, at which point the top floats begin to move or are pulled beneath the surface. The nets are then hauled in.

### Seining (ring-netting)

The seine net is really a drift net that is shot in a circle, to surround a shoal. Traditionally, seining was often done from the shore. One end of the net was held on the beach while the remainder was paid out from a rowing boat in a circle that brought the other end back to the beach again. Then the whole net was hauled in – at once, for if the shoal had not been caught it could not enter and the net had to be shot again.

Today, most seining is done from one or sometimes two boats. Where two boats are used, each carries her own net, but the first to locate a shoal shoots, casting one end of the net overboard, attached to a buoy, and paying out the remainder. The second boat picks up the buoy and as soon as the net is shot, the two boats sail towards one another, closing the circle. The net is hauled aboard the boat that shot it, the crew often being augmented by men from the second boat.

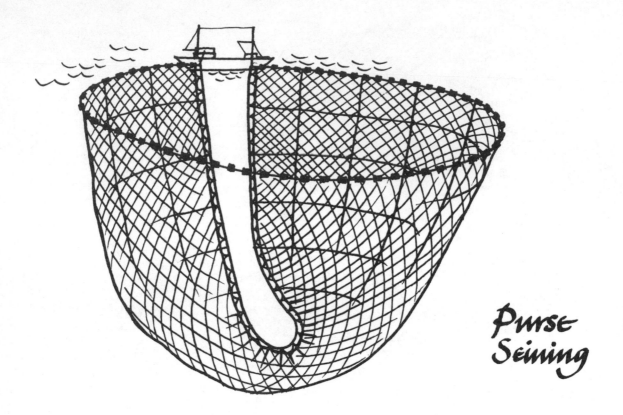

**Purse-seining**

High technology – and powerful engines – have made purse-seining a logical extension of seining. The difference between the two is that the purse-seine net closes at the bottom to form the 'purse'. The nets are often large: a circumference of about 550 metres and a depth of 150 metres is common. A new purse-seine net, at 1977 prices, costs over £40,000.

The shoal is located and if it is of the size and density required, the whole of it is taken. The vessel shoots her net in a circle, then pulls it to the side. This forces the fish closer to the surface and they are pumped out of the net directly into the holds. The method tends to damage fish, and much of what is caught can be used only for fishmeal.

**Trawling**

Basically, trawling consists of towing through the water a net shaped rather like a sock, the 'toe', or cod end, being narrower than the rest. The trawl may be towed by a single trawler, from the stern or the side (stern- or side-trawlers), or by two (pair trawlers), which can tow a much larger net together than either of them could singly.

Trawling is used to catch almost any kind of fish. If there is a universal fishing method, this is it. By towing the net it is possible to work dense shoals, dispersed shoals, or fish that are not in shoals at all. All that varies is the length of time spent trawling.

This is critical, for in a dense shoal too long a trawl (in a dense mackerel shoal, three minutes is about the maximum length of trawl possible) may carry away the net, and trawling at any time is expensive in fuel consumed.

'Beam trawling', for catching bottom-feeding (demersal) fish, uses a heavy beam fastened across the lower part of the open mouth of the net, which is dragged along the sea bottom. The method is traditional, but as practised by modern vessels using very large nets and very heavy beams, it can scoop up a great deal of bottom sediment and destroy the creatures that dwell in the mud, on which large fish depend for food.

A trawl towed through the water but well clear

of the bottom is called a mid-water trawl, used to catch pelagic fish. It was the large mid-water trawlers that used to fish in Icelandic waters, and that have been working in the western Channel during the mid 1970s.

The trawl net is held open by pairs of 'otter boards', made of wood or metal and looking a little like doors, which are attached in such a way as to move apart when they are dragged through the water.

## Dredging

Some shellfish – such as scallops – that live in deeper waters, are caught by dredging, using metal gear that scoops up the bottom sediment, and its occupants, and lets the mud settle out again.

## Potting

Potting is used very close inshore, around wrecks and in sheltered bays and estuaries to catch lobsters and crabs. Weighted, baited pots, attached to marker buoys, are placed on the bottom and then visited from time to time. Sometimes it is possible to use pots without even bothering with a boat: there are a few fishermen in isolated coves who are able to wade far enough out to make a living from these high-value fish. Mostly, however, the pots are set from small (10 metres or less) boats.

## Who does what?

Whether or not these methods can be called industrial depends only on the scale of the operation. All the techniques are traditional, there is nothing new, and all are used by vessels of every size, or have been in their time. Fashions change, according to the kinds of fish being hunted, but the all-round fisherman (or woman) should be familiar with all of them. Drifters are less common than they used to be now that the herring have been fished out, and purse-seining on a large scale is undertaken by specialized boats (to do it effectively from one boat you need bow and side propellers for manoeuvrability), but if you were to invest in a fully equipped, 20-metre or so boat you would expect it to have the necessary gear for trawling, lining and dredging, together with Decca navigation, echometer and radios.

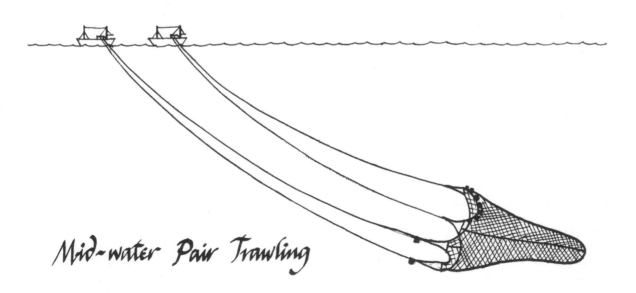

Mid-water Pair Trawling

# Freshwater aquaculture

Since all commercial fish production – in the West, anyway – aims for the top end of the consumer market, the fish most exploited in this way is the trout. Trout have been farmed for many years, originally to restock rivers for anglers, but more recently for retailing through supermarkets. As cod becomes increasingly a luxury food, it may not be long before the local fish and chip shop changes its menu from cod and chips to trout and chips.

Trout require clean, flowing water with a high oxygen content, which means that the water will be cold.

As with salmon (see p.206), the adults kept for breeding are stripped of their eggs and milt to provide fertile eggs. These must be stripped by hand. Hold the fish in one hand and apply a firm but gentle pressure with the fingers of the other hand to the belly, moving backwards from the pectoral fins to the vent (the pectoral fins are those at the front of the body, behind the gills). The fish will lay eggs naturally in late October or November. The milt is stripped in the same way as the eggs, and the two are placed together in trays. Rock the trays gently for a few minutes (in water, of course) and the sticky eggs will become free.

The trays are placed in running water, filtered to remove sediment. The temperature of the water affects the length of time it takes for the eggs to hatch, but in general, eggs laid in mid November will hatch in late February or early March.

Like salmon larvae, trout larvae are called alevins, and also like salmon (salmon, *Salmo salar*, and trout *Salmo trutta*, are close relatives in the family Salmonidae) the alevins feed at first on the large yolk sac associated with each egg.

After a month or six weeks, the yolk sac will be exhausted, the alevins will have grown into fry, and they will want to feed. At this stage they eat aquatic insect larvae and nymphs, which naturally they take from the water flowing past them. You may need to provide larvae to supplement the natural supply that is present in all open water.

By their second year the fry have become parr, like salmon parr but distinguishable from salmon by different-coloured markings. The diet is now similar to that of adult fish: smaller fish, freshwater shrimps, insects and their larvae, and any terrestrial snails, earthworms, slugs or caterpillars that have the misfortune to wander or fall into the water. Commercially raised trout are fed on proprietary 'trout pellets'. These are made mainly from trash fish, but they also include prophylactic drugs.

The adult trout are kept in cages in the flowing water. Virtually all their food is provided by the farmer.

The parr change gradually into smolts, and when they acquire adult markings and coloration they are ready to harvest. Probably this will be after three or four years from the time they hatched.

Trout can grow to a large size. The British record for a rod-caught brown trout was won in Scotland in 1956 for a trout weighing 8.221kg, and the record for a sea trout is held by an angler who caught one that weighed 9.072kg. At over a metre long, these fish are far too large to be of commercial interest. The supermarket likes trout that are closer to 20cm in length.

## What is a trout?

The trout is one of the most variable of fish species. It can inhabit a wide range of habitats, in fresh or sea water, or it can migrate between the two, like salmon. The main distinction is made between the sea trout and brown trout, but there are finer distinctions: the lake trout, Welsh black-finned trout, the Irish gillaroo, the Loch Leven trout – marked differently from other trout – and, of course, the rainbow, which is the variety most usually farmed. The sea trout has a life history very similar to that of the salmon, and all the varieties are distinguished by small differences in marking or colour (the Loch Leven trout are silvery with black spots but no red ones, because the red markings are caused by the presence of carotene in the diet, and Loch Leven is deficient in carotene-bearing organisms).

However, they are all of the same species and can inter-breed. When sea trout are crossed with brown trout some of the progeny retain the migratory instinct and others lose it, but all the progeny are viable. For that matter, trout have been crossed with salmon in the Centre Océanologique de Bretagne, near Brest. Until quite recently, the different markings were believed to indicate different species, and so in some older books you may find trout given distinctive, but misleading, taxonomic classifications.

## Commercial possibilities

Commercial trout farming is well established in Europe and in North America, and there are openings in Britain for newcomers, either to work on existing farms, or to start their own (see p.218).

Yields can be impressive. The world record, for rainbow trout cultivated intensively in running water in America, stands at 2,000 tonnes per hectare per year. This works out at an in-credible 170kg of fish per litre of water per *second*! At a more modest level, brown trout farmed in Denmark in the early 1960s produced a yield of 163 per cent. That means that for every kilogram of fish introduced, 1.63kg was harvested each year.

With yields as high as this, and an initial capital investment much lower than that for any kind of dry-land farming (where the most expensive item is the land itself, of which the fish farmer needs very little, followed by costly machinery and livestock, both of which are smaller and simpler, and so cheaper, for the fish farmers, it is surprising that more people have not entered what may well become a boom industry within the next few years.

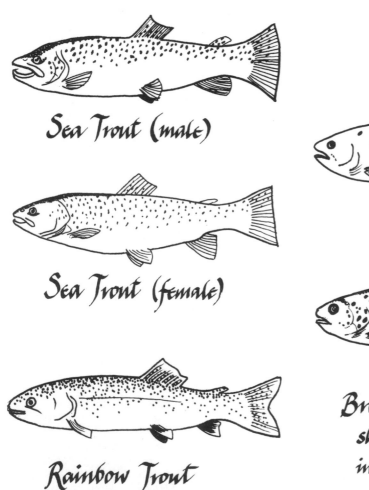

Sea Trout (male)

Sea Trout (female)

Rainbow Trout

Brown Trout:
showing variations
in marking

# Broiler salmon?

Farmed fish are expensive fish, because most of them are carnivores. If all the fish we eat were produced on farms, fish would be the highest-priced form of meat, at least until total systems are devised that make the fish farmer as independent of bought-in feed as his land-based colleague.

The relatively high production cost explains why fish farming has developed most rapidly at the top end of the market. In Britain, Norway, France and other countries, farmed salmon is now being produced commercially by an industry that is expanding.

The potential yield is large. By maintaining a high standard of husbandry it is possible to produce 50 tonnes of salmon per hectare of water surface per year, and there are estimated to be suitable sites in Scottish sea lochs whose combined area is about 1000 hectares.

Since the salmon spends part of its life-cycle in fresh water and part in the sea, the salmon farmer needs two separate establishments.

No one knows for certain why salmon spawn in some rivers and not in others. Certainly they cannot tolerate much pollution, but there is more to it than that. Rather than trying to analyse river water and simulate a spawning environment, it is much simpler to site the freshwater hatchery on a known salmon river.

The seawater site must experience little variation in salinity, temperature or dissolved oxygen content. Fresh and salt water do not mix very readily, the fresh water tending to ride over the salt water to produce an inclined 'front' that moves upstream with the incoming tide and downstream as the tide ebbs. The temperature of the two bodies of water is also likely to be different, and onshore winds can drive the fresh water into 'pools' that are much deeper than the river water that surrounds them. This means that the site must be chosen with great care, after it has been monitored at different points, at different states of the tide, and at different seasons of the year.

## Marine Harvest Ltd

Much of the development of salmon farming in Britain has been done by Marine Harvest Ltd, a subsidiary of Unilever, whose freshwater hatchery is at Invergarry, and whose seawater site is in Lochailort, sixty miles away.

The production cycle begins in October to December, when the breeding adult fish are stripped of their eggs and milt, and the eggs are fertilized.

The fertilized eggs are taken to the hatchery, where they are placed in trays through which river water is allowed to flow after it has been filtered to remove sediment. The eggs require oxygenated water, but no nutrient, of course.

The eggs hatch between March and May, and the larvae, 'alevins', spend their first few weeks eating food contained in the eggs. When this is exhausted they begin to feed. This is a critical time with all fish species, for the larvae are poorly coordinated and their behaviour is erratic. Mortality is likely to be high. Once they start feeding, however, growth is rapid.

In a matter of weeks the alevins develop barred markings, indicating that they are salmon parr. They remain in freshwater throughout the winter, and continue to grow.

The following spring, some of the parr become silvery in colour, indicating that they are smolts and ready to migrate to the sea. They are packed in tanks and taken by road to the sea loch site, where they are placed in cages.

After one year, some of the smolts have matured. These are harvested as grilse, with an average weight of 2kg. The rest of the fish remain in the cages for a further year before they are harvested as mature salmon, with an average weight of 3.8kg.

The cycle is completed by selecting suitable adults for breeding and taking their fertilized eggs back to the hatchery.

## Problems

The main biological problem with the farmed salmon is the tendency of the fish to reach sexual maturity too early. This means that instead of gaining weight they convert feed into useless roe. The problem has been overcome, experimentally at least, by feeding anabolic steroids – hormones – to retard sexual development. The treatment increased the rate of growth and the drug was lost from the flesh within ten days of the cessation of treatment. There is a possible

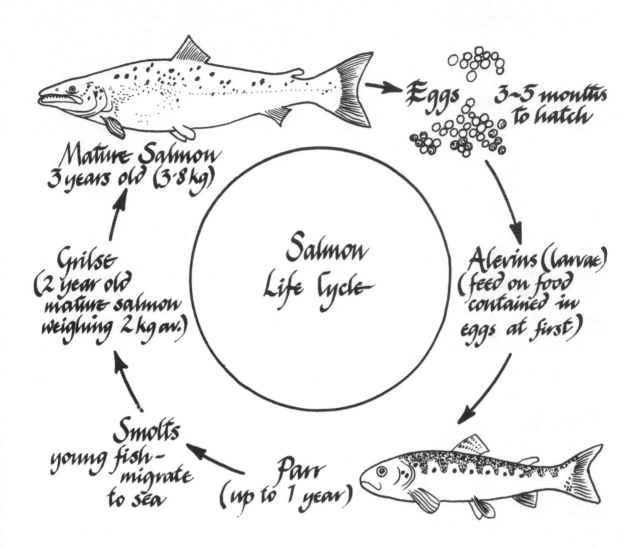

**Salmon Life Cycle**

Mature Salmon 3 years old (3·8 kg)

Eggs 3~5 months to hatch

Grilse (2 year old mature salmon weighing 2 kg av.)

Alevins (larvae) (feed on food contained in eggs at first)

Smolts young fish – migrate to sea

Parr (up to 1 year)

alternative approach through selective breeding (see p.216).

The other problems are legal. At present, British law does not recognize fish farming, but it does recognize poaching and it does guard jealously the right of any citizen to sail a boat, or fish, in salt water. Thus the fish farmer must obtain separate permission from five or six different authorities before he can install any permanent equipment in the sea, and he will need quite different permission to erect any buildings on shore–and for rating purposes they will be assessed as industrial, not farm buildings. Having overcome all these difficulties, he may find that technically he is poaching when he harvests his salmon – even though he raised them himself!

Happily, the law is likely to be changed. There is now a Fish Farmers' Union, affiiliated to the National Farmers' Union, and under proposed Common Market regulations fish farmers (seen naively as providing alternative employment for displaced fishermen) become eligible for grants.

It is distinctly possible that in a few years' time the salmon you buy in the shops will be cheaper, in real terms, than it is now, and that it will have been produced on a farm. Salmon farming has solved its technical and scientific problems, is close to solving its legal and administrative problems, and is poised to expand.

# Pond farming

If the yield possible from an intensive trout farm is impressive (se p.205), that from a farm rearing coarse fish is not far behind. The Japanese are able to produce between one and four thousand tonnes of fish per hectare per year, an average of about 100kg of fish for every litre of water per second.

The fish they use are carp, and the system is highly intensive. It shows, though, that the productivity of coarse-fish farms can be as high as from farms producing members of the Salmonidae.

At a less intensive level, the productivity from certain species of coarse fish should be higher. The distinction that anglers make between coarse fish and the surface-feeding insectivorous species, such as the Salmonidae, corresponds roughly to the saprobic classification used by biologists to categorize degrees of water pollution by the species present. The Salmonidae will survive only in very clean water; coarse fish can tolerate much 'dirtier' water. If we exclude toxic chemicals, which will kill almost anything, clean water by and large is water that contains few nutrients (oligotrophic), and dirty water is richer in nutrients (eutrophic). So the fish that live in clean water must subsist on a high proportion of airborne food – insects – while in dirty water there is likely to be much more to choose from. The nutrients will support the growth of unicellular algae and other plants, and these form the basis for a complete ecosystem. Coarse fish therefore are usually living in a richer environment.

Further, some of them at least are herbivorous and many more are omnivorous. Although most of the fish we eat consume an exclusively meat diet, the coarse fish live on a diet consisting mainly of plants. There is an ecological rule of thumb that says that whenever energy (as food) passes from one level of organisms to the next, about 90 per cent is lost – in fact it is used up almost entirely by respiration. So in terms of

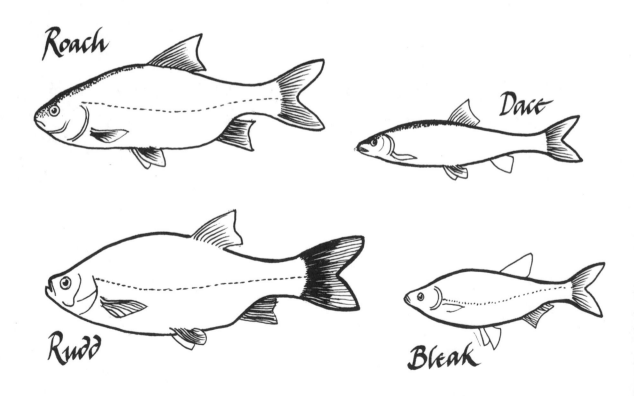

Roach

Dace

Rudd

Bleak

total mass, there will be something like ten times more plants than animals that eat plants, and ten times more herbivores than carnivores. It is to be expected, then, that fish production from herbivorous species will be greater than from carnivorous species.

Unhappily, the economics of fish farming are no simpler than those of any other livestock enterprise, and the same dilemmas occur. If you feed carnivorous salmon or trout with bought-in feed, their production increases dramatically. So does the production of herbivorous fish if you feed them intensively. This tends to dispense with their main ecological accomplishment, however: like pigs and poultry, they are splendid waste-converters. Then again, although herbivorous species can be raised more cheaply, because they will find much of their own food, they can look after themselves properly only if they are part of the complete, and complex, kind of ecosystem to which they are adapted by evolution. The carnivores can be managed more simply. Finally, Europeans and Americans are accustomed to eating carnivorous fish, and quite

unused to eating herbivores. The latter taste 'earthy', which we expect in potatoes or Jerusalem artichokes, but not in fish. So no one knows how easy it might be to market them, for no one has tried.

All the same, for the farmer who has a pond or can make one – a swimming pool whose novelty has worn off would do splendidly – it is possible to produce a very useful quantity of fish protein at a very low cost.

### Which fish?
Some years ago reports reached Europe of high levels of fish production that were being achieved in America with *Tilapia*. These are very prolific and grow at a phenomenal rate. Unfortunately, they are tropical and in our waters they will not even survive without heating. If you have access to cooling water from a power station (and this warm water is sometimes used for aquaculture) then *Tilapia* might be the fish for you.

Otherwise you will have to settle for one that will flourish in our temperatures, and the most

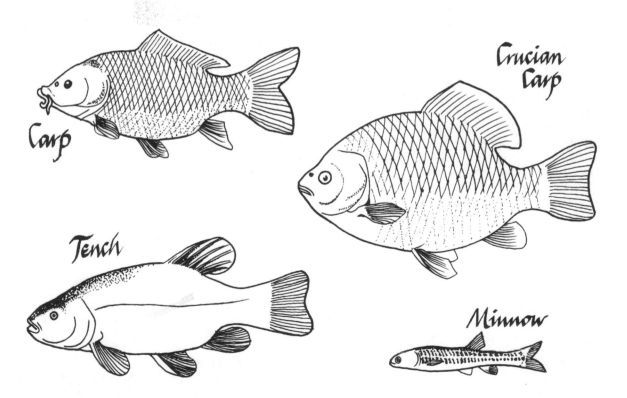

Carp

Crucian Carp

Tench

Minnow

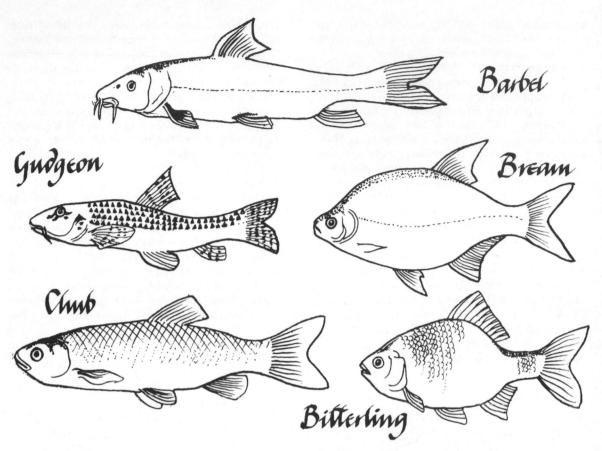

Barbel

Gudgeon

Bream

Chub

Bitterling

likely candidate is a member of the family Cyprinidae, which includes the carp, barbel, gudgeon, tench, minnow, orfe, chub, dace, roach, rudd, bream, bleak and bitterling. Of these, the best bet is probably the common carp (*Cyprinus carpio*) or Crucian carp (*Carassius carassius*), which grows faster but to a smaller full size. The common carp will grow to about 2–3kg and the Crucian to about 1.5–2kg. The Crucian is a cousin of the goldfish.

### What do you need?
Obviously, you need a pond, and it should have a flow of water, filtered to remove excess sediment. In the pond you will need to introduce oxygenating plants, as you would in a garden pond; algae, which you can buy from a garden centre but which will turn up all by themselves if you leave the pond alone; and a nutrient source, such as sewage – but not too much. The sewage will supply the nitrogen, phosphorus and potassium that feeds the plants.

Even with carp, it will help if the pond is heated: the optimum temperature ranges from a minimum of 15°C in February to a maximum of about 31°C in August. The best source of heating is provided by an array of flat-plate solar collectors, of the kind used to heat outdoor swimming pools, provided they can be moved aside when the summer temperature threatens to rise too high, and moved to shelter the pond from the wind in winter when there is little warmth in the sun: this amount of protection will prevent a good deal of heat loss that would occur otherwise.

Lights also help at night, especially in summer, because they attract insects, and the insects and their eggs and larvae all add to the food supply. The lights need not be large: one or two car headlight bulbs will do, and if you have, or can build, a small windmill, the operating cost is minimal.

### Management and yields
As with any other form of aquaculture, yields are measured in terms of the weight of fish produced per unit surface area of water. The surface area is much more important than the depth, which

in most cases need be no more than about one metre. The stocking rate and feeding rate are calculated in the same way.

The system used in parts of China for raising common and grass carp starts an annual cycle in February, when the water is at its coldest (15°C). Seventy kilograms of fish per hectare are put into the pond, but are not fed. Feeding starts in March, and the food is chopped grass, insect pupae (silkworms, in fact), silkworm waste (consisting mainly of the empty pupae), and rice bran. In Britain other insects could be substituted for the silkworms. Some fish farmers hang a piece of rotten meat over the pond, in which various flies breed: the larvae fall into the pond in a fairly constant flow. However, it should be possible to improve on this rather nauseating method!

The fish are fed more food each month from March to August (when the temperature averages 31°C): about 1.5 tonnes of grass in March increases to just over 5 tonnes in August; 1 tonne of silkworm waste increases to 3.4 tonnes; 0.6 tonnes each of pupae and bran to 2 tonnes.

At the end of July the first harvest is taken, of 800kg of fish per hectare. After August, as the water begins to cool again, the rate of feeding declines. A further 500kg of new stock are added in August, but by December the fish are receiving 1 tonne of grass, 0.7 tonnes of silkworm waste, and 0.4 tonnes each of pupae and bran. The second harvest, of 1.6 tonnes of fish per hectare, is taken in December, and in January the operation begins all over again.

The quantities of food consumed are large, but almost $2\frac{1}{2}$ tonnes of fish per hectare are being produced each year, from wastes.

This semi-industrial system can be made to work on a backyard scale, although at a lower level of production. The principles are the same.

As with any other enterprise, a high standard of hygiene is essential, and new fish should be quarantined before being added to established stocks.

From an economic point of view it is quicker and cheaper to raise a large number of small fish than to raise a small number of large fish, so you should learn to eat the fish small. The idea of farming minnows may sound absurd, but their productivity is high and (we are told) they are rather like whitebait to eat.

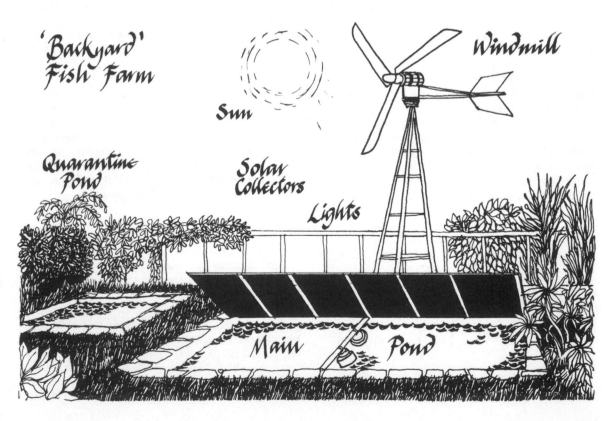

'Backyard' Fish Farm

Sun

Windmill

Quarantine Pond

Solar Collectors

Lights

Main Pond

# Farming the seas

As the cost of conventional sea fishing rises, so the operation tends to become counter-productive. Rising investment requires larger returns: the boats become larger and more powerful, and are fitted with more advanced equipment, in order to increase catches. Then over-fishing depletes stocks, or tightly enforced conservation measures protect the stocks – usually inadequately – but only by reducing the size of catches. This forces up fish prices.

At some point in this spiral it will become cheaper to raise fish in captivity than it is to hunt them. On that day, the fish farmer will come into his own, culturing marine fish. Most of the research has been done. The information he needs is ready and waiting for its first customers.

### Farming or ranching?
The would-be marine fish farmer must decide first whether he is farming or ranching. The difference lies in the degree of husbandry involved, and in the species most suited to each kind of management.

Ranching is really a sophisticated form of stock management. In France, for example, there is interest in the Imperial Prawn (*Penaeus japonicus* and *P. Kerathurus*). This is the large prawn used for scampi, and most of the European supply is imported from Japan. The prawn will feed and grow only in warm water (20°C or more) and in northern waters it cannot survive the winter. However, it is possible to import juveniles early in spring, 'sow' them in – at present – the Mediterranean, and harvest them later in the year when they have grown to a satisfactory size. Research is aimed at breeding the prawns in captivity and cross-breeding to

produce a prawn that will survive at 11 or 12°C. This would make it possible for farmers to buy juveniles in the autumn, sow them straight away and harvest them the following year. They do not feed during the winter, and when they do begin feeding, a diet of chopped-up mussels suits them well.

Molluscs, such as scallops, are managed by collecting the juveniles, raising them in captivity and away from predators until they are 2–3cm across, then returning them to the sea.

Lobsters are cultured by breeding them on shore then sowing them in protected areas, where they are left until they are large enough to be caught conventionally.

Other species–including many of the flatfish – do not travel far from a source of food. To ranch them all that may be needed is to protect them from predators and feed them.

With still other species, for example the salmon, it is possible to breed the fish in captivity and then release them into the open sea, simply to increase general stocks. In the case of the salmon, which is said to return to spawn in the river in which it hatched, the advantage is obvious. So is the disadvantage: already salmon are being caught far out at sea by drifters.

Farmed fish remain in captivity the whole of their lives. Fish farming is not new, although it has been practised more commonly with freshwater than marine species (see p.204). Tidal-barrier traps are common in Mauritius and Hawaii, in the Black Sea, in Corsica (where there is a 1,500-hectare lagoon) and in Japan. Yield from traditional brackish-water lagoons is usually low – 50kg per hectare per year – unless the fish are given additional food. When they are fed, however, productivity rises dramatically, up to 5 or 6 tonnes per hectare per year.

### 'Accommodation'
Farmed marine fish will spend their early lives in large tanks on shore, and their adult lives in closed lagoons, or tidal traps that use the seawater to flush them out twice a day and to bring in food.

The capital cost of building such lagoons is high, and under present British law planning permission is difficult to obtain; however, the sides need not be solid – netting will do provided the fish cannot leave, nor their natural enemies enter – and the law is certain to be amended within the next year or two. In practice, it will

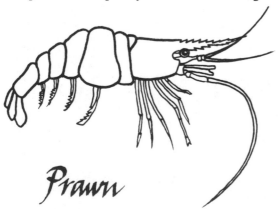

*Prawn*

probably prove impossible to operate marine fish farms except at coastal sites, for although the salinity of sea water can be simulated, the complex ecosystem cannot.

The most suitable site, then, will be on the coast, in a sheltered cove, or sea loch, or perhaps in an estuary, where the temperature of the water remains fairly constant and the salinity does not change much between tides. Most fish have a low tolerance to changes in either. There must be space on shore for a few buildings and tanks, and, of course, adequate access by road.

## Which fish?

You will want to farm the most valuable fish. In Britain these are, in order: Dover sole, turbot, halibut, hake, lemon sole, brill, red mullet, grey mullet, plaice and red sea bream. The French are also working with sea bass. All of these species can be bred and raised in captivity, although some must be helped with spawning, either by being stripped of their eggs by hand or by being fed pituitary hormone. Very large fish, such as halibut, cause some problems because of the space needed by the breeding population.

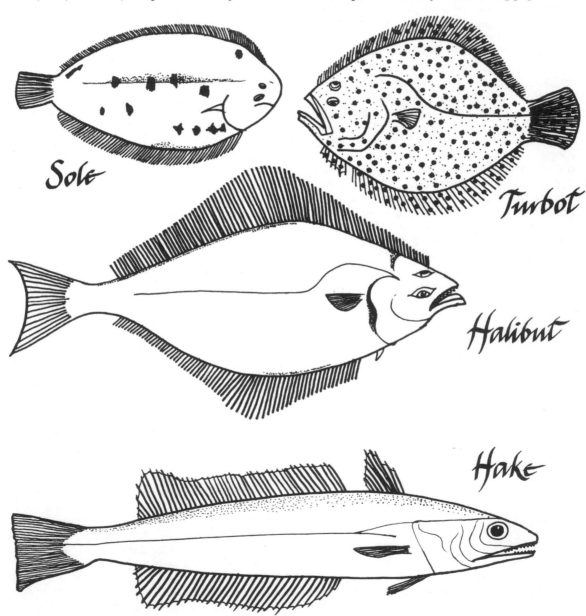

Sole

Turbot

Halibut

Hake

## Feeding

A problem with all the fish that we eat (although not all that we might eat) is that they are carnivores, high on food chains. This means that feeding them is either complex – if we do it by providing a total ecosystem that produces its own fish food – or expensive, or both. A main research problem has been to reduce feed costs.

The commercial farmer could help himself to some extent. The fish feed on the bottom at some stage in their lives, or for all of their lives in many cases, and so the growth of plankton (floating organisms) is not to be encouraged, but that of bottom-dwellers is. Thus the farmer will not want soluble fertilizers leaching into his water to promote algal growth, but will welcome organic detritus that accumulates on the bottom.

Feeding requirements change as the fish mature.

Juvenile *Dover sole* eat crustaceans and the larvae ('nauplii') of brine shrimps. Brine shrimps eat algae, and the US National Oceanic and Atmospheric Administration has demonstrated that brine shrimps (*Artemisia salina*) can be fed on algae grown on sewage. So the essential raw material is a modest supply of sewage. Adult Dover sole eat brine shrimps and molluscs.

Juvenile *turbot* eat brine shrimps, and the adults eat fish (trash fish or, more expensively, proprietary feed pellets).

*Halibut* eat crustaceans and fish at all stages, and the adults enjoy a little cephalopod (squid, octopus or cuttlefish) if they can get it.

*Hake* eat nothing but fish.

*Lemon sole* eat the same foods as Dover sole.

*Brill* eat crustaceans, and when they are adult supplement this diet with fish.

*Red mullet* eat crustaceans when juvenile, and the adults also eat molluscs and brine shrimps.

*Grey mullet* eat molluscs, crustaceans and algae.

Juvenile *plaice* eat brine shrimps, crustaceans and molluscs, and the adults eat just molluscs and shrimps.

*Sea bass* eat fish.

Pelleted foods have been developed for feeding farmed trout (see p.204), but for sea fish these are expensive. Alternatives are mostly based on fish that is not fit for human consumption, that otherwise would be used to make fishmeal.

Many species of demersal fish will eat only if some live food is present, though once they start feeding they will eat dead food. This does suggest that in the semi-natural environment of a lagoon they will fare better than in the entirely artificial laboratory environment.

## Diseases

Anyone who has kept fish in an aquarium or garden pond will know that, like any other animal, fish have their share of parasites and diseases. Farmed fish are no exception.

In the wild, the transmission of disease may be limited because of the dispersal of the hosts, and the effects of disease will be to eliminate the weaker members of a population. A farmer cannot afford this rate of mortality, and the close proximity in which his fish are confined means that diseases reach epidemic proportions more easily.

It is virtually impossible to cure an epidemic among fish, but to some extent disease can be prevented. The first step is to ensure that the water is changed regularly (as it will be by tidal movements in a coastal lagoon). This is simple hygiene.

The second step is to adopt the same all-in all-out stocking procedure that every good stock farmer follows. If you must introduce new individuals into an established colony, quarantine them for a few weeks first, just to make sure.

## The future of fish farming

The commercial farming of sea fish is still in the future. In nutritional terms it can be justified only where it uses a product that otherwise would be wasted. If caught fish is not to be eaten by humans, then it may be as sensible to feed it to other fish as to feed it to mammalian livestock – but no more sensible.

The technique will be very similar to that involved in dealing with any other intensive livestock enterprise, and it seems inevitable that there will be some loss of flavour and texture with fish, just as with broiler chickens.

Having said that, however, the fact remains that we are soon to see the last phase of the old 'neolithic revolution', as the only animals that are still hunted become domesticated. If fish farming attracts you, there is little doubt that in a few years' time it will be highly profitable.

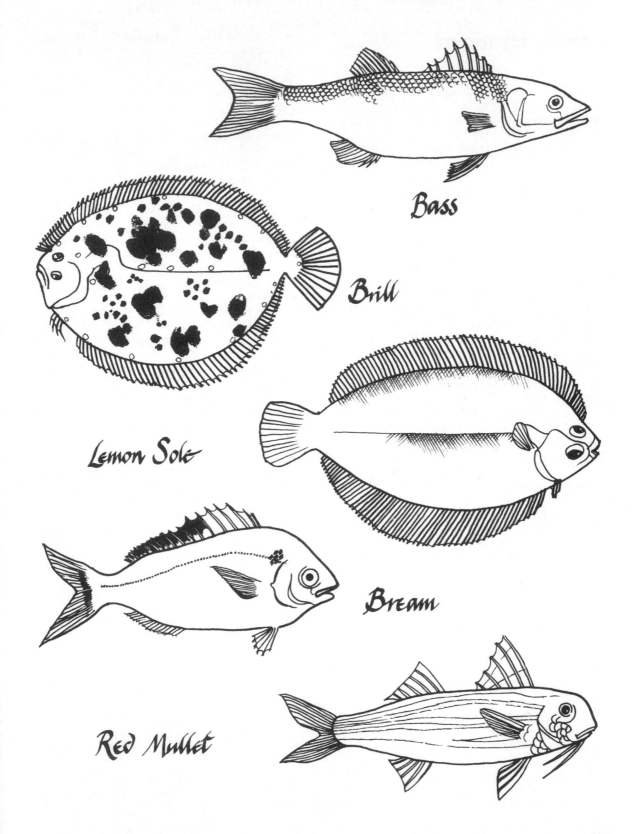

Bass

Brill

Lemon Sole

Bream

Red Mullet

# Fish for tomorrow

As we have seen with domesticated birds and mammals, no sooner do farmers enclose animals than they begin a never-ending process of selective breeding. Generally, this begins spontaneously as the domesticated population is isolated from its wild relatives, but soon it becomes deliberate, as breeders try to improve on nature and to emphasize characteristics they consider desirable.

Fish are no exception, and much of the current research into fish husbandry centres on improving the wild species, so that before long the fish that are farmed will bear a similar relation to wild fish as that which exists – or existed, before the wild species became extinct – between, say, a Friesian cow and her wild ancestor the aurochs (Bos primigenius).

Not only is the selective breeding of fish well known, it is far from new. The decorative goldfish that ornament many a garden pond are descended from crucian carp, bred to exotic – sometimes bizarre – forms.

The possibilities for fish breeders are greater than those open to the breeders of terrestrial species, for two reasons. The first is that there are many more species available in the wild. Our domesticated farm animals are descended from a very limited number of wild species; there are many more species of fish from which to choose. The second reason is that fish hybridize very readily in the wild (much more readily than do warm-blooded animals) and new techniques have been developed to accelerate hybridization under controlled conditions.

With the exception of the goldfish (Carassius auratus) which is purely decorative, fish breeders have few doubts about the qualities that are desirable. They are not in the least interested in 'show fish': appearance is of no importance. The desired qualities are those of growth rate, adult size, fecundity, amenability to management, and resistance to disease.

As you would expect, the greatest experience of fish breeding has been obtained with those species of highest commercial value. In France salmon and trout have been crossed experimentally (see p.204), and in Seattle the rainbow trout (Salmo gairdnerii), a native of North American rivers, and the Pacific salmon (Oncorhynchus tshawytscha) have been improved greatly. If you farm trout in Europe it is almost certain that the fish you use will be 'improved' rainbow trout, not native wild trout.

The common and crucian carps have been crossed in the Soviet Union to produce a variety of common carp that has the crucian's resistance to the disease known as red spot. In many parts of the world, domesticated carp grow to a much larger size than their wild relatives.

Hybrid vigour can also be achieved. Soviet breeders have achieved spectacular results with back-crossed sturgeons. There are two species of sturgeon involved, the beluga (Huso huso) which grows to a weight of more than a tonne, and the sterlet (Acipenser ruthenus) which seldom grows to more than about half a kilogram. When a male beluga is crossed with a female beluga x sterlet, the resulting progeny grow faster than the beluga.

Among sea fish, the plaice and flounder hybridize spontaneously in the Baltic, and in the North Sea a turbot x brill is encountered occasionally.

Obviously hybridization is more likely among animals whose eggs are fertilized outside the body. Species of very different sizes can be crossed (such as the beluga and sterlet) and none of the behavioural problems arise that make the cross-breeding of mammals so difficult. At the same time, the results of fish hybridization are more difficult to evaluate, because the growth rate, reproduction and adult size of fish are determined by environmental conditions to a much greater extent than obtains among land animals, so that a hybrid displaying what appears to be hybrid vigour may be merely responding to the more favourable environmental conditions of the hatchery.

## Desirable characters

The plaice x flounder could be useful commercially. The hybrids are viable and combine desirable characteristics from both fish. The flounder is hardier than the plaice, but it is very difficult to raise in a hatchery because its eggs are minute and the larvae almost impossible to feed. The hybrid has the hardiness of the flounder, but produces large, plaice-sized eggs. The hatching rate is good and mortality among the larvae is low.

It may be possible to improve on the plaice in other ways. It does not grow especially quickly and the quality of the fish is not high. A cross

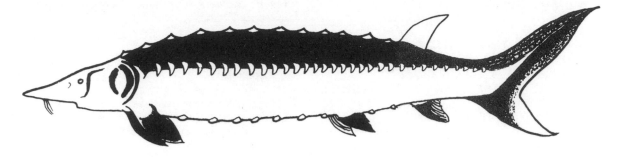

*Sturgeon ~ the largest species can weigh more than a tonne*

between a plaice and a halibut *(Pleuronectes platessa* x *Hippoglossus hippoglossus)* might produce a fish that is as suitable for cultivation as the plaice, but that grows at the rate of a halibut into a fish of halibut quality.

It might be possible, too, to produce flatfish that avoid a major problem in flatfish husbandry. The fish tend to form social hierarchies, and the position of an individual in the hierarchy determines its size. If fish are raised individually, they all grow at much the same rate to much the same size. Raised together, there is a wide variance. When fish are grouped by size in an attempt to overcome this problem, the hierarchy reasserts itself, some individuals grow hardly at all, and in the end the variance is, if anything, wider than it would have been had the population been left alone. Roundfish are much less affected by hierarchies and so, theoretically at least, it should be possible to breed out this undesirable character in flatfish.

### Chromosome engineering

Hybridization is not the end of the breeding process, but the beginning. As with any other species, most of the improvements are achieved by careful selection of the breeding stock. Hybridization may provide the initial stock, but after that selection takes over.

Selective breeding must begin with pure lines, however. These exist for almost all domesticated animals and plants, and they are the result of many generations of inbreeding. When crossed, quite different inbred lines often produce progeny that display hybrid vigour. This fact has been used widely in plant breeding and it is the basis of the intensive poultry industry.

It is a long, slow business, however, if the pure line can be produced only by about twenty generations of brother–sister matings. In fish it is possible to accelerate the process by a technique called gynogenesis. This involves the fertilization of eggs after they have been laid, but without involving the spermatozoan nucleus. In fact, it is a form of parthenogenesis. The spermatozoa are irradiated sufficiently to destroy the chromosomes, but not to kill the cells. These are used to fertilize the eggs. Fifteen minutes later the eggs are cooled to 0°C and kept at that temperature for four hours, which arrests a process that otherwise destroys most of the eggs. The survival rate of eggs after this cold shock is high, and the offspring possess only maternal genes. This is equivalent to about fourteen generations of brother–sister matings.

The cold shock ensures that when the single set of chromosomes divides into two, both parts are retained to produce a diploid egg. The process can then be extended to produce triploid eggs (three sets of chromosomes) and tetraploid (four sets). A tetraploid produced from a sterile hybrid would probably be fertile, and so tetraploidy could be used to produce entirely new kinds of fish (in nature, the salmonids and sturgeons are tetraploid). The tetraploids would provide the initial breeding stock, and the 'production line' would be composed of triploid individuals, which would be sterile but fast-growing.

The techniques may sound futuristic, reminiscent of *Brave New World* even, but they are no more than an accelerated version of the genetic manipulation that plant and animal breeders have used – often unconsciously – for thousands of years.

217

## Further reading

*Marine Fish Farming* by A. Jones. Laboratory Leaflet (New Series) No. 24. Ministry of Agriculture, Fisheries and Food Fisheries Laboratory, Lowestoft, Suffolk.

*The Farming of Fish* by C. F. Hickling. Pergamon Press.

*Fish and Shellfish Farming in Coastal Waters* by P. H. Milne, Fishing News (Books).

*Farming the Edge of the Sea* by E. S. Iversen. Fishing News (Books).

*Marine Aquaculture: Selected papers from the conference on marine aquaculture, Oregon State University.* Oregon State University Press.

## Information

Fisheries Laboratory, Ministry of Agriculture, Fisheries and Food, Lowestoft, Suffolk.

Marine Biological Association, Citadel Hill, Plymouth, Devon.

Field, Stream and Covert (England) Ltd. (Fish farming managers, engineers and scientists) Meriden, Warwickshire.

# Why grow more?

Since the early 1970s, energy prices have risen, world food prices have risen, and the economies of the industrial nations in general and of Britain in particular have stagnated. It is hardly surprising, therefore, that many students of the situation have urged us to re-examine the philosophy that has guided our agricultural policies for a century or more, and have pointed out both the advantages to be gained by achieving a higher level of self-sufficiency in food supplies, and the dangers of not doing so.

This does not mean, necessarily, that they are right. Their case needs to be argued, for we should not abandon lightly a method of feeding ourselves that has served well for longer than any of us can remember.

Britain has achieved a unique position among nations. It is, at one and the same time, a major producer of food and also one of the world's leading importers of wheat, meat, butter and feedgrains. We eat roughly twice as much as we produce, yet our farmers attain crop yields that compare favourably with those anywhere in Europe (they are much higher than North American yields) and the amount of food produced by each worker in agriculture is very large indeed. If we are to become more self-reliant can we do so by growing more food, or will we need to eat less? Probably we will do both. Already we are consuming less of the more expensive foods than we did a few years ago – without obvious ill effects – and, as we have seen, there are many ways in which agricultural productivity can be persuaded to increase.

## Cheap food

Our dependence on imported cheap food dates from the first half of the nineteenth century. At that time our great-great-grandparents were acquiring a taste for white bread. The milling that provided white flours extracted the bran and most of the germ from the whole grain. These were not wasted: they were fed to animals. However, the proportion of the grain that went to feed humans fell by about 20 per cent (modern white flour consists of about 70 per cent of the original whole grain). So in effect the demand for grain increased, and we began to import wheat.

Then, in 1846, following the Irish Famine, the Corn Laws were repealed. The domestic market was opened to imported food and British farmers were afforded no economic protection. At first nothing happened, but by the end of the century the North American plains were producing cereals and railways had been built to transport the grain to the eastern ports, the Civil War had ended and Americans were thinking of economic recovery based on expansion, it was possible to transport fresh meat long distances by sea in the refrigerated holds of merchant ships, and Australians and New Zealanders were beginning to export food to their motherland. Exporters everywhere knew of the ease with which their surpluses could be dumped on the British market.

This was the cheap food policy. It was based on the concept of liberal free trade, whereby we devoted ourselves to doing that which was most profitable – manufacturing – and used some of the income from the sale of high-priced industrial goods to buy low-priced primary foods. British agriculture became deeply depressed, but Britain became rich. Around the turn of the century it was being suggested that agriculture be run down completely, so that all our investment and energy could be absorbed by industry. Until quite recently there were still a few economists who supported this view.

## What went wrong?

Provided the world as a whole had surplus food, the policy made a great deal of sense. There were few years when it was not possible to find someone, somewhere, producing the commodities we required more cheaply than our own farmers could produce them.

The only really persuasive argument for retaining a thriving agriculture was the strategic one. As long as Britain remained an imperial power there was always the risk of war and a blockade of our sea routes. Agriculture revived a little during the First World War, only to collapse again in the depression that followed it, and despite some efforts to stimulate the industry we approached 1939 with abandoned farms and very low levels of productivity.

After the war much more vigorous policies were introduced. Although we did not abandon the cheap food policy (and there were vast grain surpluses in the world) farmers were guaranteed agreed prices for all major products, which encouraged investment, and a system of grants for farm improvements and subsidies to increase the use of fuel and agricultural chemicals encouraged modernization.

Today, the world has no food surpluses. Indeed, the major producers are struggling to rebuild their depleted stocks in order to provide a cushion against violent fluctuations in prices that threaten to become cyclical: shortages increase prices, so stimulating production, which increases supplies, leading to a fall in prices and a reduction in output, so starting the cycle again. Food is no longer cheap and it is very unlikely that it will be cheap again for as far ahead as anyone can see. The combination of increasing human numbers and rising prosperity ensures that the demand for food rises at least as fast as output can be made to increase.

The effect of population growth is less obvious than it seems. It is not merely the existence of a person that creates an effective demand for food, it is the existence of a person with money to spend. The effect of over-rapid population growth is to absorb too large a part of the capital that otherwise could be providing industrial employment. So poverty increases, and it is poverty that causes hunger, not simply the size of a population and certainly not the failure of farmers, who will grow only as much as they are able to sell.

When incomes rise, so does the demand for food, and when a certain economic threshold has been crossed, diets change. If people can buy as much as they need of the staples, more expenditure on food will take them into higher-priced items, which invariably include meat and other animal products. These are derived from animals fed on grain, and in the world as a whole it takes about 5kg of grain to produce each kilogram of animal produce. It is this change to a meat-based diet which has exhausted the granaries and which guarantees that, no matter how much vegetable matter we grow, as incomes continue to rise food surpluses and low prices will be rare accidents.

Theoretically, there would be more to eat if we were all vegetarians – though not subsisting on an entirely vegetarian diet, since large areas of the world can produce food only in animal form – but the argument is purely academic. When poor people become a little more prosperous they want to eat meat, and no amount of moralizing by those who are already rich will alter that. For us in Britain, though, a reduction in the amount of animal produce consumed, compensated for by an increase in the amount of cereals and potatoes, would increase the national level of self-sufficiency and make us more secure.

## The Common Market

Even if the world is short of food there is plenty of food within Europe, and as members of the European Economic Community we can depend on its availability to us.

In a limited sense, this is true. The Common Agricultural Policy (CAP), to which our farming systems are adjusting, is concerned much more with disposing of surpluses than with remedying deficiencies. Its aim is to improve farm incomes and facilitate trade by removing tariff barriers within the Community and by removing short-term advantages that members might gain by changing the value of their currencies. If the value of a currency should fall, as the value of the pound has done, imports will be more expensive and exports cheaper. It is to avoid this situation that we have the 'green pound' whose value is fixed at a pre-devaluation level. British consumers benefit but producers suffer, and for the Community as a whole – which has to finance the system by compensating those farmers who sell to us – it is very expensive.

The Community as a whole is about 90 per cent self-sufficient in food, and the CAP has grown out of the policies of countries more interested in protecting their farmers than in importing food they could produce themselves. The range of products is very wide – as wide as the geographical range of the Community, which extends from Sicily to the Shetlands, from Central Europe to Ireland.

Yet a snag remains. The food is there, but it must be bought, and despite the 'green pound', it is not cheap and never will be.

## Choices

Unless we are very confident that in the years ahead the world will have food for us to buy, at prices we can afford to pay, we have no choice but to grow more food for ourselves.

How shall we do this? The arguments are complex, but one necessity will be that far more people should become directly involved in food production. To grow more food we will need more people on the land. Agriculture, horticulture and aquaculture will come to play a much more important part in our national life – and that means in the life of each of us.

This sounds more earnest, more solemn, than it needs to. On the smallest scale, there is considerable pleasure and satisfaction to be gained from growing food. There is no flavour to compare with that of the food you have grown yourself and are eating fresh. If the urban food complex becomes a reality several stages more advanced than the allotment, it will contribute much to the quality of city life quite apart from providing food. On the larger scale the problem is not finding people who want to work on the land or to fish, but finding ways of helping them to achieve their ambitions. If Britain is to produce more of its own food it must devise strategies that enable large numbers of people to do what they already want to do.

Freedom, said Hegel, is the recognition of constraints. As we come to recognize that we can no longer be sure whether the world outside can supply us with our food, we may discover in that constraint more freedom than we thought possible.

# Index